Atlas of Avian Hematology

Alfred M. Lucas, A.B., Ph.D., Cytopathologist

Casimir Jamroz, B.S., A.B., Medical Illustrator

Regional Poultry Research Laboratory, East Lansing, Mich.

Animal Husbandry Research Division

Agricultural Research Service

Agriculture Monograph 25

UNITED STATES DEPARTMENT OF AGRICULTURE

WASHINGTON : 1961

Preface

An atlas of hematology is a picture book that functions as a dictionary. Minot, in his foreword to *Atlas of the Blood in Children,* by Blackfan, Diamond, and Leister (1944), aptly expressed the need for illustrations in hematology when he stated, "Illustration is essential in hematology. The inadequacy of language to convey the appearance of disease to the mind renders an appeal to the senses desirable whenever it can be employed, and when the objects themselves cannot be presented the best substitute for them is to be found in pictures."

It is hoped that this Atlas will enable investigators to forge ahead without the necessity for long delay in determining how the normal cell types and developmental stages should appear. The identification of the early and intermediate stages of development for most of the cell types has been worked out for the first time. The results of this research have been integrated with previous knowledge. All of the illustrations are original.

With the population expanding at an ever-increasing rate, the demand already is upon us to have available a stockpile of sound biological information on many subjects in order quickly and accurately to solve future problems of agriculture that will grow out of the necessity for making farm production more efficient. The control of disease is an obvious method of increasing our efficiency and is the objective of the long-range program on normal avian hematology that was undertaken at this Laboratory.

The subject matter covers not only the circulating blood of the adult bird, but also that of the embryo during its incubation from 2 days to hatching, and it includes the developmental stages found in blood-forming organs of both the adult and the embryo. The illustrations and text are concerned not only with the appearance of typical blood cells but also with the recognition of the atypical, the unusual, the abnormal, and the false. It is believed that future investigators of blood diseases of poultry will rarely find a cell in their preparations that has not been illustrated here, except cells invaded by organisms such as protozoan and other parasites.

A biopsy that involves blood is simpler and easier to procure than is a biopsy of any other tissue of the body, and even from a drop of blood much useful information concerning the health of the organism can be obtained.

It is intended that this publication shall serve the needs of the poultryman, the veterinarian, and the research worker in zoology, embryology, endocrinology, physiology, virology, and nutrition when these persons are confronted with the problem of identifying blood cells in birds. It will serve the ornithologist and the research worker in bird wildlife, in that representative studies have been made on species other than the domestic chicken; and where cells of wild species differed from those of chickens, they have been illustrated and described.

Innumerable names have been applied to the different blood cells and their developmental stages. Many of these are synonyms, many carry the implication of adherence to a particular theory of hematopoiesis, and many are the products of the clinical laboratory and of the anatomical laboratory. Whether all workers agree on the suitability of the names that, in this book, have been attached to the drawings and are summarized in table 2 is not important but it is important that the mental image of a particular cell should be the same in the minds of all who discuss it, and to this end an atlas functions as liaison among many persons.

No attempt is made to champion any theory of hematopoiesis; the total effort has gone into recording what was seen and putting the cells in serial order whenever possible. In some cases it has been impossible to carry a series back to a stem cell and, rather than force a point, blanks have been left in the record. In the avian field, we are just beginning a study of normal blood morphology and thus are now at the stage attained in the human field 50 to 75 years ago. When investigations on histology and anatomy in the mammalian and human fields were being vigorously pursued at about the turn of the century, the counterpart of such studies in the avian field was neglected, perhaps because it was not realized that the same kind of prerequisite information was needed to form the foundation for later exact investigations in poultry diseases, pathology, physiology, embryology, and nutrition.

Critical studies in the field of blood diseases of poultry have been retarded because a reference work on the morphology of normal and abnormal cells has not previously existed. The *Atlas of Avian Hematology* is the first publication within the framework of a broad program on the basic histology and anatomy of the fowl. It is hoped that the program can be carried to completion.

In the interim following the completion of the manuscript, new information on the subject of avian and mammalian hematology has been published. Therefore, a few references have been added on page 242. Two addenda, one on page 93 and another on page 140, have been inserted at the end of chapters so that pagination would not be disturbed.

ALFRED M. LUCAS
CASIMIR JAMROZ

Contents

CHAPTER 1

General Remarks and Definitions

METHODS OF STUDY

Blood cells may be studied in a variety of ways. A perusal of the literature sometimes gives the impression that one technical method is far superior to another; but actually each method has its particular merit, and it is often found that the advantages of a different approach compensate for the shortcoming of the method that has been selected as the one generally to be followed.

Some of the principal methods for studying blood and some of the advantages and disadvantages that have been claimed for each method are listed in table 1. The method chosen for this Atlas is the air-dried smear. It was chosen for the reasons given in table 1 and because it is the method most commonly used for routine blood examination.

Wright's stain was employed for the circulating blood because it is the stain that is most familiar to a large number of veterinarians and research workers who are not specialists in the field of blood. Other stains would undoubtedly have made it possible to carry out certain phases of the study with greater precision, but Wright's stain, in solution, keeps well, is easy to apply, and may be procured from any medical or biological supply house.

Table 1.—**Advantages and disadvantages of various methods that have been used to study blood cells**

Method of study	Advantages	Disadvantages
KILLED CELLS	1. This method permits a great variety of technics to bring various components and reactions of cells into view. Many technics can be used that are sufficiently specific to be microchemical tests.	1. Considerable alteration occurs in the transition from life to death; thus it becomes difficult to distinguish between structures that existed in life and artifacts brought about by death.
1. Tissue, fixed, sectioned, and stained. An example would be to drop a piece of tissue such as embryo spleen in Zenker formol, wash, run through alcohols, embed, section, and stain in hematoxylin and azure II eosin.	1. Cells are fixed in approximately their normal shape; that is, they are not flattened as in dry smears. 2. Maintains topographic relationship of cells so that daughter cells and clusters of cells having a common ancestor can be identified by their proximity. 3. Shows fixed cells of tissue as well as blood cells. 4. Some regard the cytological appearance of fixed and sectioned blood cells as more reliable than smears for distinguishing differences.	1. Cells are not killed as quickly in the center of a mass of tissue as they are in a smear, so that alterations in shape and organization can occur. 2. The method is time consuming, especially if a celloidin technic is employed. This imposes a greater limitation on a survey type of study than does the smear method. 3. Most investigators consider that minute differences in nuclei and cytoplasm are not as clearly differentiated in tissue sections as in dry smears.
2. Wet fixed smears. A thin smear of blood or other tissue cells on a slide that is dropped into the fixative before it dries. Usual techniques from here on.	1. Cells by this method duplicate the appearance they have in fixed preparations so that cells studied by either method can be readily compared. 2. A fixing agent can be chosen that will serve a particular purpose—i. e., the use of methyl alcohol for preservation of granules in blood and tissue basophils. 3. Requires less time and equipment than the fixed-tissue method. 4. Cells usually not as severely flattened as in dry fixed smears.	1. Topographic relations with other cells and tissues are lost. 2. Cells do not show the delicate structural and tinctorial gradations seen in dry smears. 3. Has some practical disadvantages in the field, since it involves carrying a number of solutions.

Method of study	Advantages	Disadvantages
3. Dry fixed smears. A thin smear of blood or other tissue cells on a slide, dried in the air, stained, and dried again after staining.	1. Reveals maximum structural and tinctorial gradations that permit differentiation between closely similar cells. 2. Easy to prepare. A technic useful for work in field or laboratory research. Minimum equipment and time required.	1. Lose topographic relations with other cells and tissues. 2. Because cells in dry smears appear structurally different from cells in fixed-tissue preparations, they cannot be readily compared with cells in fixed tissues.
4. Electron microscopy. Spread cells on a gelatin screen and place in a vacuum chamber of the apparatus. Killed cells sometimes previously treated with osmic acid or other metals.	1. Offers higher magnification and resolving power than any previous method. Its greatest usefulness is to make visible minute structural details within the cell.	1. It is necessary, not only to kill the cells, but also to dehydrate them completely in vacuum, thus removing all volatile molecules. 2. This treatment of tissue cells may produce distortions even greater than those that occur in the usual fixed and stained preparations. 3. Staining technics thus far are limited to the use of metallic stains. 4. In order to see most cells with the electron microscope, the material needs to be cut into sections thinner than one micron.
LIVING CELLS	1. Living cells are generally thought to give a better standard for measuring reality of structures than do killed and stained cells. 2. Measurements of size are more accurately made on live than on dead cells.	1. The perception of the cell and its internal structure is dependent upon differences in refractive indices. Therefore, the fact that an object cannot be seen within a living cell is not proof that the object's presence in killed and stained cell is an artifact.
A. *In vivo* methods. All technics where cells are studied within the body, such as the blood studies made on the living tadpole tail, the transparent chamber built in the rabbit ear, and the use of the quartz tube to concentrate light for the study of vascular problems in the internal organs.	1. Study of cells in their natural location within the body bathed by normal body fluids gives the most reliable information of any method. That which can be clearly seen may be regarded with considerable assurance as a true picture. 2. The same cell can be followed over a considerable period in all of its reactions to surrounding cells of the body. Valuable in following the transformation of an individual cell from one type into another.	1. Technic difficulties are often insurmountable. Low-power studies have their usefulness, but individual cells are scarcely visible. Use of water or oil immersion lenses means a short working distance with all its limitations. 2. It is often difficult to transmit enough light through the tissues to illuminate adequately the field for high power work. 3. Sometimes light itself, even free from heat, will disturb the normal physiology of cells. 4. Often an operation is required to see the cells and this introduces a disturbing factor.
B. *In vitro* methods. Tissue culture chiefly, but it includes, also, all technics where living cells are studied outside the body.	1. Cells taken outside the body can be subjected to a wider variety of technical methods, and the cells can be followed more closely than within the body.	1. Cells removed from the body are no longer bound by the same physical and chemical environmental forces that existed inside the body, and new equilibriums are set up that may be atypical. 2. In temporary mounts expected to last for merely a matter of hours, the cells begin their degenerative process as soon as they leave the body, and it becomes difficult to determine between the extremes of normal variability and the early stages of irreversible degeneration.

Method of study	Advantages	Disadvantages
1. Vital staining. Methylene blue (vital), neutral red, Janus green B, and brilliant cresyl blue are examples of vital dyes that have been used extensively.	1. Motility and reactivity can be correlated with cell cytology. 2. Gives a sharper separation of lymphocytes and monocytes than with other technics. 3. Some degenerative reactions may be useful, such as the occurrence of vacuolization in granulocytes that appear 30 to 40 minutes after the preparation is made.	1. Vital dyes used in studies of this sort are usually slightly toxic. 2. Clean slides are very important in supra vital technics and may require 3 to 4 weeks to prepare properly. Thus this technic cannot be set up on short notice. 3. Fails to show variations in cytoplasmic basophilia and in nuclear details as well as they are shown in dry smears. 4. Degenerative processes inherent in vital preparations are a limiting factor in the number of slides that may be studied at one time; thus, weekly counts on 25 birds would be more of a task by this method than by using dry smears.
2. Darkfield illumination. A microscopic technic (usually with a special condenser) whereby light enters the field at such a wide angle that the field appears black except where the light strikes a particle and bends upward toward the observer.	1. Often reveals extremely delicate protoplasmic processes such as filaments of erythrocytes and the undulating membrane of monocytes. 2. Useful for study of formed structures within the cell and movements of cells without the introduction of toxic agents.	1. Not adaptable to routine study of cells or to making differential counts. 2. The reflected light gives a distorted impression of the real size of lines and dots.
3. Phase microscopy. A microscopic technic that utilizes some principles of darkfield, interference phenomena, and differences in refractive indices of various materials within the cell.	1. Has advantages of vital staining in showing movements and the existence of preformed structures such as granules and mitochondria without the disadvantage of introducing toxic dyes. 2. Reveals almost as wide a variety of structures as may be shown in fixed and stained preparations. 3. Excellent for exposing technic artifacts induced by killing and staining cells.	1. Does not get the full range of tinctorial variations obtained in stained slides.

Wright's stain is often capricious when applied to circulating blood of embryos, to bone marrow, to spleen, and to pathological blood that contains blast cells. The chief objection is its frequent failure to penetrate adequately and stain the nuclei; the nuclei remain pale blue and seemingly structureless, but close examination under oil immersion reveals that the structures are actually present, and duplicate slides stained with May-Grünwald Giemsa demonstrate that the lack of staining is not due to degeneration of the cell. Additional comments on Wright's stain are given in chapter 7, page 228. May-Grünwald Giemsa has been used routinely in this Laboratory for a number of years and in this study has been applied to all embryonic blood and to impression smears of embryonic and adult hematopoietic tissues.

The great variability of approaches to the study of blood-cell morphology has been brought out in table 1, and it is quite evident that no one method has all the advantages with no disadvantages. The numerous theories of blood-cell genesis and developmental potentialities often have been associated with a particular technic; for example, the Maximow school developed and used celloidin on fixed and cut sections and arrived at the unitarian theory of hemocytogenesis, and many proponents of this theory continue with the same technics. The clinical hematologists use the smear method extensively and, in general, hold to the polyphyletic theory. The statement that the theories are determined by the technic used would, of course, be too broad, but technic has certainly exerted an influence that cannot be ignored.

Much of the early basic concept of general cell cytology was procured from sectioned material, and the hundreds of textbook figures depicting the nucleus of the typical cell show its internal structure only, the surface structure being practically ignored. Studying only the internal structure of a cell, or only the surface structure, is comparable to gaining an impression of a house by noting the arrangement of the rooms or by looking at it from the outside; thus it is no wonder that hematologists seem so far apart in their basic concepts when often a particular school sees only one aspect of the nucleus.

The realization that the internal structure and external surface of a nucleus can present entirely different pictures came with the study of the cytology of intranuclear inclusions produced by viruses. In these cells the chromatin that marginated did not disappear (Lucas and Herrmann, 1935), and the appearance of a thin line against the nuclear membrane was not a line at all but part of a reticulum just beneath the nuclear membrane (Lucas, 1940); that this was actually a reticulum could be seen only by focusing on the membrane surface. Then, during degeneration, the marginated chromatin aggregated into larger and larger clumps. In cross-section these appeared to be a string of closely set beads, but in surface view they proved to be rather widely spaced, irregular clumps, arranged at the interstices of a network. Still another example illustrating that what appears as

dots in cross section may be a network upon surface view came from study of a prophase figure of a liver cell containing a plasmosome nucleolus (Lucas and Riser, 1945, fig. 29).

A cell that has been fixed and sectioned has approximately its normal size and shape, whereas a cell fixed by the smear method is spread out and distorted into a very thin, flat disk. The rough treatment might seem to be ample reason for discarding the latter method as reliable procedure, but cells flattened in this way show many cytological details that are never seen in a sectioned cell. A series of three diagrams (fig. 1, A, B, and C) illustrates what an observer sees when viewing a sectioned nucleus, A, as compared to a surface view of a flattened cell, C, and, as already pointed out, this is a change from the study of the interior of the nucleus to the surface of the nucleus. These figures are merely diagrams but if A and C of figure 1 are compared with the nuclear structures seen in section and surface views, as illustrated in the detailed drawings presented by Kirschbaum and Downey (1937), the similarity is striking.

In order to determine what happens to a cell when it is spread on a slide, an experiment was performed in which a slide was first coated with a thin layer of celloidin and, when dry, a blood smear was made in the normal manner on the surface. The celloidin with the flattened cells was peeled off and embedded in fluid celloidin, hardened, and sectioned transversely to the blood cells. When these flattened cells were finally located under the microscope, they were found to be exceedingly thin, certainly no more than a micron in thickness. The region of the nucleus was scarcely thicker than that of the cytoplasm alone. This means that the whole content of the cell lies in the same level and, being thin, the

---

FIGURE 1.

A, B, C: *Three stages in the shift of viewpoint from the interior of the nucleus to the surface.*

A Cut section of a nucleus, showing nuclear membrane, chromatin clumps, and a plasmosome nucleolus (stippled disk).

B A transitional step showing both interior and surface views of the nucleus.

C A flattened nucleus as it appears in a blood smear in which the nuclear plattern is determined by the chromatin reticulum at the nuclear membrane.

D, E: *Scales for measuring cells.*

D Scale for measuring cells drawn at low magnification, 1,370×.
E Scale for measuring cells drawn at high magnification, 2,470×.

F, G: *Appearance of blood smears from chickens.*

F Smear from young birds, males and nonlaying females.
G Smear from laying hens. Clear areas due to droplets of fat that flatten and spread when the smear is made.

4

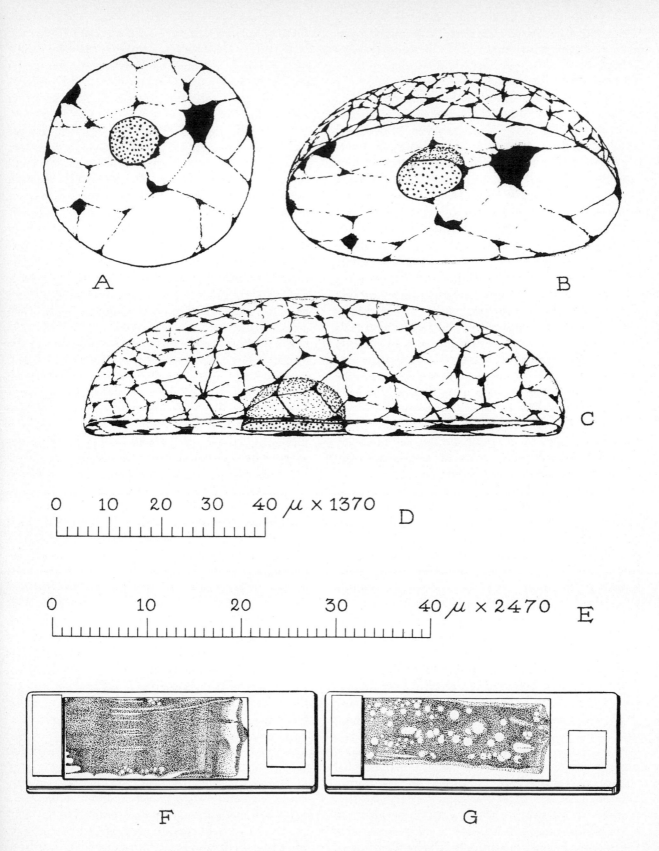

A

B

C

0   10   20   30   40 μ × 1370   D

0   10   20   30   40 μ × 2470   E

F   G

whole cell falls within the depth of focus of even the oil immersion lens. This is readily confirmed by looking at any dried blood cell of average size.

The cytosome is flattened in the same way as the nucleus, and the disk-shaped nucleus is covered by a thin layer of cytoplasm above and another below. The stainable bodies of the cytoplasm may thus be superimposed on the nuclear structure; likewise stainable particles in the fluid around the cell may come to lie upon the flattened cell, and it is impossible, because of the shallow depth of focus, to tell whether they are inside or outside the cell.

There are numerous illustrations of the points that have been presented thus far. Figures 70, 71, and 72 show examples of substances outside the cell that appear to be inside; in figures 70 and 71, parts of smudged nuclei from other cells fell upon the cytosome and produced stained bodies. In figure 72, stained serum granules fell upon the cell, and had not other granules around them been stained also, they might have been considered as lying within the cell instead of on it. In other instances, granules having an identical appearance may lie inside the cell. Considerable judgment may be required to determine what is artifact and what is real.

Figures 103, 105–107, and 110 show cytosomal inclusions that appear to be in the nuclei; they stain intensely, and the nuclei in some cases are lighter than normal, so that the particles stand out in contrast to the background. Cytoplasmic inclusions such as pale straining azurophilic bodies of the monocyte usually are not visible when they overlie a darkly stained nucleus (figs. 132–134) but they may appear to be located inside the nucleus if they stain intensely (fig. 135).

There is need at this point to explain more fully what has been said regarding the desirability of viewing both the outside and the inside of the nucleus. It was stated that in the flattened, dried cell one sees primarily the surface of the nucleus rather than its interior. It is the coarseness of this network at the surface that in part determines the extent to which objects within become visible. It is the same experience that one has in attempting to view an object through a very fine screen, as against a coarse wire net; the former almost completely blocks the view of things beyond and attention is automatically focused on the structure of the screen itself; the latter offers very little obstruction to a clear view of the objects beyond; in fact, attention must be shifted in order to see the wire net. Examples will bring out these differences as they occur in avian blood cells.

Erythroblasts and thromboblasts are characterized by the presence of nucleoli; whereas, granuloblasts, lymphoblasts, and the most immature monocytes that we have been able to find, do not appear to have nucleoli, owing in part at least to the difference in screen effect as determined by the coarseness of the chromatin reticulum. Whether nucleoli actually exist in all blast cells is not the point for consideration at this time. Granuloblasts (figs. 366 and 367) have a close screenlike pattern of chromatin reticulum and, if a nucleolus exists, it cannot be seen. The same is true for the lymphoblast (fig. 334). So far, all efforts to demonstrate a nucleolus in the granuloblast and lymphoblast of chicken blood have failed. Yet, in a few cells, a vague bluish image seemed to be present below this network (fig. 382). For practical purposes of cell-type identification, it makes no difference whether a nucleolus is actually present or not, but it is important and would have a bearing on the acceptance of one hematopoietic theory over another. In the box-turtle the immature heterophil possesses a blue-staining plasmosome nucleolus, according to Ryerson (1943). In sectioned chick material studied by Dantschakoff (1908b) a nucleolus was present inside the nucleus of the granuloblast.

The blast stages of both erythrocytes and thrombocytes show nucleoli (figs. 345, 346, 357, and 358); the former is shown more clearly than the latter, which is to be expected, since the latter has a denser chromatin layer at the nuclear surface. Yet, at best, these plasmosome nucleoli are never sufficiently sharply defined to show clearly the boundary of this body. There seem to be two reasons for this—(1) the masking effect of overlying surface chromatin particles which has already been discussed, and (2) the penetration of the stain.

Normally, when the cell dries it does not rupture; instead, the cell and nuclear membranes remain intact and merely flatten out like balloons partly filled with water, and membrane resistance to penetration is far more effective in a dried cell, even though the cell is compressed to a thickness of less than one micron, than it is in sectioned tissue of 5 to 7 microns in thickness. Drying, like tanning, seems to toughen the membranes. Lack of stain penetration is well illustrated in the use of Wright's stain on heterophils (figs. 154–167) where the nucleus does not stain in those portions that lie within the central part of the cell. When the character of the membrane is changed by a strong fixative, the stain penetrates readily and colors the chromatin brilliantly (figs. 203–214). Another example is the basophil nucleus, which often appears to be pale and ghostlike with no evidence of chromatin or other structure. This effect is in addition to the masking of the nucleus by the basophilic granules (figs. 190 and 191). In these illustrations, the stained bodies simulating chromatin clumps within the boundary of each nucleus are actually cytoplasmic basophilic granules; yet when the membrane resistance is broken down, the cell proves to have a normal nucleus capable of internal staining (fig. 221).

Dried immature cells appear to offer greater resistance to penetration of stain than do mature cells, and thus Wright's stain, which is able to penetrate the membranes of normal circulating cells, does not readily do so in the case of precursor cells found in bone marrow, spleen, thymus, and other hematopoietic organs. On the other hand, May-Grünwald Giemsa can penetrate immature cells quite well, with an occasional exception (figs. 259, 281, and 334). Neoplastic blood cells are usually at various stages of immaturity, and it is for this reason that following Wright's stain they often appear as basophilic rings with empty nuclei. A May-Grünwald Giemsa stain on these cells will generally bring out the details of nuclear structure. Although Emmel (1936) did not give the stain used in his studies on hemocytoblastosis, many of the figures he has depicted as degenerated cells are identical in appearance with cells that have been inadequately colored with Wright's stain. His figure 3B is a good example. In this study such conditions are regarded as defective technic, not as degenerated cells.

Jones (1948) discussed the problem of the appearance of nuclei in cut sections versus dried smears for embryo rat blood, and on most points we are in agreement, except that he considers the nuclear pattern as due to overlying mitochondria; whereas, we recognize that cell organelles may play a part, yet believe that the pattern is due chiefly to the arrangement of chromatin at the nuclear membrane.

The question can justifiably be raised, How should the study of normal hematology be approached? In one book on human hematology approximately the first hundred pages are devoted to the cytology of blast-cell types and their derivatives. These figures form the basis of comparison for the subject matter of the body of the book on blood diseases, yet approximately 85 percent of the cells selected for illustration and description in the section illustrating stages in development of each blood-cell type came from patients suffering from different types of leukemias or infectious diseases. Only a few were taken from normal, healthy individuals, and usually these were the mature stages of cell lines. It is recognized that pathologic conditions often reveal what cannot be deciphered readily from the normal, where all processes of formation and destruction of blood cell lines are in balance; yet from our limited experience with pathologic avian blood, undoubtedly we would have gone astray had the picture of the normal been built upon abnormal blood conditions. It was observed for example, that heterophil myelocytes found in circulating blood after irradiation were slightly different in general appearance and cytologic detail from those found in normal bone marrow of the chicken. In leukemias as well as in this example from irradiation, immature cells have been pushed into a new environment, and thus two variables are operating, either of which may be responsible for their slightly different appearance—(1) the chemical constitution of the new environment and (2) the abnormal conditions that produced them.

Isaacs (1928) was dealing with essentially the same problem when he noted that bone-marrow cells and tumor cells stained more brilliantly when mixed with blood serum than when imprints from these tissues were made directly on the slide.

As a side effect, the fact must not be overlooked that often disease conditions weaken and change the permeability of the cell membrane; thus it may well be that some of the differences we see are merely a matter of degree derived from the more effective penetration of the blood stains used. Determination of the correct answer must await further collection of data.

The same complaint was made by Dantschakoff (1908b) against the use of blood from cases of leukemia and other blood diseases as source material for establishing the normal. She says (p. 477), ". . . Nach meiner Meinung ist es z. B. heute bei der verwirrenden Menge von einzelnen, nicht systematischen Beobachtungen geradezu aussichtslos, aus Beobachtungen an krankhaft verändertem Blut des erwachsenen Menschen z. B. bei den verschiedenen Leukämien etc., auf die normale Entstehung und die Verwandtschaft der verschiedenen Blutzellenformen zu schliessen, wie es jetzt von vielen tatsächlich gemacht wird."[1]

TERMINOLOGY

One of the big problems in morphologic hematology is the choice of an acceptable terminology. Theories of hematology have influenced the terminology and for the early stages, at least, each school has its own set of names. This fact makes a selection of working terminology, independent of any particular theory, often impossible to find. The reader should bear in mind, therefore, that when a particular term is applied to a cell, the authors have selected it without any implication that they favor the theory of hematopoiesis commonly associated with the term. No single investigator has been able to encompass the whole field of hematology from his own researches, and the terms he uses in his own studies are influenced by the appearance of the cells as revealed by the particular technics he has used. Were one unbiased person able to thoroughly review the whole hematologic picture of the normal and abnormal of the embryo and of the adult for just one species of reptile, bird, or mammal, by sectioned tissue, by smear method, and by vital technic, supplemented by tissue culture, probably all conflicting theories could be merged into a uniform concept of hematopoiesis in health and disease. A similar thought was expressed by Doan (1932) when he said, ". . . It is agreed that all [blood cells] take their first beginnings from the mesenchymal cells of the mesodermal layer in the embryo. But thereafter the theories and hypotheses diverge more or less radically, though I would venture to assert that the differences arise more in the interpretation than in opposing objective observations, where experiments have paralleled in materials and methods." A survey of comparative hematology by Jordan (1938) brings out the point that regardless of the wide differences in form and habitat from fish to man, the general blood patterns are remarkably constant and similar.

Kindred (1940), using the rat, illustrated the appearance of the same cell type as seen by the section and by the smear method. This work brought out clearly the difference in appearance of the nuclei of cells by these two different technics. A still more striking comparison was made by Kirschbaum and Downey (1937) when they placed some of Maximow's drawings (1909) derived from celloidin sectioned material beside drawings of corresponding cells made from air-dried smears. The material for both came from 14-day-old rabbit embryos. The wide differences in cell identification and even terminology that can be attributable largely to the different appearance of similar cells in two different technics is provocative. Our own studies on cell identification agree closely with those of Kirschbaum and Downey, except that we have avoided the use of the term "megaloblast" because of the controversy associated with the identity of the cell and the correct usage of the term (Jones, 1943).

Kracke and Garver (1937) and Osgood and Ashworth (1937) emphasize in their atlases the need for standardized terminology and in the first of the books mentioned, the origins of the words commonly and uncommonly used are discussed rather fully. Exact terminology often moves contrary to simplified terminology. Proposals made by a committee for standardized terminology are highly commendable (Anonymous, 1949), but the names proposed are specifically adapted to man and are not broad enough to fulfill entirely the needs for terminology in other classes of vertebrates. Although a serious effort has been made by the authors to fit the terminology of the bird into the exact framework designed for clinical medicine of the human, the effort did not succeed and one cannot avoid the conclusion that any satisfactory universal terminology should be broad enough to include

[1] Translation: In my opinion, it is downright hopeless, for instance to draw conclusions about the normal origin and the relationships of the various blood cell forms from today's bewildering mass of separate unsystematic observations of pathologically altered blood of adults in various leukemias, for example: but this is actually done today by many students.

all vertebrates and, if possible, all theories of hematopoiesis.

Table 2 shows the lineages of cell lines as seen in the birds. For each line, there is listed at the top of the column a primordial stem cell or blast cell. In human hematology, blast cells are pictured and described as containing one or more nucleoli that appear as pale blue homogeneous bodies following the commonly used blood stains. In avian blood, no more than one nucleolus has been seen in any cell line except in the primary generation of embryonic erythrocytes, and nucleoli are absent from granuloblasts, lymphoblasts, and probably monoblasts, at least by the same technics that have revealed them in human blood.

Erythroblasts, thromboblasts, lymphoblasts, granuloblasts, and primordial osteogenic cells of birds are somewhat more easily distinguished than in the human species. Each represents the earliest recognizable member of its respective line, and although some do not show nucleoli, each is believed to be equivalent functionally to the same blast cell by the same name in the human series. The important point is that in many cases they can be separated on the basis of their structure, even when isolated from the other cells on the slide. This does not alway hold true in the human field, and in the atlas by Osgood and Ashworth (1937) it is stated (p. 36), "In the author's opinion [Osgood], the individual granuloblast (myeloblast) is morphologically indistinguishable from the most immature lymphoblast, monoblast, plasmoblast, or karyoblast (megaloblast). The differentiation of the type of cell has to be made by identification of the cells found associated with the stem cell under consideration. A stem cell found in association with a progranulocyte (promyelocyte) is classed as a granuloblast." (References to figures have been omitted in the quotation just given.) It is this type of dependence upon the presence of more highly differentiated cells in the same field for exact placement of the different blast cells that has led the unitarian hematologist to suggest that if blast cells all look alike and are all characterized by a narrow rim of blue-staining cytoplasm around the nucleus, and the nucleus contains a nucleolus, it is just as logical to say that there is a single common stem cell capable of differentiation into any blood cell type. As already mentioned, the criticism leveled at this view of blast cells in mammals cannot be applied as readily to avian blood because, as seen by the smear method, cytologic differences do exist among the blast cells.

All schools of hematology recognize the fact that if the genealogy of cell types is carried far enough back into the embryology of the organism, there will be a common cell for all blood-cell types. The point of controversy is not on this matter but on whether a blast cell of a particular cell line is a fixed type, incapable of differentiation under stimulus into other cell types. Answers to such questions must come from experimentation and, as far as the present study is concerned, there is no evidence that blood cells have or have not any potentiality beyond the particular line that they represent.

On the basis of what has been observed in the chicken, its embryology, and its hematopoietic organs, a blast cell may be defined as the earliest recognizable cell belonging to a particular cell type, and all following stages observed consist of progressive steps toward the mature cell. To this should be added the observation that if, antecedent to the blast cell, there does exist a totipotent cell type other than mesenchyme, reticular, and possibly connective and endothelial tissues, it has not been found in this study. It should be added, also, that the terminology presented in table 2 is based on the assumption that the usual medium and small lymphocyte found in circulating blood is a mature cell, on a par with all other fully differentiated mature cells found in the circulating blood, and that it is not a totipotent primordial cell capable, at least in the course of normal hematopoiesis, of producing all other blood-cell types. In normal blood only two types of mature lymphocytes exist, medium and small; the large lymphocyte is not a mature cell but is an immature cell usually standing early in the lineage of the cell line to which it belongs, which may not necessarily be the lymphocyte line.[2]

More than one erythrocyte series exists in the life of the embryo up to hatching. There is a primary series representing the first generation of red cells in the embryo; then follow several generations, each less precocious in its hemoglobin formation than the preceding one and,

---

[2] For further clarification of viewpoint see:
Lucas, A. M. 1959. A discussion of synonymy in avian and mammalian hematologic nomenclature. Amer. Jour. Vet. Res. 78: 887–897.

Table 2.—Stages in development of blood-cell types

Erythrocyte series	Thrombocyte series		Nongranular leukocytes		Plasmocyte series
	Embryonic series	Definitive series	Lymphocyte series	Monocyte series	
Erythroblast.	Thromboblast.	Thromboblast.	Lymphoblast.	Monoblast (not seen).	Plasmablast (not seen).
Early polychromatic erythrocyte.	Large embryo thrombocyte.	Early immature thrombocyte.	Immature lymphocyte.	Early immature monocyte.	Early immature plasma cyte.
Mid-polychromatic erythrocyte.	Medium embryo thrombocyte.	Mid-immature thrombocyte.	Mature lymphocyte. Medium. Small.	Late immature monocyte.	Late immature plasma cyte.
Late polychromatic erythrocyte.	Small embryo thrombocyte.	Late immature thrombocyte.		Mature monocyte.	Mature plasmacyte.
Reticulocyte.		Mature thrombocyte.			
Mature erythrocyte.					

Granular leukocytes			Osteogenic cells	
Heterophil series	Eosinophil series	Basophil series	Osteocyte series	Osteoclast series
Granuloblast.	Granuloblast.	Granuloblast.	Primordial osteogenic cell.	Primordial osteogenic cell.
Metagranuloblast.	Metagranuloblast.	(Metagranuloblast—combined with succeeding stage).	Immature osteoblast.	Mononuclear osteoclast.
Promyelocyte.	(Promyelocyte—combined with succeeding stage).	Promyelocyte.	Mature osteoblast.	Multinuclear osteoclast.
Mesomyelocyte.	Mesomyelocyte.	Mesomyelocyte.	Osteocyte (not studied).	
Metamyelocyte.	Metamyelocyte.	Metamyelocyte.		
Mature heterophil.	Mature eosinophil.	Mature basophil.		

finally, the definitive cell line arises. Thrombocyte stages of development in the embryo differ morphologically also from those found in the definitive stages. Therefore, to cover all these variations, definitions must be broad.

ERYTHROCYTE SERIES

Erythroblast.—A large cell with more cytoplasm in relation to the nucleus than in most blast cells. The cytoplasm of the primary generation is strongly basophilic, but in the definitive cell line it stains less intensely. The cytosome shows mitochondrial spaces and may have an amoeboid shape. The nucleus is an open, coarse network with chromatin that is clumped more than usually found in other blast cells. The plasmosome nucleolus is large and more conspicuous than in the thromboblast.

Early polychromatic erythrocyte.—A smaller cell than the blast stage, and the cytosome is rounded. Mitochondrial spaces are largely replaced by a more homogeneous cytoplasm. The cytosome has a strong basophilic color. The chromatin of the nucleus is definitely clumped. The nucleolus is smaller than in the blast stage but is often visible.

Mid-polychromatic erythrocyte.—This cell is usually smaller than in the preceding stage, of rounded shape, and has a gray cytoplasmic color that ranges from nearly basophilic to slightly eosinophilic. No mitochondrial spaces are visible but the cytosome often shows an artifact of fractured spaces usually concentric to the cell perimeter. The nucleus is small relative to the cytoplasm. It is round and has a clumped chromatin pattern. No nucleolus is seen in the definitive cells.

Late polychromatic erythrocyte.—This cell is round to slightly oval. Staining of the cytoplasm varies from an eosinophilic gray color to a pale eosin and, in the older cells, to a moderate eosin color. Fracture artifacts tend to appear in the younger forms of this stage. The nucleus is round to slightly oval and there is irregular clumping of the chromatin.

Reticulocyte.—Without special stain, this cell appears as a late polychromatic erythrocyte with almost full development of hemoglobin or even as a mature erythrocyte. A reticulocyte stain reveals the presence of granules in the cytosome, concentric to the nucleus. The basophilic granules characteristic of a typical reticulocyte may be found at earlier stages of development, after the appearance of hemoglobin in the cell.

Mature erythrocyte.—This cell has an oval shape and a cytosome of uniform texture, colored a reddish orange. The nucleus is elongated, oval, and sometimes rodlike with rounded ends. The nucleus is leptochromatic to pachychromatic. Aged cells have dense homogeneous or nearly structureless nuclei.

THROMBOCYTE SERIES

Thromboblast.—A cell with basophilic cytoplasm that is amoeboid in the early embryonic generations. The cytosome forms a narrow rim around the nucleus. Spaces are present in the cytosome. It has a round nucleus with a plasmosome nucleolus that may be masked by the density of chromatin granules. The chromatin tends to be punctate in contrast to that of the erythroblast, where it is more angular, merging into the linin network.

Thrombocytes appear to be functional in the embryo from an early stage and hence probably should not be called immature; thus, in table 2 two columns of terms are given for the thrombocytes—one for the embryo and one for the bone marrow of the adult and circulating blood.

Embryo Thrombocytes

Large embryo thrombocyte.—This is a large cell with a moderate amount of cytoplasm around the nucleus. The cytosome shows partial to nearly complete vacuolization and stains more lightly than in the preceding stage. The nucleus has large irregular chromatin clumps and no visible nucleolus.

Medium embryo thrombocyte.—A cell of medium size with about the same nucleocell ratio as before. The cytosome is fully vacuolated and specific granules sometimes are present. Early degeneration is marked by pinkish coloration and by crumpling of the borders of the cytosome. The nucleus is pachychromatic.

Small embryo thrombocyte.—A small cell of which the cytosome is highly vacuolated and pale staining. The nucleus is dense and individual chromatin clumps are fairly distinct. Nearly all cells of this type, as seen in the smear of embryo blood, have lost most of the cytosome and are clumped.

Definitive Thrombocytes

Early immature thrombocyte.—A large cell, often not round, and with the nucleocell ratio less than in the preceding stage. The cytoplasm is basophilic but the overall color is lightened by the presence of vacuoles. The nucleolus may still be visible and the chromatin is aggregated into clumps of nonuniform size.

Mid-immature thrombocyte.—A cell of medium size that is often elongated slightly or has an irregular shape. The cytoplasm is vacuolated and stains a light blue color. Specific granules may be present. The chromatin is clumped extensively but linin network is still visible.

Late immature thrombocyte.—This cell is elongated but the nucleus fills up a larger proportion of it than at the mature stage. Clumps of chromatin are still clearly visible. Specific cytoplasmic granules are generally present.

Mature thrombocyte.—The mature definitive thrombocyte has an ovoid shape and is slightly smaller than the mature erythrocyte. The cytosome takes on a pale blue color with most blood stains. The intensity of color is varied by the presence of vaguely defined rarefied areas.

The nucleus is usually round rather than elongated as in the mature erythrocytes. The chromatin is clumped and the clumps are closely packed, which gives to the nucleus an effect of density equal to or greater than that of the small lymphocyte.

One or more specific granules, having a weak affinity for acidophilic dyes, are visible in most mature thrombocytes. These granules usually lie at one end of the cell.

LYMPHOCYTE SERIES

Lymphoblast.—This is a large round cell with a narrow rim of cytoplasm that stains dark blue but may contain colorless spaces. The chromatin forms a delicate reticular pattern. No nucleolus is visible.

Immature lymphocyte.—General appearance the same as in the blast stage, except that the chromatin of the nucleus shows clumping and the cell is smaller.

Mature lymphocyte.—Nucleocell ratio is similar to that of the blast cell. The chromatin of the nucleus is definitely clumped but not always in massive blocks even in the small mature lymphocyte. The separation of size into "medium" and "small" is purely arbitrary.

MONOCYTE SERIES

Monoblast.—Thus far the monoblast stage has not been definitely identified.

Early immature monocyte.—The cytoplasm of this cell stains a clear blue color with or without basophilic granules. Azurophilic granules may be present. The nucleus has a granularity on a reticulum quite similar to that of the mature cell. The cytosome is large relative to the nucleus.

Late immature monocyte.—The cytoplasm often shows a basophilic granulation, or reticulum, and azurophilic bodies may be present. The nucleus is round and has an eccentric position in the cell and a *Hof* may be present.

Mature monocyte.—The cytosome is large relative to the nucleus. The cytoplasm has a reticular structure and contains azurophilic substances, either on the reticulum or as discrete granules. The nucleus usually is indented and adjacent to it is a *Hof* area with spheres faintly stained an orange color present in the vacuoles. The chromatin is usually a delicate reticulum but may be composed of coarse blocks.

HETEROPHIL SERIES

Granuloblast.—A large round cell with a narrow rim of cytoplasm around the nucleus. The cytosome stains an intense blue color and is only slightly interrupted by light-staining areas. The chromatin forms a reticulum more delicate than for any other blast cell. The smear method would indicate that a nucleolus is absent. The morphology of the granuloblast is the same for heterophils, eosinophils, and basophils.

Metagranuloblast.—The cytoplasm on the side opposite the eccentrically placed nucleus is vacuolated with spaces of approximately equal size. The nuclear chromatin may be aggregated slightly, but more often the chromatin remains in the form of a delicate reticulum, and the boundary between the nucleus and cytoplasm becomes indistinct. At this stage no granules characteristic of this cell line have appeared.

Promyelocyte.—This stage also precedes the appearance of specific granules. The boundary of the nucleus often becomes indistinct and in the cytosome there appear dark-stained magenta granules and rings. The magenta bodies are highly characteristic for the heterophil but are not specific for it. Orange-stained spheres are present in the vacuolated cytoplasm and these are the precursors of the definitive rods.

Mesomyelocyte.—From the precursor orange spheres come the definitive rods. Cells with less than half the number of definitive rods are included in this stage. Magenta rings and granules may still be present. The nuclear boundary often is still vague. In some cells there is evidence of nuclear condensation.

Metamyelocyte.—This cell usually is smaller than the preceding one. The cytosome contains more than half the normal complement of rods. The chromatin of the nucleus is condensed and in older stages the nucleus may have a bean shape. The nucleus begins to show staining refractiveness characteristic of adult cells.

Mature heterophil.—The cell contains a full complement of rods and the nuclear lobes may vary from 1 to 5 or more. The chromatin of the nucleus is aggregated into clumps.

EOSINOPHIL SERIES

Granuloblast.—Morphologically this cell is the same as described for the heterophil series.

Metagranuloblast.—The nucleus is eccentric and this position produces a crescent of cytoplasm at one side. The vacuoles are more uniform and more sharply defined than in the heterophil at this stage. The nuclear structure is more definite than in the heterophil, and chromatin clumps are larger.

Promyelocyte.—This stage is defined as the one in which only precursor substance that produces the definitive specific granule is present, but in immature eosinophils, all degrees of development from the precursor substance to the definitive granule may be found. Therefore, this stage overlaps the next, and the term "mesomyelocyte" has been used to cover both stages.

Mesomyelocyte.—Definitive granules arise at this stage, and all cells are included under this term that have less than half the usual number found in the adult cell. The nucleus is more definite and chromatin more condensed than in the heterophil.

Metamyelocyte.—This is an immature myelocyte with more than half the number of specific granules. The nucleus may be round, indented, or constricted, and its chromatin clumped irregularly.

Mature eosinophil.—Contains a full complement of specific granules, and the number of lobes in the nucleus may vary from one to five. The chromatin clumps are close together.

BASOPHIL SERIES

Granuloblast.—Morphologically this cell is the same as described for the heterophil series.

Metagranuloblast.—This stage is present but, concurrently with the characteristic vacuolization of the cytosome, the magenta granules appear also, and thus the term "promyelocyte" has been used for the two stages combined.

Promyelocyte.—Scattered magenta bodies are present. They are closely similar to those of the heterophil, except that there is less tendency to form rings. If rings are present, they are usually small. Vacuoles are present in the cytoplasm but they are less uniform in size than for the other two preceding granulocytes. The nucleus is eccentric and has a coarse chromatin pattern.

Mesomyelocyte.—This cell is smaller than the preceding one. The nucleus usually is not in the center but is not completely eccentric. The cytosome contains less than half the number of granules found in the adult cell. The water solubility of the granules is a confusing factor in estimating number.

Metamyelocyte.—This cell contains more than half the total number of basophil granules. The nucleus is near the center and is composed of a dense chromatin network.

Mature basophil.—This cell contains a full complement of granules. The nucleus is a single body in most cases, but occasionally it is divided into two lobes.

OSTEOGENIC CELLS

Primordial osteogenic cell.—A large amoebid cell with lightly stained cytoplasm containing clear vacu-

oles. There are relatively few mitochondrial spaces. The cytosome is large relative to the nucleus. The nuclear chromatin is finely punctate and a nucleolus is present that stains light blue.

Osteocyte Series

Immature osteoblast.—The nucleus is placed eccentrically. Large and definite mitochondrial spaces are present. Usually there is a clear area on the side of the nucleus toward the center of the cell. Clear spherical vacuoles are present in the cytosome. The nucleus stains darkly with uniform granulation, and usually one blue-stained nucleolus is present.

Mature osteoblast.—A darkly stained cell with well developed, clear areas adjacent to the nucleus. All parts of the cytosome are filled with mitochondrial spaces. The nucleus has a pattern of granular chromatin, and a nucleolus is present.

Osteocyte.—This cell has not been seen in smear preparations of bone marrow since it is embedded within the substance of the bone.

Osteoclast Series

Mononuclear osteoclast.—This cell closely resembles the primordial osteogenic cell. The nucleus may be in the center of a round cell or at one end of an elongated cell. It contains a mixture of delicate vacuoles composed of mitochondrial spaces and eosinophilic accumulations. Also present are some clear vacuoles with a definite spherical shape. The nucleus is composed of particulate granules on a linin network and beneath this a nucleolus is visible.

Multinuclear osteoclast.—This is the only giant cell of the avian bone marrow. The cytosome contains basophilic and sometimes eosinophilic substances, and the latter usually are concentrated in the central part of the cell. Many vacuoles and granules and sometimes irregularly shaped bodies are present in the cytosome. The borders of the cell are poorly defined. The nucleus is large and round; it contains relatively fine, punctate granules; a single nucleolus is present.

PLASMACYTE SERIES

Plasmablast.—This cell may be a primordial osteogenic cell or a reticular type cell. It has not been identified thus far.

Early immature plasmacyte.—The ratio of cytosomal to nuclear size is about the same as in the monocyte. The cytosome contains vacuoles and mitochondrial spaces, and the ground substance stains a clear blue that is more transparent than the basophilic cytoplasm of most other young cells.

Late immature plasmacyte.—The cytoplasm in this cell is colored the same shade of blue as in the preceding stage, but there are fewer mitochondrial spaces

13

and more vacuoles. The nucleus is small in relation to the cell area, and is darkly stained. There is a clear area in the cytosome at the side of the nucleus.

Mature plasmacyte.—The cell may vary in size from large to small, and the cytosome contains numerous granules, ranging from large to small. The nucleus contains condensed blocks of chromatin and is located against the cell wall. A clear area adjacent to the nucleus is present in most mature plasmacytes.

The definitions that have been presented are in reality brief descriptions of each cell type, and the use of these, combined with the illustrations, should make it possible to put together quickly the necessary facts for identification of any mature or immature cell without extensive reading.

Brief mention of some terms used in general cytology may be helpful. The cell is composed of two main parts—nucleus and cytosome; the former contains nucleoplasm and the latter, cytoplasm. If a large dense mass of basichromatin lies within the nucleus, it is called a karyosome or karyosome nucleolus, and if the mass or sphere takes acidophilic dyes, it is called a plasmosome or plasmosome nucleolus, and if both karyosome plasmosome are present, the two form an amphinucleolus.

Wherever color is mentioned, it is understood that Wright's stain was used on smears of the circulating blood of the hatched chicken, and May-Grünwald Giemsa was used for immature cells found in embryos and in hematopoietic organs of both embryo and hatched chick. Any exceptions to this have been noted in the legends or text. These two stains give closely similar colors on the same cell, but the latter produces a somewhat more intense coloration.

MAGNIFICATION

The measurement of blood cells is an important field of study, and especially so on erythrocytes, which have a definite shape and are held by a firm stroma. Some measurements of length and of width of elongated cells and of diameters of circular cells and of areas of irregularly shaped cells have been undertaken in this study. Not as much emphasis has been put on cell size as in some atlases on human blood.

Size is a helpful adjunct to cellular morphology for the categorizing of cells into types and into stages of development, but if one takes away color, form, and internal structure, then size alone becomes a rather inadequate tool for cell identification. This is especially true of cells prepared for study by the smear method, which flattens them as broadly as their membranes will permit. Smears from bone marrow and other hematopoietic organs showed this quite clearly: in an area where the smear was thick, the cells were smaller, but at the edges of a group of cells they were larger and, in many cases, were stretched to the breaking point in drying. In the wet-fixed smear the cells are much smaller than in the dried smear and they often appear shrunken. Compare, for example, the size of basophils that have been fixed by drying in air (figs. 385–387) with similar cells fixed in methyl alcohol (figs. 388–390).

Most often the visual impression of size as seen microscopically forms the basis for the statement that a cell is large, or medium, or small and, only rarely, is the filar micrometer taken out of the box and actual measurements of size made. True, actual measurements should be taken more often than they are, but the fact remains that we depend to a great extent on mental impressions for a comparative estimate of the size of objects. Therefore, in order to avoid confusion in making these impressions from the illustrations, only two magnifications have been used—one called low power and the other, high power. Two scales have been constructed (fig. 1, *D* and *E*). One, *D*, is equivalent to the measurements in microns at a magnification of $1370\times$ and the other, *E*, at $2470\times$. With these scales the size of any cell or its part can be estimated fairly closely, since all cells, both at low and high magnification, were drawn carefully with a camera lucida.

The low-power drawings were made at an optical magnification of $400\times$ and a magnification when projected on drawing paper of $913.3\times$. The high-power drawings were made at an optical magnification of $1125\times$ and a projected magnification of $2470\times$. By optical magnification is meant the theoretical value obtained when the magnification of the objective is multiplied by the magnification of the eyepiece. The low-power drawings were made by using a $20\times$ objective and a $20\times$ ocular, and the high-power drawings were made with a $90\times$ objective and $12.5\times$ ocular. During the engraving process, all the low-power drawings that originally were approximately 3 x 3⅞ inches were increased in size 50 percent, so that, as presented here, they are 4½ x 5¹³⁄₁₆ inches or slightly more. Therefore, in the low-power drawings, the cells are shown at about 1370 times their natural size.

The purpose of the low-power drawings is to give the overall impression that one has when looking through the microscope and observing different kinds of cells in the same field. Under such conditions one can distinguish minute differences in color, tone, or texture that often vanish when single cells are removed from the environment of other cells, even when they have been drawn at a much higher magnification. The low-power drawings serve another purpose in that they contain about four times as many cells as are represented in the high-power drawings; therefore, the same cell type shown at high magnification can be presented sufficiently often so that deviations from the typical are fully illustrated. If all these variations were presented as high-power drawings the Atlas would be unduly large.

An outline of the individual cells of each low-power drawing is given on the facing page along with the legend. Identification of the cells in the field is made by numbers placed on or near the cells of the outline drawing.

Blood from mammals often spreads unevenly over the slide when the smear is made and in particular shows a clumping of platelets and an aggregation of leukocytes along the margins of the preparation. In order to reduce this tendency as much as possible, the mammalian hematologist has often used coverglass smears. This has not been necessary for preparations of avian blood because the cells in the average well-made smear do not segregate, there is no clumping of thrombocytes, and the erythrocytes do not rearrange themselves in rouleaux formation. The simplest and easiest method is to place a small drop of blood on the end of a "pusher" slide and to touch this to one end of another slide where it is held for a moment—long enough for the drop to spread to each edge of the pusher slide. The latter slide is then steadily and rather quickly slid to the opposite end of the "smear" slide at an angle of about 45 degrees.

The appearance of the typical blood smear in which there is a relatively even distribution of cells is obtained from all hatched chickens, except laying hens, as shown in figure 1 *F*. The scratches and abraded spots that often come when the slides are blotted or handled roughly are included. The appearance of a smear made from the blood of a laying hen is shown in figure 1 *G;* the fat globules in the serum spread when the smear was made and pushed the cells of the undried layer aside. This, however, disturbed only slightly the uniformity of distribution of cells and did not cause certain cell types to segregate.

ARRANGEMENT OF SUBJECT MATTER

It is often helpful to the reader of a scientific book if the writer reviews briefly the general plan of organization and what was in his mind when seemingly unrelated things sometimes were placed beside each other. In this study, the list of chapter headings reflects the scope and sequence of the fields covered.

More emphasis has been placed on the subject matter of the second chapter than on any other. It contains almost as many drawings as do all other chapters combined. The purpose of this emphasis is to give as much help as possible to the field worker in poultry diseases, whose first consideration when confronted with an unknown condition is to arrive as quickly as possible at a preliminary diagnosis.

The four categories into which the study of each cell type is grouped is best exemplified in the erythrocyte series from the circulating blood of the hatched chicken. These series fall into the following classifications: (1) Normal mature cells, (2) normal immature forms found in circulating blood, (3) abnormal cells, and (4) artifacts. Sometimes the variety of immature cells found in circulating blood is so great that these cells appear to represent the complete developmental series, but they were included under the circulating blood to indicate the range of cell types that might be picked up in a general examination. In the study of embryo circulating blood and blood from hematopoietic organs, these cells are shown in their proper setting in the form of a complete series. This may appear to be a duplication of effort, but it has proved to be of great help in the exact characterization

15

of a cell type or stage of development because, as already mentioned, immature cells when they are carried by the circulating blood often have an appearance that is different from that presented when they are in the environment of the organ from which they came.

A distinction has been made between abnormal cells and artifacts; actually there is a third category, namely, variations from the typically normal, and to place each atypical cell in the correct one of these three categories has taken far more study and experimentation than finding, illustrating, and describing the "typical" cells. Likewise, the possibility of error is greater, so that future research may well discover that what has been called abnormal is, in reality, an artifact, or merely a variation of the normal. Cells are called abnormal on the assumption that the abnormality in them was present within the body of the bird, and artifacts are considered to be deviations from the normal that presumably were caused in the process of taking blood, or drying it, or applying the stain. Since so much less is known of the cytology of immature blood cells than of the mature types, the series of examples showing abnormalities and artifacts are much fewer in the chapters on embryo blood and on bone marrow cells than in chapter 2.

Chapters 3, 4, and 5 have much in common in regard to their subject matter; they all deal with cells during development. This is true, whether the cells were collected from functional circulating blood of the embryo or from various hematopoietic organs of embryo or adult.

Chapter 6 is devoted primarily to a description of blood cells of avian species other than the chicken. It was soon discovered that similarities in the morphology of blood cells of different species were much greater than differences. Included also in this chapter is tabular material on cell sizes and cell counts.

A chapter on technic was included at the end of the volume. Sometimes it happens that seeming differences in cell morphology can be traced to the use of different technics by different investigators. It was hoped that this difficulty might be avoided if the technics used in this study were set forth. Many methods in addition to those discussed here have been applied to avian blood studies.

CHAPTER 2

Circulating Blood of the Hatched Chicken

ERYTHROCYTES

Normal mature erythrocytes (figs. 4–8)

The "typical" erythrocyte of birds has often been described as an oval cell with an oval nucleus (Goodall, 1909; Foot, 1913; Magath and Higgins, 1934; and many others). Forkner (1929) has described in detail its appearance in vital stained preparations. The nucleus is not quite concentric with the contour of the cell; there is a wider margin at the poles of the cell than at the sides. The cytoplasm takes an orange pink color with Wright's stain and with May-Grünwald Giemsa gives a distinctly more reddish color. The nucleus stains intensely but reveals a pattern of chromatin clumps more or less uniformly distributed. If the nucleus has an oval shape, there are no massive chromatin clumps. If the nucleus is contracted to an elongated rod-shaped structure, dense clumps of chromatin are usually present. A nucleolus is absent.

Low-power views are presented in figures 2 and 3. The slide from which figure 2 was made came from the flock of Single Comb White Leghorn chickens maintained at this Laboratory, and figure 3 was drawn from a set of 25 slides obtained from the same breed at another location, which for convenience has been designated as Laboratory No. 2. Thus, even in these two samples, differences can be observed and probably could be extended if a careful study were made of blood from many sources.

A typical cell is shown in figure 4. It was necessary to do considerable searching to find this "typical" cell. Examples are shown also in figures 2, 7 and 3, 7. All the other cells deviate from it in shape of nucleus or cytosome or both. The cells may be too round or too elongate or irregular (fig. 3, 5). The nuclei may be too large or too small for the cytosome (figs. 2, 10 and 3, 10); the long axis of the nuclei may not coincide with those of the cells that contain them, or they may be eccentrically placed (figs. 2, 9 and 3, 9); the nuclei may not be in the center of the cells and may be blunt at one end and pointed at the other. Most conspicuous of all are the indentations (figs. 2, 11, 12 and 3, 11, 12), constrictions (fig. 2, 13), and protrusions (figs. 2, 14 and 3, 14). Even duplications of the nuclei (figs. 7, 8, and 29) may be found. As far as can be determined, these are all normal cells and in spite of their multiplicity of shape they are all instantly recognizable as mature erythrocytes, because the hemoglobin gives to the cytosome a strong affinity for acid dyes and a nearly homogeneous texture. In some cases a narrow rim of cytosome around the nucleus stains lighter than the more peripheral part, but this is probably an artifact that developed when the cell was flattened in the process of making the smear. This perinuclear space is shown in figure 2 but not in figure 3. The clear space, as suggested, may arise as an artifact but its occurrence in one smear and not in another may be worthy of further study. A perinuclear space appears in all types of blood cells, except the heterophil, when the smear has been fixed in Petrunkevitch No. 2, and stained in May-Grünwald Giemsa (figs. 198–202, 215, and 221). Following this technic the nucleus of the erythrocyte appears to be almost a solid chromatin mass.

Suggestions concerning the origin of multipolar and giant erythrocytes and leukocytes in man have been given by Schwarz (1946). He believes these conditions can be traced back to multinuclear conditions in the immature stages.

Certain types of variability have significance. Among the 25 blood smears received from Laboratory No. 2 there were several in which the nuclei of the erythrocytes were longer and narrower (figs. 3, 8, and 5) than any found in smears from our flock. Also, the chromatin was more condensed and more heavily stained. The significance is not known but the same type of erythrocyte has been observed in some of the smears

17

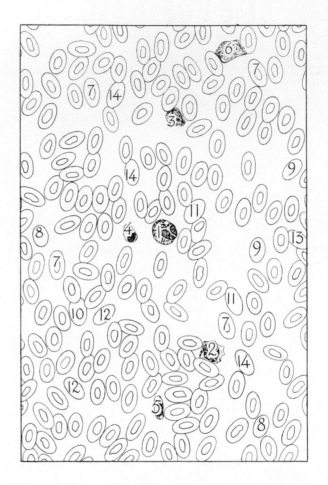

FIGURE 2.—Appearance of a typical smear made from the blood of the basilic (cubital) vein of a Single Comb White Leghorn chicken. This bird, raised in isolation, was 2,095 days of age when the smear was taken. 1,370×.

1 Heterophil.	9 Erythrocytes with eccentrically placed nuclei.
2, 3 Lymphocytes.	10 Round undersized nucleus.
4, 5 Thrombocytes.	11 Erythrocyte nuclei indented at one end.
6 Squashed erythrocyte nucleus.	12 Erythrocyte nuclei indented on one side.
7 Typical erythrocytes.	13 Erythrocyte with constricted nucleus.
8 Erythrocytes smaller than average.	14 Erythrocyte nuclei with protrusions.

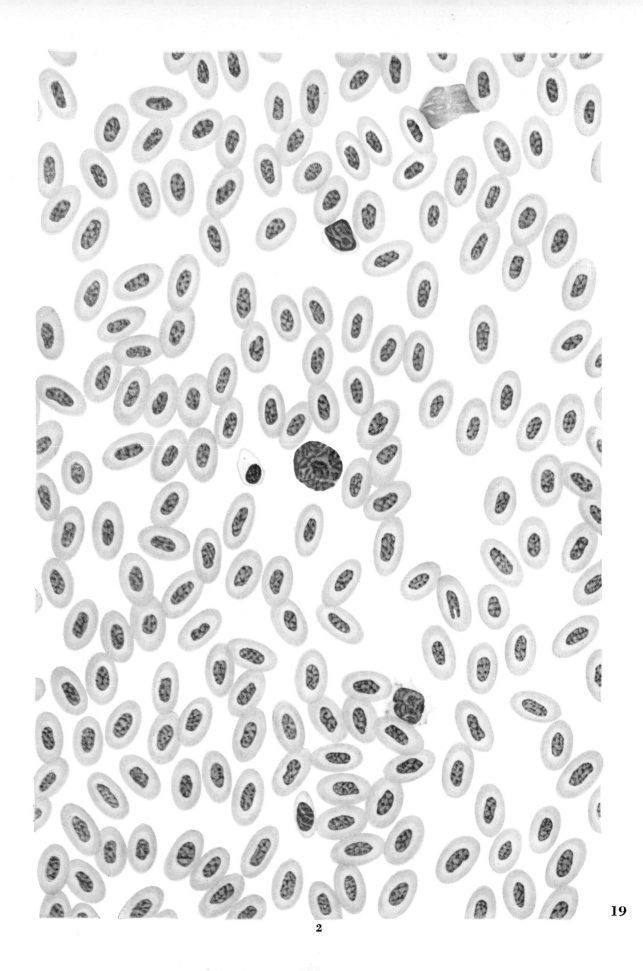

FIGURE 3.—Appearance of an atypical smear from a Single Comb White Leghorn. The cause of the chromophobic bands in the nuclei of heterophils and of erythrocytes is not known.   1,370×.

1	Heterophil showing chromophobic bands across the nuclear lobes.
2	Erythroplastid.
3, 4	Late polychromatic erythrocytes.
5, 6	Erythrocytes in which the distorted shapes may have been acquired during the making of the smear.
7	A "typical" erythrocyte.
8	Erythrocyte with an elongated, dense nucleus.
9	Erythrocyte with nucleus eccentrically placed.
10	Erythrocyte in which the nucleus is undersized and almost round.
11	Erythrocyte with nucleus indented at one end.
12	Erythrocyte with nucleus indented on one side.
13	Erythrocyte with a pyknotic nucleus.
14	Erythrocyte nucleus with a protrusion.
15–22	Erythrocytes showing chromophobic bands across the nuclei.

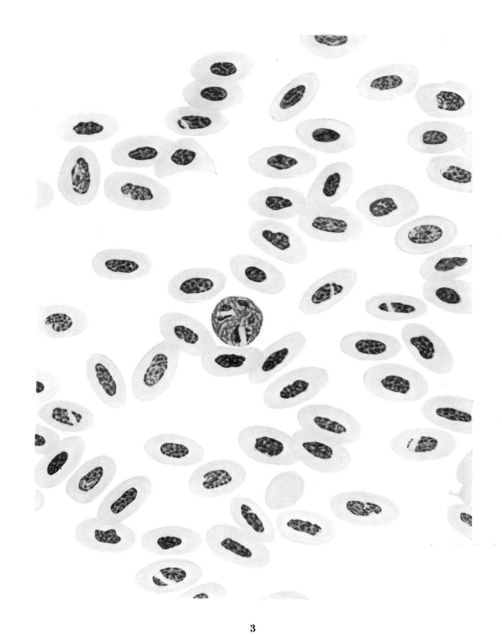

3

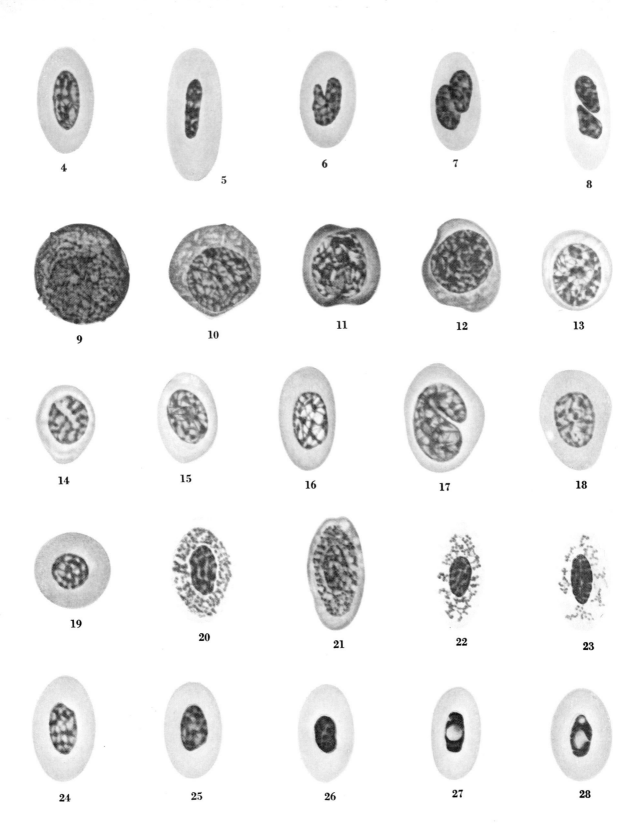

from wild birds. In starling blood, for example, the condensed chromatin beneath the nuclear membrane produces a bumpy contour like that of a mulberry. A narrow condensed nucleus is found also in the common mallard duck. In fact, in this species cells showing the two nuclear types are found in the same smears. For convenience, one (fig. 4) may be designated as the ovoid, leptochromatic type, and the other as the elongated, pachychromatic type (fig. 5). Breusch (1928) makes the statement (p. 224), ". . . Allgemein kann man weiterhin feststellen, dasz je junger die orthochromatische Zelle is, um so mehr bezitzt der Kern Blaschenform. . . ." [1] However, no data to support this opinion are presented.

Studies are needed on blood physiology and chemistry that would aid in the evaluation of the

[1] Translation: In general one may state that the younger the orthochromatic cell is, the more its nucleus has the vesicular form.

relative merit of each type in relation to the general vigor of the bird. This is a point of more than academic interest. One hypothesis might be that a smaller, more condensed nucleus permits the existence of a proportionally larger cytosome and hence a greater content of hemoglobin. Another hypothesis stems from the fact that an oval leptochromatic nucleus is characteristic of immature cells and a condensation of chromatin is associated with older cells. The condition in the common mallard duck of a mixture of these two types of erythrocytes is some evidence for this hypothesis. Therefore, it is possible that in our Laboratory stock the erythrocytes show a type of nucleus not fully developed because the cells are destroyed before they reach full maturity.

The existence of amitosis in mature erythrocytes has been suggested in amphibians (Charipper and Dawson, 1928). Up to a certain point

---

FIGURES 4–28.—Normal erythrocytes—immature, mature, and aged—found in the circulating blood of the hatched chicken. 2,470×.

FIGURES 4–8: *Typical mature erythrocytes and variations.*

4 Mature erythrocyte, typical for our Laboratory stock. Nucleus—oval leptochromatic type.
5 Mature erythrocyte, typical for some other stocks and breeds of chickens, for other domesticated birds, and for wild birds. Nucleus—elongated, pachychromatic type.
6 Normal erythrocyte with nucleus indented at the end; similar to figure 2, *11*.
7, 8 Mature erythrocytes with two nuclei. The cell in figure 8 shows that the two nuclei may be completely separated.

FIGURES 9–23: *Immature cells.*

9 An erythroblast, equivalent to that in figure 255, which is from the embryo.
10 A late erythroblast, equivalent to, but smaller than, that in figure 347, which is from the bone marrow.
11 Early polychromatic erythrocyte, equivalent to those in figures 264 and 348, which are from the embryo and the bone marrow, respectively.
12 Early polychromatic erythrocyte. A few lightly stained spaces characteristic of the erythroblast are still visible in the cytoplasm.
13 Mid-polychromatic erythrocyte, equivalent to those in figures 350 and 351, which are from the bone marrow.
14 Mid-polychromatic erythrocyte.
15 Transition between mid- and late-polychromatic erythrocyte, but included with the latter type.
16 Late polychromatic erythrocyte.

17 An atypical late polychromatic erythrocyte.
18 Late polychromatic erythrocyte. This and figure 16 are typical of cells at this stage.
19 Mature erythrocyte. Nucleus and stroma differentiated ahead of changes in cell shape, and thus the round shape is fixed. A similar reaction is often found in first generation of erythrocytes in the embryo.

FIGURES 20–23: *Reticulocytes from the circulating blood of 1-day-old chicks.*

20 Early stage of reticuloycte; granules are abundant.
21 Same stage as preceding cell. The color obtained with Wright's counterstain indicates that reticulocytes have full complement of hemoglobin.
22 Partial loss of reticulocyte granules.
23 Granular material is minimal in amount but is sufficient to establish the cell as a reticulocyte. Smaller amounts are confused with precipitated stain.

FIGURES 24, 25: *Mature erythrocytes.*

24 The type characteristic of Laboratory stock.
25 A cell approaching senility in Laboratory stock but typical for most other stocks of chickens and for most other birds. Compare with figures 2 and 3.

FIGURES 26–28: *Aged erythrocytes.*

26 Aged erythrocyte, undergoing pyknosis.
27 Aged erythrocyte with vacuolization of the nucleus.
28 Aged erythrocyte showing continuity between intranuclear vacuole and cytosome.

there is some evidence for it in birds, such as shown in figures 2, *12* and *13*; 3, *12*; and 6, 7, 8, 17, and 29. Some indentations extend rather far into the nucleus and sometimes there are two completely separate nuclei in the cell. Figure 29 demonstrates fairly clearly that a cell with two nuclei such as shown in figures 7 and 8 can be derived by constriction of a single nucleus and not by mitosis in which the cytosome failed to divide. Figure 17 is an early stage in the process of nuclear constriction. Cells *A* and *B* of figure 29 were from chickens used in an irradiation experiment. The history of the birds that furnished these cells is given in the legend. Neither of these two cells can be considered normal, but in *B* the cytosome is partly divided and even though abortive, as it obviously is in this cell, fulfills some of the criteria for amitosis.

Charipper and Dawson (1928) believed that the erythrocytes of amphibians, which showed the same range of morphological variations found here in chickens, offered evidence for the occurrence of amitosis. As already discussed, cells with two nuclei or cells with constricted cytosomes (figs. 34, 35, and 36) may be found in avian blood, but the same two processes have not yet been found in the same cell except in figure 29 *B* and in a primary erythrocyte (fig. 246). The idea of amitosis would be more convincing if one could find series of stages in which the nucleus was first involved and divided into halves and each half moved to opposite poles when the cytosome divided. The point will be discussed again when artifacts are considered.

Developmental stages found in circulating blood (figs. 9–28)

Cells more immature than reticulocytes are so rare in the circulating blood of the normal, healthy mammal that the presence of even an occasional one in a smear is suggestive of a pathological condition. In avian blood the presence of immature erythrocytes is common and as far as we know now, an occasional immature cell does not indicate a blood dysfunction. Immature stages are found in birds of all ages, and three birds that were over 5 years of age contributed examples of polychromatic erythrocytes in the series of figures presented here. If one seeks stages earlier than polychromatic erythro-

cytes, considerable searching is necessary, but even erythroblasts so immature that they might be classed as large lymphocytes have been found (figs. 9 and 10).

Since blast cells of various sorts and potentialities have close morphologic similarity among themselves and in turn resemble what has been called a large lymphocyte, it seemed best as far as circulating blood is concerned to discuss them under the subject of lymphocytes, and four examples have been illustrated (figs. 121–124). Some differential counts given in the literature would indicate that large lymphocytes were present to the extent of 1 percent and over. This must be a different cell from the one described here since the "large lymphocytes" observed in these studies occurred so infrequently that they would not be included in a differential count. Further amplification of the point will be made later (p. 50), but figure 121 has the characteristics that identify it as an erythroblast and thus could be included among the series of developmental stages shown in figures 9–23. A discussion of other structural features that distinguish an erythroblast from other blast cells is given on page 9.

When development has reached the stage of an early polychromatic erythrocyte, there is no longer confusion with other cells, and typical examples are shown in figures 11 and 12. Mitochondrial spaces may or may not be present in the cytosome, and cells at this stage of development have not as yet acquired the homogeneity of cytoplasm that comes later. Sometimes the cytoplasm is vacuolar as shown in basophil erythrocytes from bone marrow (figs. 348 and 349). In figure 11 there is a faint suggestion of a nucleolus near the lower nuclear margin. The term "erythroblast" has been reserved for the early stages of development where a nucleolus is present, yet in the red-cell line the nucleolus may still be visible at the early polychromatic stage and in the primary generation of the embryo, even to the mid- and late stages. The early polychromatic erythrocyte often has been called a basophil erythroblast, but actually some hemoglobin has already been acquired at this stage.

The polychromatic phases of erythrocyte development are represented by cells in which the cytoplasm possesses an affinity for both basophilic and acidophilic dyes in various proportions. Thus, there may be found a complete range of color from a basophilic cytoplasm with a trace of hemoglobin (fig. 11) to a cell that has a high hemoglobin content and only a trace of basophilia (figs. 16–18). The early polychromatic erythrocyte is characterized by a blue cytosome, the mid-polychromatic erythrocyte by a gray coloration, and the late stage by various tints of orange. A mixture of blue and orange produces gray, and in some cases the yellow portion of eosin mixed with blue adds a slightly greenish tinge. With a shift from a predominantly basophilic to predominantly acidophilic cytoplasm there is an accompanying progression of changes involving cytoplasmic texture, nuclear structure, nucleocytoplasmic ratio, and cell shape. Each cell passes through an infinite number of steps, but for purposes of communication we arbitrarily break up a continuous series into segments; three seems to be the most workable number, and these, as already indicated, are called, early, mid-, and late.

The color of the cytoplasm serves as the primary criterion in identifying each of these three phases. Figures 11 and 12 are examples of early polychromatic erythrocytes, as has already been mentioned. An important nuclear change is an increase in the amount of chromatin clumping beyond that observed in the erythroblast. The cytoplasm has taken on some of the homogeneous textural characteristics found in the mature erythrocyte. This is variable, as shown in these two figures, and is not very closely synchronized with the degree of basophilia. The size of nucleus in comparison with the size of cytoplasm usually shows a definite decrease in the shift from erythroblast to early polychromatic erythrocyte, but this, also, is not constant. In general, this cell is somewhat smaller than the erythroblast but size in itself is not a reliable criterion for separating the two stages of development. These points are examples of the lack of close synchronism between different parts of the cell during development. Actually the cell in figure 11 is relatively rare, even in bone marrow. Its homogeneous cytosome combined with strong basophilia is not typical. Figure 12 is more typical in that there is some evidence of mitochondrial spaces and of irregularities in cytoplasmic structure. These may persist even up through the mid-polychromatic erythrocyte stage of development (figs. 13 and 14).

The classification of stages in the development of erythrocytes on the basis of hemoglobin content has not found general acceptance by hemotologists working on human blood, and the point is illustrated by Osgood's (1938) statement (p. 67), "However, it seems to the author unjustifiable to use the amount of hemoglobin in the cytoplasm as the criterion of the age of the individual cell since many polychromatophilic akaryocytes (nonnucleated red cells) are seen which contain practically no hemoglobin and these must certainly be more mature than nucleated red cells which contain much hemoglobin. If one uses the nucleus alone, however, as the criterion of the maturity of the cell, one can arrange a continuous series, each one differing from the neighboring cell by an almost imperceptible degree, from the most immature karyoblast (megaloblast) to the most mature metakaryocyte (normoblast) which is just losing its nucleus." This point of view is probably entirely justified for erythrogenesis of mammalian blood, but in avian blood where the red cells do not lose their nuclei, the color changes within the cytosome seem to be a much more reliable criterion of progressive cellular differentiation than the alternate ones suggested by Osgood for man. It is agreed that hemoglobin uptake and structural differentiation are not always synchronized.

Dantschakoff (1908b) faced the same problem in her use of the term "polychromatic." Her comments (p. 519) are interesting.

"Da die jungen, eben erst aus den farblosen Elementen entstandenen primitiven Erythroblasten noch sehr wenig Hämoglobin enthalten, erscheint ihr Protoplasma nach D-, EA- und G-Färbung in einem Mischton von blau und rosa tingiert, weil es eben seine ursprüngliche Basophilie nur noch zum kleinsten Teil eingebüsst hat. Hämoglobinführende Zellen mit ähnlich reagierendem Protoplasma werden bekanntlich bei verschiedenen Tieren und auch beim Menschen im erwachsenen Körper bei verschiedenen Krankheitszuständen im Blute gefunden und sie erhielten in der Pathologie den Namen 'polychromatophile Erythrocyten resp. Erythroblasten'. Das Wesen dieser sogen. Polychromatophilie wurde von verschiedenen Autoren sehr verschieden aufgefasst. Ehrlich (15 u. 16) betrachtet sie als Folge anämischer Degeneration, wobei die Erythrocyten den Blutfarbstoff ins Plasma diffundieren lassen; einen ähnlichen

Standpunkt nehmen ferner für manche Fälle auch Aschheim (2) und Pappenheim (37) ein, wobei sie jedoch in anderen Fällen die Polychromatophilie für den Ausdruck einer noch nicht vollendeten Reife der Zelle erklären. Im Gegensatz dazu halten Heinz (23) und Troje (49) die Polychromasie als Folge der Auflösung des Chromatins im Zellleib.

"In meinem Falle treten ausgesprochen polychromatophile Hämoglobinzellen, die primitiven Erythroblasten in frühen Stadien normaler Embryonalentwickelung auf; in diesem Fall ist also diese Erscheinung sicherlich das Symptom der Jugendlichkeit der Zelle. Für das Blut kann man vielleicht überhaupt den Satz aufstellen, dass die Basophilie das typische Merkmal junger, noch nicht differenzierter Zellformen ist." [2]

Cells of the mid-polychromatic erythrocyte stage of development (figs. 13 and 14) are usually smaller than they are in the preceding stage. The nucleus may be large or small in relation to the total cell size, and the pattern of chromatin condensation is intermediate between the two extremes represented by the erythroblast and the mature erythrocyte, in that there is considerable condensation, yet there still remain numerous open spaces in the linin network through which the nonstaining nucleoplasm is exposed. The cytosome in many cells is not entirely homogeneous, and vague traces of mitochondrial spaces

often remain. The characteristic by which this stage is identified is the presence of a gray-stained cytoplasm that may vary from bluish gray to a slightly orange gray.

The late polychromatic erythrocyte is the third stage of the polychromatic series. The cytoplasm shows a definite orange tinge. In figures 15–18, which are examples of this stage, the cytosome, both from circulating blood (fig. 3, *3* and *4*) and from bone marrow (figs. 352–354), is about as homogeneous as in the mature erythrocyte. Clumping of nuclear chromatin has progressed almost to that of the mature erythrocyte but the nucleus itself is not as compressed laterally as it will be later. Even at this stage there is evidence of the variability in nuclear form found in the mature cell; the nucleus in figure 17 is deeply indented on one side. It may be a stage leading to a binucleated cell but, as already stated, this is insufficient evidence that amitosis is a common method of multiplication for these cells. Figure 29, *A* and *B*, which clearly shows separation of the nucleus into two parts, was made from late polychromatic erythrocytes, also.

The cell shape in the late polychromatic erythrocyte is approaching that of the mature erythrocyte but, like the nucleus, is still less compressed than it will be later. The slight angularity of cells found in dried smears has no biological significance; it is part of the tendency toward a hexagonal form due to crowding on the slide. As already mentioned, shape alone is a poor criterion of cell age—some cells assume an oval shape quite early during the process of hemoglobin acquisition while others accumulate their full complement of hemoglobin and still retain the spherical cell and nuclear shape usually associated with a relatively undifferentiated cell. Such a cell as figure 19 cannot be cataloged properly as a mature erythrocyte. It might be labeled an orthochromatic erythrocyte, or with equal justification a cell showing anisocytosis.[3]

---

[2] Translation: Since the young primitive erythroblasts that have just appeared from the colorless elements still contain very little hemoglobin, their protoplasm appears tinged a mixed tone of blue and pink, after D-, Ea-, and G-coloring, since it has so far lost just the least bit of its original basophilia. Hemoglobin-containing cells with protoplasm of a similar reaction are known to be found in the blood in different animals and also in men in the mature body, under various pathological conditions. In pathology these have the name "polychromatophilic erythrocytes or erythroblasts." The nature of these so-called polychromatophilia has been conceived of very differently by different authors. Ehrlich (15 and 16) viewed it as the result of anemic degeneration, in which the erythrocytes let the blood pigment diffuse into the plasma; a similar viewpoint is taken for many cases by Ascheim (20) and Pappenheim (37), who explain the polychromatophilia even in other cases as the expression of a still uncompleted maturity of the cells. On the other hand, Heinz (23) and Troje (49) consider polychromasia as the result of the dissolution of the chromatin in the cell body.

In my case, pronounced polychromatophilic hemoglobin cells appear in the early stages of normal embryonic development: the primitive erythroblasts; thus in this case this phenomenon is certainly the symptom of the younthfulness of the cell. Perhaps one can establish the principle generally for the blood, that basophilia is the typical sign of young, still undifferentiated cell forms.

The numbers in parentheses refer to references in Dantschakoff's bibliography. "D-," "Ea-," and "G-" refer to Dominici, Eosin-azure, and Giemsa stains.

---

[3] Another interpretation might be made from the observations of Shattuck (1928), who followed the changes in shape of red cells under the action of lysins. He noted that chicken cells lost their oval shape and became round. A similar change from an oval to a round shape was noted by Nesterow (1935) as an initial degeneration reaction when chicken erythrocytes were injected intravenously into dogs and rabbits. Therefore, it is at least possible that the round shape of an erythrocyte in the chicken might, in some cases, indicate the first stage in degeneration.

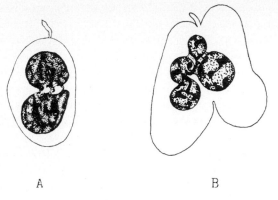

A   B

FIGURE 29.

A   A double nucleus in an erythrocyte from a 6-week-
    old Single Comb White Leghorn that, 3 days earlier,
    had received 900r total body irradiation.
B   An atypical erythrocyte found in a nonirradiated bird
    from the same stock and the same age.

This again points to the fact that the shape of the cell is not closely synchronized with color change, and not infrequently a cell may show its full complement of hemoglobin and yet remain as round as an early polychromatic erythrocyte. Thus, in any attempt to pigeonhole cells, one must select one "chief" criterion and let all others become subsidiary to it. Color, in the erythrocyte series, has been selected as the chief criterion, whereas nuclear development, vacuolization of the cytosome, and cell shape are regarded as subsidiary. This does not minimize the importance or significance of these subsidiary criteria. They are indispensible for identification of cells and for an understanding of progressive change, but terminology based on multiple criteria leads to ambiguity and contradictions.

It was probably some such cell as that represented by figure 19 that led Bizzozero and Torre (1881) to divide erythrocytes into three types— (1) the typical erythrocyte, oval in shape; (2) the type that is spherical but has an oval nucleus and is intensely stained; and (3) a rare type distinguished from the typical erythrocyte by its more delicate contour, weaker staining, and somewhat shorter length, as well as by its larger and sometimes almost spherical nucleus. That type 2 includes immature cells is suggested by the further statement that these spherical forms appear somewhat more abundantly in the blood of anemic animals and correspond to an earlier

developmental form found in bone marrow. Their type 3 might be a thrombocyte, since thrombocytes are not otherwise mentioned in their paper.

Reticulocytes have been mentioned occasionally in avian literature. Magath and Higgins (1934) found that the percentages of reticulocytes for adult mallard ducks varied from 16.6 to 27.7 percent. This is considerably higher than the normal value of 1.47 percent given for children of various ages (Osgood, Baker, and Wilhelm, 1934). Wills (1932) demonstrated that in pigeons, reticulocyte counts do not remain at a steady and low level. Individual birds showed high counts during the holding period, for no accountable reason. Peabody and Neale (1933) had a somewhat similar experience. During 25 days confinement, the counts usually fell from 15–22 percent to 8–10 percent, but in some individuals the counts went up again to 11–13 percent. To our knowledge no one has as yet carried out a study on the changes in reticulocyte counts in birds from the day of hatching to maturity, such as was done by Orten and Smith (1934) on rats. According to Magath and Higgins, the reticulations in the avian erythrocyte are composed of little dots along the strands of a basket network. As the cells grow older, the network disappears, leaving a few strands and dots.

Their description agrees closely with the cytology of this stage as observed in the day-old chick, where at first (fig. 20) there was an abundance of granules arranged on a reticulum. These form a band of uniform width around the nucleus, and when cells of this type are given a counterstain it is evident that the cell, if the reticular granules had not been revealed, would be classed as a mature cell (fig. 21), but others with reticulations appear to be late polychromatic erythrocytes. During the final step in the maturation of the cell the reticulum breaks apart and the amount grows less, but it still retains the perinuclear arrangement (fig. 22) and later becomes dissipated throughout the cytosome (fig. 23). It was hoped that the last stages in the disappearance of the reticular granules could be traced, but with the technics used (ch. 7, p. 230), there always persisted a certain amount of precipitate over the slide, which, as it fell on the cells, resembled in size and color those granulations. These illustrations for reticulocytes are similar to those given by Hewitt (1940) in the frontispiece.

Richardson (1937) counted only those cells as reticulocytes in which the granules completely surrounded the nucleus. In his material he found the normal count to be 7.8 percent with a standard deviation of ±2.39. Robertson et al. (1947) showed that chicks that had been deprived of folic acid for 4 weeks held a relatively low percentage level of reticulocytes. One injection of folic acid gave a sudden increase in proportion of reticulocytes. The peak of the increase was reached on the sixth day. The percentage curve subsided to a normal level by the thirteenth day.

An excellent review of the occurrence of reticulocytes among various classes of vertebrates and of the significance of the basophilic granulations in these cells has been presented by Orten (1934). His statement that sometimes nearly all of the erythrocytes in pigeons, chickens, reptiles, frogs, and fishes may be in the reticulocyte stage, is based on observations made by Seyfarth (1927). Graam (1934) found a similar result in pigeons when she stained for 10 to 30 minutes, but Seyfarth was aware of the fact that staining for a long time damaged the cells. He found that reticulocyte granules took up the stain in a few seconds. Yet, in spite of the precaution to keep the staining time short, sometimes he obtained preparations from lower vertebrates with a large proportion of the erythrocytes with reticular granulations. From his colored illustrations of reticulocytes in the bone marrow and blood of the fowl, he has included in the last one or two steps of his developmental series, cells which contained only a few granules. Had we included such cells in our studies as being reticulocytes, then we also would have been forced to the point of view that practically all erythrocytes in the circulating blood of either chicks or adult birds were reticulocytes because, as mentioned (last paragraph, p. 27), a precipitate was present over these slides and stainable granules existed both between the cells and on the cells. Those on the cells resembled reticular cell granulations.

From our study of blood from normal adult birds, the reticulocytes are extremely rare and the possibility at least exists that the chicken would be a better experimental animal than the pigeon for the types of study that in the past have been applied to pigeons.

These are all points that can be settled by further study, but more significant at present are the observations of Seyfarth (1927) that reticulate granulations in mammalian blood are not limited to the phases of erythrocyte maturation that follow the extrusion of the normoblast nucleus. By the use of reticulocyte staining on cells from bone marrow, he found that these granulations were present at very early stages of development, when the cytoplasm was only a narrow rim around the erythroblast nucleus. As the nucleus became pycnotic at the late normoblast stage, the granules retained a perinuclear position, forming a ring around the last of the chromatin. After the chromatin had been entirely discharged, the reticular granules (he calls them substantia granulo-filamentosa) again scattered throughout the cytosome of the erythrocyte and then gradually disappeared.

An exactly comparable series of stages was presented by Seyfarth from studies on the bone marrow and blood of the chicken, except that the nucleus was not eliminated from the cell. In birds the reticular granulations almost entirely fill the narrow rim of cytoplasm in the late erythroblast or the early polychromatic erythrocyte and as the nucleus condenses, the granules accompany its peripheral margin, thus leaving the periphery of the cytosome free from granules. There is no normoblast stage in birds at which stage the nucleus is eliminated, but the behavior of the reticular granules gives an indication when this stage of development has been reached in the maturation process of the avian reticulocyte. This is indicated by the change from a condensed band of reticular granulation around the nucleus to a subsequent scattering of the granules throughout the cytosome. Disappearance of the granules is taking place at the same time.

From these observations, it would appear that the mature erythrocyte of the bird is homologous to the mature erythrocyte of the mammal, and not to the erythroblast of man, as suggested by Burckhardt (1912).

The reticular granulations first appear in the cell, immediately following the development of hemoglobin in the cell (Seyfarth, 1927). This agrees with Dawson's data on the occurrence of vitally stained granules in primary erythrocytes over a wide range of developmental stages (Dawson, 1936a).

A normal mature erythrocyte (fig. 24) has been included in order to make the developmental series complete. This forms the point of departure for the discussion of over-aged cells that follows. In summary, it is quite evident that all stages in erythropoiesis from the erythroblast to the mature erythrocyte may be found in the circulating blood. It would appear that birds in general, including the chicken, have a more labile hematopoietic system than mammals, and the presence of an occasional immature red cell cannot, at present, be regarded as abnormal or indicative of a pathological or diseased condition in birds. Wirth (1950) also observed greater reactivity in chickens than in mammals and stated that regeneration in the chicken was very vigorous; that it ends in about a week, and that in mammals about 3 weeks are necessary for the same result. Polychromatic erythrocytes and erythroblasts occurred in very large numbers (up to a half million per cubic millimeter) and the reticulocytes became so numerous that they rose from 0 to 33 percent.

Splenectomy in pigeons (Toryû, 1930) raises the number of polychromatic erythrocytes from a control level of none to a quarter of a million and more. This increase comes the first day after splenectomy and continues for about 2 weeks and even after 50 days the level of immature erythrocytes does not return to the normal. Jordan and Robeson (1942) observed that splenectomy in pigeons increased the number of plugged vessels and lymphoid foci in the bone marrow. These authors interpret this as a compensatory reaction but the possibility of a different interpretation is discussed on page 181.

Toryû (1931) also performed splenectomy on pigeons and an abstract of his article (1933) states:

"After complete splenectomy the marrow of the femur and tibia becomes fatty and inactive for erythrocyte formation, but active for lymphocyte formation; new haemopoietic tissue appears in the lobules of the liver and various stages of erythrocytes are seen in the central veins and the capillaries of the acini. Splenectomy in adult carrier pigeons brings about a general circulation of polychromatophil cells, which amount to 3–8 percent of the red corpuscles in the blood. The hemoglobin content after the operation does not reach the normal level, probably owing to the presence of polychromatophils in the circulation."

Some physiological differences between mature and immature erythrocytes of birds, the rate of maturation and the differences in these respects between birds and mammals have been brought out in studies made by Wright (1930a and b) and Wright and VanAlstyne (1931), and reviewed by Orten (1934). Wright made use of the well-established fact that immature erythrocytes have a lower specific gravity than mature erythrocytes. By centrifugation he separated the reticulocytes and other more immature erythrocytes from mature cells of chicken blood. He obtained the immature cells by repeated bleeding of adult birds and by injection of phenylhydrazine hydrochloride. He established the fact that the oxygen consumption of all types of immature cells was greater than for mature cells. This was true for mammals also, and it has been suggested that perhaps most of the respiration which occurs in mammalian erythrocytes is due to the reticulocytes present. In summary, Wright (1930b) says (p. 213):

"A comparison is made of the respiration of the reticulated nucleated red cells present in the blood of anemic fowls and the nonnucleated reticulated red cells of rabbits. On the basis of equal volumes of cells, the respiration of the former is about twice that of the latter, while this in turn is about six times as great as the nucleated but nonreticulated normal red cells of the fowl."

Wright and VanAlstyne (1931) has brought out some significant points concerning the rate of maturation of avian erythrocytes that may help to account for the fact that recovery from injury apparently is more rapid in birds than in mammals. They found *in vitro* that young red cells could differentiate into mature erythrocytes within 36 hours, with a full complement of hemoglobin. In fact, they state (p. 36):

". . . the conclusions are drawn that the basophilic staining characteristic of the more primitive cells is no indication of any lack of hemoglobin. Indeed the most primitive cells examined seem to have possessed almost, if not quite, as much of this substance as the ordinary red corpuscles."

On the subject of rate of maturation they observed (p. 32):

"This maturation of the fowl's blood takes a shorter time than the equivalent development of mammalian cells. Erythropoiesis can be mobilized much more rapidly in the fowl than in the rabbit, as can be seen from the regeneration curves for the two (Wright, 1930a, and 1930b), even though on the basis of relative blood volumes the loss of blood is greater in the fowl. Possibly the delay in the mammal is related to the additional time necessary for the disposal of the nucleus."

Since immature stages are not hard to find in circulating blood, it was thought that over-age cells might also be easy to find. A few were discovered but only after much searching. They are not nearly so common as are the immature stages. However, this statement is applicable only to stages showing pyknosis and degeneration; the early indications of aging are fairly abundant (fig. 25). Within any one slide there usually exists considerable variability in the intensity of nuclear staining. This variability is illustrated in figure 2 and particularly in figure 3; the chromatin in some nuclei has the form of fine particles and gives to the nuclei a light color, but in others the chromatin is condensed and the nuclei are darkly stained. It is these latter that presumably are the older cells, and were they not removed from the circulation by the spleen, they would go on to a pyknotic condition (fig. 26). The pyknotic stages are rare.

In pyknosis the first reactions consist of chromatin condensation and nuclear contraction, and the spaces between the chromatin clumps are no longer clear but take the same staining reaction as the chromatin, although in a lighter shade. On sectioned material it is hard to decide whether this reaction is due to dissolution of basichromatin into the nucleoplasm or to the filter effect of underlying chromatin clumps that are out of focus because the nucleus has greater thickness than the oil immerision lens has depth of focus. The flattened nucleus of a cell in a blood smear, however, lies within sharp-focus range of the lens; thus, the conclusion may be justified that in the process of pyknosis some basichromatin is dissolved in the nucleoplasm. This conclusion is in agreement with observations made on a previous study (Lucas, 1940) in which the Feulgen test gave a positive reaction on the nucleoplasm of degenerating tissue cells.

As pyknosis proceeds in most tissue cells of the body, there is usually extensive contraction of the nucleus that brings about considerable change in the nucleocytoplasmic ratio. Some evidence of this shift is shown in figure 26 but a different type of reaction is equally common, namely, vacuole formation within the nucleus (figs. 27 and 28). This would appear to be a compensatory reaction. The nucleus during pyknosis should shrink but apparently the attachment of nucleus to stroma will not permit an overall retraction of the nuclear membrane. The goblet-shaped vacuole in figure 28, with its stem extending to the nuclear surface, suggests that cytosomal fluids have been sucked in to form these vacuoles, permitting increased condensation of the chromatin without loss of nuclear volume.

Degenerating erythrocytes in the spleen exhibit predominantly nuclear contraction without vacuolization; some show karyorrhexis. The latter has never been observed in circulating blood in mature erythocytes from normal birds.

These degradation changes in the cell and its nucleus are included under the section describing normal circulating blood because aging and the processes leading to death, as well as death itself, are all normal phases of life's progression. But whether degenerating cells normally occur in the circulating blood of a healthy bird is another question for which there is no answer at present. A study on the occurrence of over-aged cells in the circulating blood under various experimental conditions should produce some interesting results. The bird lends itself to this type of study because the nucleus is a more delicate indicator than is the hemoglobin-bearing cytosome. In mammalian blood there is no means for recognizing the old erythrocyte because the nucleus is ejected or disintegrated before the cell enters the circulation.

Atypical and abnormal erythrocytes (figs. 30–49)

Cells included in this group are those in which, presumably, the atypical condition observed existed in the bird before the blood was drawn, but there is always the possibility that a particular result observed was produced by the technic employed.

Spindle cells (figs. 30–32) are rare in blood from normal birds. It is conceivable that the occasional cell of this type in normal blood is a technic artifact, produced when the smear is made by the mechanical stretching of the cell. On the other hand, poikilocytosis does occur in chickens; it is indicative of a disturbance in the blood, and among the various shapes are many that have a spindle form. Poikilocytosis obviously develops within the bird and is not a technic artifact, but this does not exclude the possibility that technic can play a role. Spindle cells have been seen in the counting chamber of the hemocytometer and, of course, under these conditions there would be no stretching effect on the cells.

Such spindle cells have been observed by others, even in the embryo. Sugiyama (1926) in his study says (p. 134), "It is noteworthy that there are a few spindle-shaped red cells in the blood of chicks, not only in embryonic life but also after hatching. These red cells ordinarily vary from medium size to exceedingly small, sometimes with one end pointed and the other rounded, sometimes with both ends pointed. Such red cells have appeared by the time the embryo has 22 to 29 somites, ahat is to say, from the stage of early erythroblasts; at this stage they are usually pointed at one end and rounded at the other (figs. 17, 18)." His figure 17 is similar to our figure 32 and his figure 18 is equivalent to our figure 30. He goes on to say, "As an evidence that such spindle-shaped red cells are by no means to be considered as artificial products, one finds them in the circulating blood within the vessels of the area pellucida."

Distortions of cells often produce rarefied areas in the cytosome; an example of this is shown to a slight extent in figure 30 and more clearly in figure 31. A variation in the production of a spindle cell is shown in figure 32. One end is round and the other drawn out into a long tapering point. The fact that intermediate stages between figures 31 and 32 can be found leads to the suggestion that all these various distortions of cell shape have a common underlying cause.

Distortion of cells may not necessarily produce pointed ends. There may be a slight break in the side of the cell (fig. 34), a splitting apart of the nucleus (fig. 33), a constriction of one end of the cell (fig. 35), an elongation of the cell (fig. 36), and the production of erythroplastids of various sizes (figs. 41–43).

The erythroplastid is probably produced by some process such as indicated in figures 35 and 38, and the anisocytosis sometimes observed in cells could be accounted for by a diminution in size following the production of an erythroplastid. It is conceivable that a small one (fig. 41) could be derived from a cell like figure 37, and a medium-sized erythroplastid (fig. 42) from figure 40, and large ones (figs. 3, 2, and 43) from such a cell as figure 39. Primary erythrocytes of embryonic blood break off anucleated portions of cytosome more frequently than do the definitive erythrocytes.

Amitosis has already been mentioned in connection with the study made by Charipper and Dawson (1928) on the blood of *Necturus*. They include the elongations of cells and constrictions of either nucleus or cytosome under their evidence for amitosis, but, as already pointed out, only rarely has there been any evidence of division of nucleus followed by division of cytosome. The opinion is held that they are extending the definition of amitosis too far when they include the formation of erythroplastids. They state, "Their formation may be considered to be by an amitotic division of the erythrocytes involving only the cytosome." Wilson (1925) in his glossary defines amitosis as "mass-division of the nucleus without the formation of spireme, chromosomes or spindle-figure." Erythroplastid formation is equivalent to the throwing off of blebs of cytoplasm, which occurs so frequently in lymphocytes, or to the pinching off of pseudopodia. After discussing the evidence for and against amitosis as a normal process of cell multiplication involving genetic continuity of cells, Wilson (1925) states (p. 221), "It is clear, therefore, that evidence of amitosis, unless based on direct study of the living cell, must be received with the greatest caution; . . ." This point deserves reemphasis. The existence of amitosis in avian blood can only be established after careful *in vivo* studies of the type Speidel (1932) has carried out on the tadpole tail and Knisely, et al. (1947) on mammals.

In birds, erythroplastids are relatively common and somewhere during the course of evolution from reptiles to the ancestor of the mammals the process of erythroplastid formation became fully established. It would be interesting to know whether the survival value of such cell fragments depended upon the more economical utilization of space without the nucleus present or came about because the nucleus aged and died before the cytosome had reached its senility and by the elimination of the nucleus, a longer life span was obtained.

The life span of erythrocytes among mammals varies greatly, from 8 or 9 days for rabbits and rats to about 100 days for monkeys (Harne, Lutz, Zimmerman, and Davis, 1945); for chickens it is said to be about 28 days (Hevesy and Ottesen, 1945). In the pigeon after hemorrhage there followed recurrent reticulocyte peaks at about 11-day intervals (Graam, 1935).

Another type of abnormal cell involves only the nucleus and is illustrated in figure 3, *15* to *22*, and figures 44–49. This defect was found only in slides from Laboratory No. 2 and has never been observed in any of the hundreds of slides made at this Laboratory or in slides made from farm stock. These cells are included here because it is not known whether these abnormal nuclei develop within the bird or appear on the slide as a result of faulty technic. The preponderance of evidence points to an abnormal cell. If this is true the cytopathology deserves thorough study since it is a very conspicuous handle, or label, that the veterinarian could easily use in the identification of a disease condition. It is the type of abnormality that could be recognized readily from field cases and requires only low-power magnification to locate the cells. Wirth (1950) in his figure 43 pictures cells showing the same type of cleft nuclei. He labels them pathological erythrocytes of birds but gives no further information about them or the species of bird in which they were found. It is possible to go one step further than this and say that it is not a breed difference since Laboratory No. 2 and this Laboratory are using the same breed, namely, Single Comb White Leghorn.

The defect appears as an achromatic or chromophobic band across the nucleus; sometimes it is narrow (figs. 3, *16*, and 44) and sometimes broad (figs. 3, *19* and *20*, and 45). Sometimes it does not cut all the way through the nucleus (fig. 3, *21*). Sometimes it cleaves straight across the middle (fig. 44) but frequently it is diagonal (figs. 3, *17* and *18*, and 45). Sometimes there are two clefts (fig. 46) and sometimes the break is subterminal (figs. 3, *15* and *19*, and 45) with nuclear substance visible at the tip, or it may appear as if the tip of the nucleus had been lost (fig. 3, *22*). These achro-matic bands are not indentations because there is usually enough of the nuclear boundary still visible to see that it is not curved inward. When individual cells are examined closely there is no evidence that the nucleus has been fractured and the two portions pulled apart by pressure in making the slide.

Sometimes the chromophobic streaks extend lengthwise in the nucleus (fig. 47), leaving a central axis of chromatin granules that stains normally. The washed-out band shows no trace of chromatin granules; it shows only a faintly stained linin network (figs. 47–49). These three figures illustrate a transition leading to a completely chromophobic nucleus. The late stage (completely empty nucleus) might be confused with the illusion of emptiness sometimes found after Wright's stain on immature cells. They are, however, different; the former is practically structureless and colorless but the latter shows a pale blue color over the nucleus although structural details are hardly visible.

The chromophobic reaction might be a type of chromatolysis but, if it is, it differs from the commonly observed liquefaction process in that there is a sharp boundary between the staining and nonstaining parts of the nucleus, whereas usually chromatolysis is a progressive process affecting all parts of the nucleus equally.

Nuclear fractures are not limited to erythrocytes. In the same set of slides they were found also in heterophils (fig. 3, *1*) and in lymphocytes (figs. 117–120). In the heterophil illustrated, the clear areas extend lengthwise down the middle of two of the nuclear lobes. The nuclear degeneration seen in lymphocytes will be described later. It is usually more vacuolar and irregular than in the erythrocytes, and rarely are the clefts of uniform width. The fact that nuclei of several different kinds of cells are affected might be considered as evidence that this is a technic artifact. If these chromophobic bands are due to faulty technic, it would be expected that some slides prepared at this Laboratory would also show them, because certainly every one of the many thousands made here has not been of top quality. Moreover, Laboratory No. 2 was asked several years later to prepare another set from the same flock and stain them, and none in the second set showed this particular defect.

Numerous visitors to this Laboratory who had

worked with poultry diseases or in the field of hematology have been asked if they had ever observed this type of reaction in any of their studies and thus far the answer has always been in the negative.

Tate and Vincent (1932) have reported the occurrence of sharply delimited spherical bodies in the cytoplasm of erythrocytes of canaries and mice treated with R59 and P25—two compounds used in antimalarial tests. The bodies stained blue in dried smears following Leishman's stain but were not visible when other types of fixatives were used, and could not be seen in dark field. The peculiar bodies were found, not only in erythrocytes, but also in eosinophils, leukocytes and reticuloendothelial cells. Their significance is not known but nothing similar to these bodies has been seen in our studies. Nor were the small spherical bodies called stigmata described by Nittis (1930) after vital staining with brilliant-cresyl-blue observed in our preparations. He found these bodies associated with nucleated erythrocytes of various classes of vertebrates. They were not visible after Wright's stain. Although Nittis did not believe that the stigmata were the same as the refractile granule found in nearly mature mammalian erythrocytes by Isaacs (1925) yet the granules resemble each other in appearance as illustrated by the two authors.

Technic artifacts (figs. 50–72)

All smears of avian blood will show some defective cells. It often becomes a difficult problem to separate those that are atypical because they are truly abnormal from those that have been made to appear abnormal by the technics used to make the smear and stain the blood. Under the previous heading were listed those abnormalities about which there might be some question of whether they occurred *in situ* or were related to the technics used, but the group of cells now to be considered are all quite probably technic defects. Since it is difficult to tell whether a peculiar appearance found in cells should be referred back to the animal or to technic, a rule of thumb has been adopted and found helpful. It is based on the distribution of the abnormal cells on the slide; if a number of cells showing the same defect are grouped in the same region on

the smear and are absent from other intervening areas, it is concluded that this is a technic defect.

The defect shown in figure 50 is commonly found in polychromatic erythrocytes and, therefore, is quite characteristic for embryonic blood at certain ages (figs. 227 and 273–275) and for leukemic blood. It is readily recognizable by the irregular pale spaces scattered through the cytosome and by a loss of homogeneity in the remaining chromophilic masses of cytoplasm. The spaces are not vacuoles in the cytoplasm or breaks in the continuity of the cell membrane, since sharp boundaries or refractile margins are never associated with this type of artifact. It occurs predominately in the mid-polychromatic and the early part of the late polychromatic erythrocyte development. This fact aids in understanding what causes this atypical reaction. The mid-polychromatic erythrocyte is in a delicate transitional condition. It has lost approximately half of its basophilic substance and has replaced it with about half of its final content of hemoglobin. The transition from basophilic to acidophilic cytoplasm in immature blood cells, like the molting of insects, is a vulnerable period. The cytoplasm is distorted when the smear is dried. The distortion occurs most readily where the serum layer is thick and the slide dries slowly; in thin portions of the smear the cells dry quickly and here the normal homogeneous appearance of the cytoplasm is retained.

Cells pulled into two pieces have already been shown (figs. 35, 36, and 38) but those illustrated in figures 51 and 52 differ from them in that the cytoplasm was already fixed before the pulling began or in that the stretching took place when the smear was made. It is obvious in the latter two figures that the cytoplasm had some rigidity before it was forced apart. Cells do not divide normally by the kind of process indicated in figures 51 and 52. In both of these cells the nuclei lie at one pole and it is quite probable that these cells were caught in the process of producing erythroplastids. The cytoplasm was weakened and the pressure from surface tension when the smear was made or when it was blotted was sufficient to pull the halves of the cells apart along the planes already set up for the separation of the cell into nucleated and anucleated portions.

Price-Jones (1910) studied the differentiation of the erythrocyte in the early chick embryo.

33

The technic used was equal parts of glycerine and distilled water, followed by drying. His colored drawings illustrate examples of lack of homogeneity in the cytoplasm of the partially developed erythrocyte, formation of erythroplastids, and elongation and distortion of the cell body. He regarded these atypical cells as evidence of degeneration, but some of them appeared atypical probably because of the technic used.

Too much pressure exerted during blotting of the slide will damage the cells in other ways, as shown in figures 53 and 54. These fractures of the cytosome and the cell membrane are of the kind that come after the cytoplasm has become rigid; the clefts have sharp borders and extend no farther than the nucleus. In figure 54 the damage is greater than in figure 53 in that the nucleus, as well as the cytosome, has been partly squashed. The former does not show fractures but the chromatin is spread out into a thinner layer than normal and stains more lightly.

The peculiar nuclear reaction shown in a series of three cells, figures 55 to 57, has been observed only once. It occurred in a routine slide made from a moribund young chick that had previously been inoculated with neoplastic lymphoid tumor cells. It is listed under the heading of technic artifacts because additional smears made from the same bird, only an hour or two later, failed to produce these odd-looking cells. The basichromatin of the nucleus was clumped into a dense mass and it seemed to pass, phantomlike, through the nuclear membrane without rupturing it or even denting it. Often the basichromatin mass lay beyond the limits of the cell, and again apparently without rupture of membranes. It must be assumed that the dense basichromatin leaves by the top of the nucleus and cell instead of laterally, so that, as viewed from above, the breaks in the membranes were not visible. Sometimes the chromatin masses did not retain their original shapes but were drawn out into elongate bodies with bizarre forms. The nuclear hull remaining behind was firmly anchored to the stroma of the cytosome and showed no evidence of displacement, and it retained nucleoplasm that was tinged with dissolved basichromatin.

The displaced basichromatin masses are so suggestive of peas popped out of a pod that slides were made later from normal birds and the unstained cells vigorously pressed against another slide laid on top of the smear. There were no effects on the nuclei. The whole phenomenon is an intriguing one and needs to be studied further.

Sometimes other slides are found in which the nuclear contents have been drawn out into long streamers. Usually they are roughly parallel and they may be straight or curved. Flies and cockroaches should be suspected when this type of nuclear dissolution is observed. Flies tend to clean up the spot touched by their proboscis better than do cockroaches, which have a different type of mouth structure. The salivary secre-

---

FIGURES 30–49.—Atypical and abnormal cells found in smears from chickens considered to be normal. 2,470×.

FIGURES 30–43: *Poikilocytes* (P), *anisocytes* (A), *and erythroplastids.*

30   Bipolar spindle cell (P).
31   Large elongated bipolar spindle cell, with light staining areas at the ends (P).
32   Unipolar spindle cell (P).
33   Cell with nucleus constricted longitudinally.
34   Transverse constriction of nucleus with infolding of cytoplasm on one side (P).
35   Constriction of the cytoplasm at one pole (P).
36   Elongated cell and nucleus (P).
37   Cell with eccentric nucleus (A). Probably a portion of the cytoplasm has been lost.
38   Cell with nucleus carried into protrusion of cytosome. Probably a stage in the formation of erythroplastid.
39   Microcyte (A).
40   Microcyte (A).

41   Small erythroplastid.
42   Medium erythroplastid.
43   Large erythroplastid.

FIGURES 44–49: *Cells showing chromophobic reactions in the nuclei. Compare with figure 3, 1, and 15–22.*

44   Chromophobic band across the nucleus and a small area at one pole.
45   A single chromophobic band diagonally across the nucleus at its lower end.
46   Two transverse chromophobic bands.
47   Chromophilic area restricted to a narrow band down the center of the nucleus.
48   Chromophilic area limited to the center of the nucleus.
49   Nucleus entirely chromophobic.

34

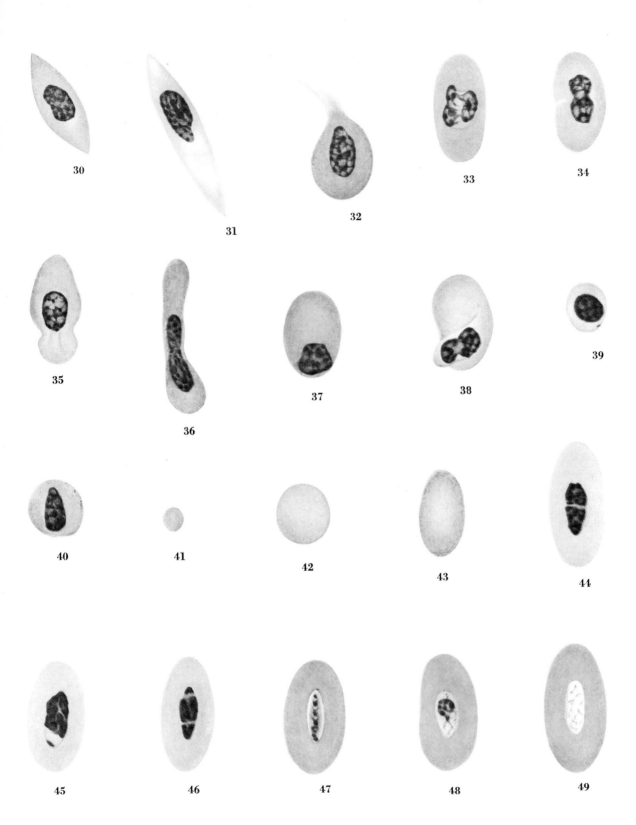

30

31

32

33

34

35

36

37

38

39

40

41

42

43

44

45

46

47

48

49

FIGURES 50–72.—Technic artifacts in erythrocytes.   2,470×.

50   Late polychromatic erythrocyte with internal fracturing of the cytosome. Probably occurs as the
slide dries.

FIGURES 51–54: *Mechanical rupturing of the cell; occurred
when smear was made or when it was blotted.*

51   Pulling apart of a cell that already had its nucleus at
one pole prior to pinching off an erythroplastid.
52   Partial rupture of a cell in which nucleus lies near one
pole.
53   Fracture of the cytosome.
54   Partial squashing of the nucleus and fracture of the
cytosome.

FIGURES 55–57: *Extrusion of nuclei, found in a bird previously inoculated with lymphoid tumor cells. Manifes-
tation of the technic artifact probably enhanced by the
disease condition.*

55   Condensation of basichromatin.
56   Shifting of the basichromatin outside the nucleus.
57   Complete displacement of basichromatin outside the
nuclear membrane.

FIGURES 58–60: *Smudged cells.   Fragile cells broken at the
time the smear was made.*

58   Partially ruptured cell with squeezing out of liquid
basichromatin.   Later stage shown in figure 2, *6.*
59   Partially ruptured cell with early chromophobic
reaction of the nucleus.

60   Partially ruptured cell in which the nucleus was
almost completely chromophobic.

FIGURES 61–63: *Cells showing varying degrees of non-
refractile vacuolization of the cytosome.*

61   A few vacuoles of varying size lateral to the nucleus.
62   Half the cytosome filled with large vacuoles.
63   Small vacuoles filling the entire cell.

FIGURES 64–69: *Artifacts due to overheating the slide.*

64—Heating has produced a few scattered refractile
vacuoles in the cytosome.
65   Large and small refractile vacuoles in the cytosome.
66   Coalescence of refractile vacuoles.
67   A single large refractile vacuole at one pole of the
nucleus.
68   Effect of excessive heat. Substance of refractile
vacuoles driven off leaving empty spaces.
69   Staining of serum granules in an overheated slide.

FIGURES 70, 71: *Artifacts due to parts of smudged cells
falling on top of normal cells.*

70   Vacuoles and chain of three bodies beside the nucleus
due to overlying smudged nucleus.
71   Two cells with a smudged nucleus overlying both of
them.
72   Serum granules which have taken the stain.   Compare
with figure 322.

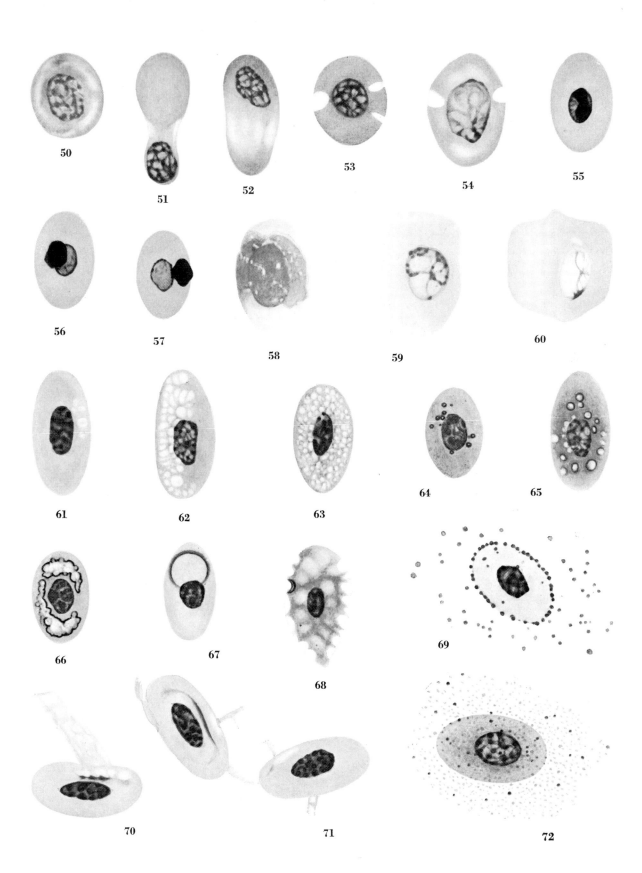

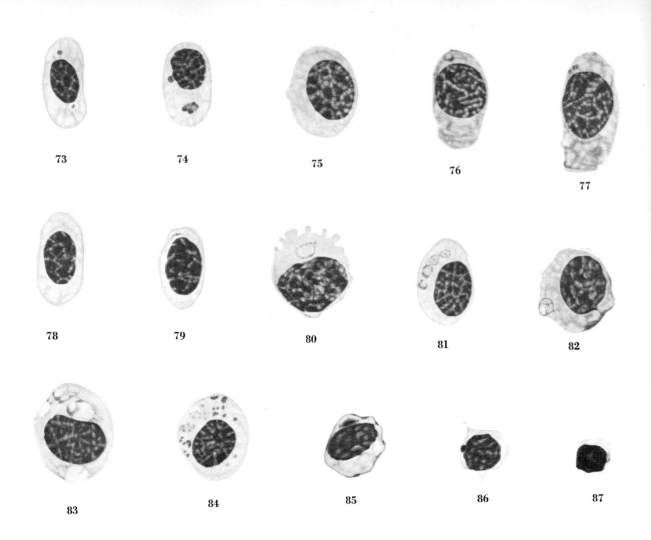

FIGURES 73–87.—Thrombocytes. 2,470×.

FIGURES 73, 74: *Normal thrombocytes.*

73 A typical thrombocyte.
74 A variation from the typical toward the reactive thrombocyte type.

FIGURES 75–79: *Developmental stages found in the circulating blood.*

75 Stage about midway in the differentiation process.
76 Early elongation stage. Cytoplasm about the same as in preceding cell. Specific granule present.
77 Early elongation, beginning rarefaction. Two specific granules present.
78 Thrombocyte character definitely established. Lightly stained cytoplasm. Granulation still very faint.
79 Nearly mature thrombocyte.

FIGURES 80–84: *Reactive thrombocytes.*

80 Multiplication of specific thrombocyte granules to form a sphere.
81 Multiplication of specific thrombocyte granules to form spheres.
82 Vacuolization of cytosome and presence of two irregular spheres.
83 Aggregation of specific thrombocyte granules around vacuoles of various sizes.
84 Numerous faint spheres and large, dark granules.

FIGURES 85–87: *Stages in disintegration of the thrombocyte when exposed to air.*

85 Early stage of disintegration of the cell membrane.
86 Mid-stage of disintegration.
87 Late stage of disintegration. Specific granule still visible.

tions put the proteins from the nucleus into solution and in the wet condition they are spread around the slide. These dry and later, when stained, appear as long strands, irregular masses, and fine filaments that take the typical nuclear stain. If the slides are on edge, there will be long streamers flowing downward.

It has been found from experience that if blood slides must be kept over until the next day before staining, the rack should be put inside a glass dish with a good cover and the edges sealed with adhesive tape. No drawings have been made showing these effects but there should be no difficulty in recognizing them and in reproducing them. If a slide held up to the light shows minute clear areas punched out here and there over the smear, those areas are a fairly good indication that flies have had access to the slide.

Squashed cells are exceedingly common in avian blood (fig. 2, 6). The part of the cell that stains is the nucleus, and in the case of the cell mentioned the cytoplasm has disappeared entirely. When it has been squashed to this degree it often becomes impossible to determine whether it had been an erythrocyte, lymphocyte, monocyte, or thrombocyte. If granulocyte cells become broken they can be identified by their specific inclusions (figs. 175, 176, 187, 195, and 196). Broken monocytes can sometimes be identified (figs. 148 and 149).

Smudged cells are much more abundant in bird than in mammalian blood, because, in birds all blood cells are nucleated and there is much more opportunity to find a smudged cell, than where only the leukocytes carry nuclei, as in mammals.

It was noted by Furth, Seibold, and Rathbone (1933) that in mice, smudged cells were rare in normal animals but very numerous in cases with lymphomatosis. They suggested that the incidence of smudged cells might represent a measure of the cells that were fragile, but they knew of no way to put this idea to the test. They were not found in the counting chamber. Although no adequately controlled studies have been made on chickens, the indications are the same as for mice, that there are fewer squashed cells from smears of normal individuals than from those inoculated with tumor transplants. Kyes (1929) found a certain proportion of erythrocytes in fowl and pigeon so susceptible to hemolysis that nucleated stromata appeared even when blood was diluted with the animals' own serum.

Smudged cells in chickens are so numerous that it is easy to find all stages. The initial reaction is liquefaction of chromatin which gives the nucleus a light staining homogeneous appearance, and the cytosome is flattened beyond its usual limits. In anything beyond this initial stage, the liquefied chromatin flows beyond the nuclear membrane (fig. 58) and the cytoplasm shows various stages of rapid disintegration.

In most smudged cells the reaction goes all the way and the nucleus is recognizable only as an irregular, magenta-colored mass (fig. 2, 6). The cytoplasm is less durable than the nucleus and even when slightly flattened it loses its affinity for the stain (fig. 60). With only slightly more pressure, the cytoplasm becomes almost completely lysed (figs. 58 and 59). When cells are severely squashed, the nucleus also disappears and the only indication that a cell previously existed is found when some of the squashed material happens to overlie the cytoplasm of another cell (figs. 70 and 71). Mere gossamer traces of squashed chromatin can be seen between the cells but that which falls on top of other cells takes an intense stain. In figure 70 the remains of the squashed nucleus have taken the form of a row of bead-like structures, and have interfered with the proper staining of the cytoplasm of the underlying cell. In figure 71 the nuclear substance has been stretched between two cells; the cell to the left received a bow-shaped strand extending half way around the nucleus. The other portion of the same squashed nucleus is only faintly visible on the cell to the right, and a small portion extends beyond the lower side. The vacuole at the upper edge of the same cell is caused by the presence of the squashed nucleus, which interfered with the straining of the cytoplasm. These small fragments of darkly stained material that fall on the cytoplasm of normal cells are confusing in that they may resemble foreign bodies, parasites, bacteria, or even Cabot's rings. Careful study may sometimes be necessary to distinguish between such artifacts and some types of pathogenic organisms.

Two drawings of partially squashed cells from Laboratory No. 2 (figs. 59 and 60) have been included because they contribute some additional information on several subjects—squashed cells, chromophobic nuclear bands, and bird differences. In the set of slides, squashed cells were rare but those that occurred did not show the type of nuclear reaction illustrated in figure 58; instead, the chromatin clumps remained discrete. There was no indication of basicromatin liquefaction and spread. The nucleus in figure 59, before squashing, was probably similar to the cell in figure 45, where a chromophobic band cut across one end of the nucleus, and the cell in figure 60 was probably something like that shown in figure 48. As the flattened nuclei with chromophobic bands expanded, their structural details became increasingly clear. When one looks at figures 59 and 60 with that thought in mind, it becomes questionable whether "chromophobic" is the best term to use in designating the clear nuclear areas. The basichromatin failed to reveal itself, not because it had lost its affinity for nuclear stains but because it had actually disappeared. A study of chromophobic reactions in lymphocytes (figs. 117–120) raises the same question.

It is pertinent to ask whether such differences between birds in respect to nuclear reactions are genetic or pathologic in origin. In any case, these differences emphasize the fact that full use has not yet been made of cytologic details that could be applied as labels in various kinds of experimental studies.

A common artifact is the presence of vacuoles in the cytoplasm (figs. 61–68). Two types are illustrated in this series of drawings—nonrefractile vacuoles (figs. 61 and 63) and refractile vacuoles (figs. 64–68). The former type was found in slides from Laboratory No. 2 and the latter in slides from this Laboratory. The cause of the nonrefractile vacuole is not known, but it is undoubtedly a technic fault since it was found on localized regions of the slides with large expanses of normal erythrocytes intervening. The vacuoles are fairly uniform in size, perhaps with some coalescence. They vary from a few to many and may fill up the entire cytosome. The nucleus was not affected by vacuole formation in the cell body even when the condition became extreme (fig. 63).

In an attempt to produce similar structures, slides were overheated; the only result obtained, however, was a vacuole that was refractile. The spheres may vary from very minute bodies (fig. 64) to relatively large ones (figs. 65–67). They

contain either air or moisture and the bubbles often break through the cell wall as shown in figure 65. An extreme condition is shown in figure 68 where all the bubbles have left the cell except one, which is in the process of extrusion, and with the extrusion of the bubbles the cytoplasm is still vacuolated but not refractile. Often the bubbles coalesce and form bizarre shapes (figs. 66 and 67). They may form one large vacuole with its margin intensely colored (fig. 67), or a refractile, sausage-shaped mass, or irregular bodies (fig. 66). The last named is a common type and often appears in slides in which there was no indication that too much heat had been applied. The problem of the cause of these artifacts still exists, and causes for their production, other than heat, are not excluded. Dawson (1931) has photographed erythrocytes of *Necturus* that appear very similar to figure 67 and they occurred in fresh, unstained blood. In conclusion he stated, "The vacuoles have been interpreted as degenerative in nature, but no specific cause for such changes in the erythrocytes has been discovered."

Some artifacts produce appearances simulating cell abnormalities (figs. 69–72). The cause of the magenta bodies found in the erythrocyte cytoplasm (figs. 70 and 71) and their possible confusion with Cabot's rings or intracellular parasites have already been discussed. A red cell falling on top of another cell produces a refractile curved line across the cell underneath and a concentric clear band of cytoplasm. It is so obvious that the clear cytoplasmic line is caused by pressure from the overlying cell that no questions are raised, but the same phenomenon originating from a small granule or dust particle falling on the surface of the cell before it dries will often lead to erroneous interpretation. The tiny particle, if it is heavy enough to depress the cell surface as it dries, will thin out the underlying cytoplasmic layer and this will look like a vacuole when the slide is stained. What one sees is a granule lying in the center of a vacuole that appears to be located inside the cytosome. Focusing does not help to determine whether it is on top or inside, because the cell is flattened to such an extent that its whole thickness lies within the depth of focus of the lens, and even if focal levels could be separated it would still look as if it were inside the cell, because the particle has depressed the surface.

Avian blood serum contains more particles than mammalian serum. Usually the serum does not give trouble in stained smears from young birds or males, but it may be quite annoying in laying birds, in circulating blood from embryos, in bone marrow of older birds, and especially in bone marrow of embryos (fig. 322). The granules in the serum (figs. 69 and 72) tend to stain more readily with Wright's than with May-Grünwald Giemsa. Whenever they stain they spread a veil or screen over the cells (fig. 72) and obviously make it difficult to observe cellular detail. In addition, they modify the color reaction of the underlying cells so that identification of cells under these conditions becomes unreliable. In some cases only the granules take the stain and in other cases both the fluid serum and its contained granules take the basophilic dye. Extreme examples are shown in embryo bone marrow (fig. 322), spleen (fig. 329), and thymus (fig. 332).

Sometimes the granules that fall on top of the cell and not between the cells will take the dye, which causes the cell to look as if it contains many small organisms. Oftentimes the serum granules will remain uncolored except near a ruptured or smudged cell (figs. 175 and 176). In these figures the small, darkly stained particles are the serum granules. Heterophil granules from the rods may closely resemble those in the serum but are larger and take a more reddish color.

Occasionally the serum bodies are larger than usual, resemble cocci, and may cluster around the cells (fig. 69). This example was from a heated slide but similar reactions have been seen in unheated specimens.

Another type of abnormality observed both in mammalian and in avian blood is the production of slender, flexible, protoplasmic processes from the surface of erythrocytes. They are not found in fixed and dried smears but the projections on cells *A* and *B* of figure 29 indicate their appearance, except that they are longer in the living cell where they are usually seen. Shipley (1916) observed them in tissue culture from cells of the area opaca, and found that they appeared to be beaded for part or all of their length and terminated in a small round knob. They were actively motile and the end of the process whipped back and forth.

Knowles et al. (1929) have depicted in color many artifacts, abnormal cells, and cellular para-

sites that are frequently found and misinterpreted. Their studies covered several classes of vertebrates, including birds. Some additional artifacts and parasites found in avian blood are shown in the colored illustrations by Balfour (1911). Neave (1906) pictured, in figures b and c of plate XXI, two pointed objects found in his blood smears. Similar objects have been found on rare occasions in smears made from the blood of chick embryos. Neave describes these bodies as follows (pp. 196–197): ". . . Length varies from 50–58μ and it occurs plentifully. It would appear to consist of a sheath pointed at each end which contains protoplasm segmented into two or more portions." Balfour (1911) considers these to be yeast cells that have fallen on the slide and which have come from the air. We are in agreement that they are contaminants on the slide from outside the specimen itself.

THROMBOCYTES

The nucleated thrombocytes of birds, reptiles, amphibians and fishes have the same function as the blood platelet in mammals.

Bradley (1937) called these cells thigmocytes. "Spindle cells" is another term used commonly, especially in the older literature. When blood is drawn, thrombocytes and platelets clump rapidly and soon disintegrate. The disintegration is part of the mechanism of blood coagulation. In mammals platelets are pinched off from the cytosome of megakaryocytes located in the bone marrow and lungs. The parent cell is large, and is easily recognized and identified. It has a polymorphonucleus in contrast to the multinucleated condition of giant cells in birds. The megakaryocyte is lacking in avian bone marrow and, instead, thrombocytes arise from antecedent mononucleated cells that have a blast stage like that of other blood cells. Blount (1939b) noted that thrombocytes of 5 x 10μ were smaller than erythrocytes of 7 x 12μ, and Magath and Higgins (1934) gave the average size at 3.9 x 8.1μ. The distribution curves for width and length, based on 10 cells measured from each of 9 chickens, gave means of 4.7 and 8.5 for these two dimensions (fig. 89). These data are discussed further in chapter 6. Similar distribution curves have been prepared for the pigeon by Schoger (1939) who gave the range in length as 7.5–8.5 microns and the width as 3.0–4.5 microns.

In birds, thrombocytes develop as mononucleated cells and remain so throughout their life span. Unfortunately, for purposes of study, they acquire early in their development a trigger-like fragility that makes them as readily reactive to damage in the immature as in the mature stages. In contrast, during the process of mammalian evolution a shift in fragility apparently arose, so that developmental stages represented by the megakaryocyte lost this high degree of fragility and retained it only in the functional platelet. It is because the avian thrombocyte is so easily and quickly damaged at all stages that we know so little about its cytomorphosis. Fewer than half a dozen papers have been written on the subject.

When the thrombocyte disintegrates, not only does the cytoplasm go to pieces but the nucleus rapidly reaches a pyknotic condition. Because the disintegration mechanism is held in such delicate balance the thrombocyte would seem to be an ideal tool for the physiologist in his study of cell equilibrium and disruption. Because the avian thrombocyte has many points of association and similarity with erythrocytes and with lymphocytes they have been placed between these two cell types in the arrangement of subject matter in the Atlas. Bradley (1937) and Blount (1939b) regard thrombocytes and erythrocytes as closely related genealogically, and the latter author mentions the existence of thromboplastids, but enucleated thrombocytes have not been observed in these studies. Hartman (1925) and Gordon (1926) extensively reviewed the various theories of the origin of thrombocytes. From Gordon's own experiments, he concluded that thrombocytes were derived from erythrocytes. This conclusion was based in part on the fact that when he bled a heath-hen repeatedly the number of thrombocytes increased when the number of erythrocytes decreased. The ratio of thrombocytes to erythrocytes was 15:1000 at the beginning of the experiment and after 5 bleedings it was 45:1000. The absolute number of thrombocytes had increased from 35,000 to 86,000 and the number of erythrocytes had decreased from 2,350,000 to 1,900,000. Hartman (1925) concluded from his studies that they were of extravascular origin and thus thrombocytogenesis was not related to erythrocytogenesis.

Normal mature thrombocytes (figs. 73, 74)

The typical thrombocyte (fig. 73) has been described many times as a cell slightly smaller than an erythrocyte, elongated with rounded ends, but not having the regular oval contour of the erythrocyte. The thrombocyte nucleus also has a slightly oval shape but is not as elongated as that of the erythrocyte. The cytosome usually consists of a framework with large spaces. Some have called them vacuoles but they do not have the discrete nature and regular contour of vacuoles. Sometimes the cytosome shows structural uniformity. Considerable variability in color is taken on by the cytoplasm—pale blue as in figure 73 or pale purple as in figure 74. Often the cell membrane appears as a distinctly purplish line (fig. 85); this is especially true in cells in which disintegration is just beginning.

Thrombocytes contain specific granules that take a pink to reddish purple color. The variability in number, size, intensity of color, and position in the cell is extremely great. In figure 73 there is a single compact granule at each nuclear pole with a suggestion of diffuse orange material beside the lower one. In figure 74 there is a definite single granule between the nucleus and the side wall, and at the lower pole there are four granules surrounding a lighter stained homogeneous mass of similar material. In figure 81 there is a chain of four rings. The intensity of staining is less than in the two cells previously described.

The outline drawings (figs. 88 a-s) have been arranged so that the cells in the first horizontal row are examples illustrating a single granule. The second row shows 2 granules per cell, the third row shows 3 granules, and the cells in the fourth row contain 4 or more granules. The granules may lie at the poles of the cell or at the side. If multiple, they may be close together or far apart, and they may be compact and dense or diffusely organized.

The significance of the specific granulation is not known. Blount (1939b) is of the opinion that these granulations do not represent hemoglobin. Possibly it is part of the trigger mechanism that brings about the rapid disintegration

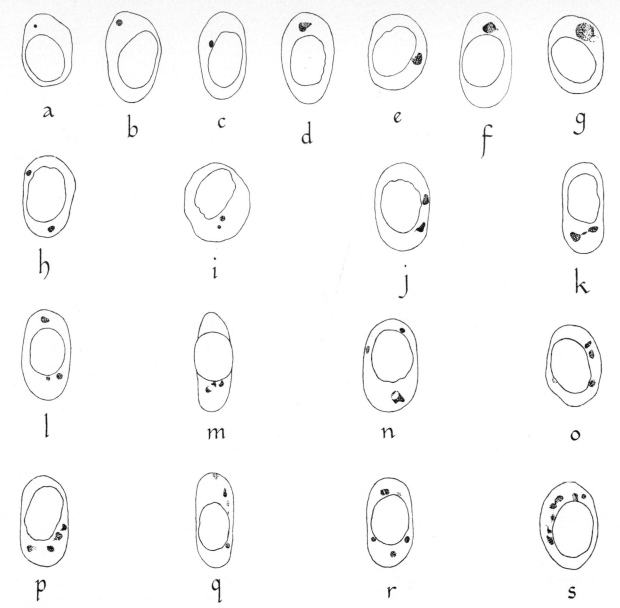

FIGURE 88.—Outlines of normal thrombocytes and their nuclei, showing variability in shape, and in number and size of granules. 2,470×.

a–g   One specific granule per cell. Size of granules ranges from small to large. Cell *g* tending toward a reactive thrombocyte.

h–k   Two specific granules per cell.
l–o   Three specific granules per cell.
p–s   Four or more specific granules per cell.

of the cell. When the specific granules are absent or are hidden by the nucleus, the thrombocyte becomes a difficult cell to identify. Forkner (1929) observed that thrombocytes have a clear cytoplasm at first but during the progress of staining with neutral red and janus green, vacuoles developed at one or both ends of the nuclei. These stained a muddy, brown color, were non-refractile, and increased in size with long exposure. If the cells are elongated, like those in figures 73 and 88, *k*, *m*, and *q*, they could pass for poorly developed erythrocytes; on the other hand, if rounded like figures 88 *g*, *i*, and *s*, they would simulate lymphocytes. Usually the nucleus is smaller than that of the lymphocyte. The nucleus of figure 80 is an exception and is

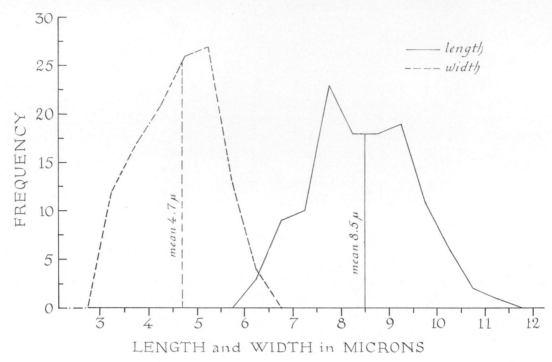

FIGURE 89.—Frequency distribution curves for length and width of 90 normal thrombocytes.

larger than that of the lymphocyte figure 102, and if it were not for a few faint specific granules it would be classed as a lymphocyte. The cytoplasm does not always contain spaces or vacuoles; instead, its texture and coloration sometimes may be indistinguishable from that of lymphocytes. Fortunately the specific orange granules are very constant in their occurrence if not in their number and arrangement.

Developmental stages found in circulating blood (figs. 75–79)

Developmental stages for the thrombocytes were first worked out from the circulating blood of the embryo incubated for about 4 days and then in older embryos. These observations provided clues for recognition of thrombocytogenesis in bone marrow and it was only following this that they were recognized in the circulating blood of the hatched chicken. Developmental stages represented by figures 75–79 were found in 1 specimen 6 days posthatching. At this early age the probability of discovering develop-

mental stages is greater that at older ages, just as immature erythrocytes are more abundant soon after hatching than they are later.

There are about 75 red cells to one thrombocyte; therefore, considerable more searching is necessary to find immature thrombocytes than corresponding stages of the erythrocyte series. None were found that were younger than about the middle of the developmental process (figs. 75–77), which is approximately equivalent to cells (figs. 288–290) found in the circulating blood of an embryo incubated 4 days, or (fig. 363) from adult bone marrow. The nucleus is still large relative to the cytosome, but at this mid-stage of immaturity the cytosome has more area than merely a narrow rim of intensely stained basophilic material as it had at the thromboblast stage. By the mid-immature stage, the cytoplasm has lost some of its basophilia and has become vacuolated. The vacuoles tend also to lighten the staining. Specific granulation may (figs. 76 and 77) or may not (fig. 75) be evident. The nuclear pattern is intermediate between the punctate reticulum of the blast stage and the closely packed, dense chromatin clumps of the fully mature cell. The areas occupied by linin network and basichromatin are about equal.

The late immature stage (figs. 78 and 79) shows certain changes from the preceding phase. The cell has usually attained a slightly oval shape but this is not always the case (fig. 364 from bone marrow); the cytoplasm has nearly the same degree of coloration found in the mature cell and it shows extensive vacuolization; the nucleus may still have a round contour or may be slightly oval, but more important is the increased density of chromatin clumping. Specific granulation is present, but a point to which reference will be made later is the faintness of the granules and the fact that there is seldom more than 1 or 2 small granules present.

Abnormal cells (figs. 80–87)

Probably neither of the two types of cells included under this heading could be called pathological. The cells in the first group have been classified as reactive cells (figs. 80–84) and those in the second group illustrate the cellular breakdown that begins as soon as the blood is liberated from the body (figs. 85–87). The latter might even be classed as a technic artifact because it takes place outside the body. Clotting, on the other hand, also takes place outside the body and yet is a normal function of blood, but from the point of view of cytology this process is degeneration.

The type of cell shown in figures 80–84 is often seen in blood smears from birds that have been inoculated with lymphoid tumor cells or filtrate, and occasionally it will be found in large numbers in seemingly normal birds. All the examples selected for illustration were taken from apparently normal birds, but the chicken that furnished the cell for figure 84 died with extensive neural lymphomatosis 44 days after the smear was taken. A 5-week-old chicken furnished the material for figures 80, 82, and 83, and in the same slide there were an unusual number of smudged monocytes of which figure 149 is an example. Not enough has been done to use the blood picture as an indicator of incipient lymphomatosis. It is a problem that should be investigated, not on the basis of a certain number of cells of each kind but rather on the basis of

various cytologic effects produced in each cell type. Cellular reactions of the kind shown for the thrombocytes appear so frequently in birds inoculated with lymphoid tumor material that they deserve further study.

Kasarinoff (1910) described hypertrophy of thrombocytes with an increase in vacuolization following the subcutaneous injection of sodium cantharidate. Schogar (1939) described the morphology of thrombocytes in pigeons and divided them into four categories: Normal, youthful forms, forms in old age, and forms under stimulus. It seems probable that our reactive thrombocytes include his last two categories. The aging of thrombocytes has received practically no attention, except by Schogar, and yet it is a subject that might be pursued with considerable profit. There seems little doubt that the reactive thrombocytes are the ones with vacuoles. Gray, Snoeyenbos and Reynolds (1954) have photographed this type of cell in their study on the hemorrhagic syndrome of chickens. Aged cells may possibly be of the types shown in our figures 81 and 84.

In the amphibian, *Necturus,* Dawson (1933b) found that thrombocytes had the power to phagocytose colloidal particles of carbon. These particles tended to aggregate at the poles, like the specific acidophilic granules of thrombocytes. Later (1936b) he showed that the particles of carbon persisted in the cytoplasm of circulating thrombocytes as long as a year, but he concluded that the individual cell probably survived only about 5 months. The thrombocyte is a highly labile cell and survival even this long seems rather surprising, yet his conclusion is justified by the data of his experiment.

This property of phagocytosis may be peculiar to particular species. Hartman (1925) in his classification of different types of thrombocytes among vertebrates, noted phagocytosis in the thrombocytes of the amphibian *Bathrachoceps attenuatus* (Eisen) and in the reptile, *Iguana tuberculata.*

Figures 80, 82, and 83 illustrate a structural series but it is not known whether progression in this series is from right to left or from left to right. As already mentioned, figure 80 closely resembles a lymphocyte except for the identifying specific granules. Figure 90 is a lymphocyte from the same slide; it has a similar cytoplasmic texture and nuclear structure. In figure 82 the cytosome is frothy and contains two irregularly shaped masses of specific granular material, and in figure 83 the entire cytoplasm has a pinkish color, and abundant specific material surrounds the vacuoles. Figure 84 shows the specific substance scattered in clusters and clumps throughout the cytosome, and the cytoplasm itself has a pinkish color. The cell (fig. 81) is probably least removed from the normal in that it is not uncommon to find thrombocytes with four clusters of specific granules (figs. 88, p–s).

When cells of the type exemplified by these figures were first observed, it was assumed that because the cells were large and tended to have a rounded shape, they were immature; but after the developmental series had been worked out both in the embryo and in the adult, and it had been repeatedly demonstrated that the specific granules of thrombocytes come relatively late in the developmental process and that when they appear only 1 or 2 small granules are present, it was concluded that the overproduction of such granules must have some other explanation. Because they often occurred in birds suspected of being in ill health or known to have been inoculated with tumor transplants, they have been called reactive thrombocytes.

A second type of abnormal cell, the degenerating thrombocyte (figs. 85–87), is very common. As previously stated, degeneration is part of the normal function of the thrombocyte; yet degeneration from the standpoint of the individual cell can hardly be considered normal. Death and the processes leading up to it are not normal for the individual; yet from the standpoint of the race and the replacement by successive generations, death must be considered as normal.

Clotting of the blood of birds proceeds at about the same rate as in mammals (Dorst and Mills, 1923). When smears are made, however, there is not as rapid clumping of thrombocytes as there is of platelets, and cytologic changes can be followed in more detail in avian cells than in the latter. The first reaction involves a shift in staining color (fig. 85) of the cell membrane from a pale blue to a reddish violet or reddish orange. Whether this is brought about by a condensation of cell substance or by shrinkage beginning at the cell surface has never been determined. Diesem (1956) has illustrated this affinity of the thrombocyte margin for eosin in his plate 1. His figure is similar to that shown in our figure 85. Usually the accentuation of the edge of the cell is accompanied by a shift in cell and nuclear shape from an oval to a more rounded condition. More often the perimeter of the cytosome breaks away from the cell and there remains only a relatively narrow rim of cytoplasm drawn out into irregular peaks (figs. 86 and 87). In both these illustrations, specific granules served to identify the cell type, but again there is considerable similarity to a lymphocyte. This is especially true when the specific granules are absent, as is usually the case in thrombocytes reaching this stage of degeneration. When the thrombocyte is small like figure 87, the possibility of confusion is not very great because this shrunken pyknotic cell is smaller than even a small lymphocyte, but a large thrombocyte with a nucleus of corresponding magnitude can often raise a question of how it should be classified.

The rate at which the thrombocyte arrives at this terminal stage of degeneration is variable, and the predisposing factors are known only in part. It has been observed that usually a smear made within a few seconds after pricking the wing vein will give well-preserved thrombocytes, evenly distributed; but with some birds, even a few seconds of delay, such as occurs in taking the second drop of blood instead of the first, will produce many cells showing early reactions similar to figure 85. The taking of the first drop is contraindicated for good smears in mammals but has been found by experience to give the best result in birds. On the other hand, in some chickens one may be quite careless, even allowing a pool of blood to accumulate on the feathers, and after waiting 20 to 45 seconds before making the smear one may yet obtain thrombocytes that are well preserved. Even a 2-minute delay may not cause much more degeneration than may be found in certain birds from which the blood is taken immediately.

Technic artifacts

No figures have been made because nothing has been found that could be so classified although it is most probable that it does occur. Just as there are many smudged erythrocytes, there are probably smudged thrombocytes. A partially smudged thrombocyte would resemble a smudged erythrocyte too closely to permit identification, and it has already been pointed out that, after the cytoplasm is gone, all smudged nuclei look very much alike.

In conclusion, it should again be emphasized that less is known about thrombocytes—their cytology, physiology, development, and reactivity—than about any other cell in avian blood. For the solution of some of these problems the phase microscope would be useful in that it reveals in the fresh living cell nearly all the details that can be seen in the stained preparation, and with it many of the rapid changes in the cell could be followed directly.

Nongranular Leukocytes

The term "nongranular leukocytes" groups lymphocytes and monocytes under one heading. The term is applicable to these two cell types because stainable granules are usually absent from the cytoplasm of these cells; however, this characteristic should not be applied too broadly, because some lymphocytes contain magenta-colored bodies and some monocytes contain azurophilic granules. In mammalian hematology these two cell types in some theories of hematology are said to arise within the lymph nodes, and have a common cell of origin. A review of the theories of hematopoiesis of lymphocytes and monocytes was given by Bloom (1938) and Bessis (1956).

The nongranular leukocytes offer many complex problems and some answers must be given to them before any workable basis of identification can be set up. It is true that practically any answers given will be arbitrary or empirical; nevertheless, they are indispensible and must be presented and discussed before considering the individual figures and the accompanying descriptive text.

Kasarinoff (1910) has reviewed the earlier literature on the number of types of leukocytes in avian blood. He demonstrated by colored drawings his division into six types: (1) Small lymphocyte, (2) large lymphocyte, (3) lympholeukocyte, (4) mast cell, (5) pseudoeosinophil, and (6) true eosinophil. In this study, small and large lymphocytes have been grouped together and his lympholeukocytes have been identified as monocytes. Mast cells are called basophils, pseudoeosinophils are called eosinophils, and true eosinophils, heterophils.

Shall lymphocytes and monocytes be treated as a continuous series extending from lymphocyte to monocyte? Maximow and Bloom (1931) have stated (p. 63), "When preparations of blood are examined and viewed objectively, it is seen that the nongranular leukocytes consist of a series of transition forms which begins with the smaller lymphocytes and ends with larger cells of quite different appearance, the monocytes, . . . But in the midportion of this series of transitions is a group of cells which cannot be classified as either typical lymphocytes or typical monocytes." The same statement is applicable to avian blood, and this might be considered as lending weight to the ideas expressed by the unitarian school, but it does not exclude assessment of the problem in a different way, as follows: Lymphocytes and monocytes show but little structural differentiation—neither cell type is far removed from the conventional generalized or typical resting cell so frequently depicted in textbooks.

In the blood there are no topographic tissue relationships. It is as if a smear were to be prepared for study from cells of the respiratory mucosa, epithelium of the digestive tract, of the liver, connective tissues, reticular tissues, and thyroid, and these cells had all been isolated from their usual habitat, allowed to round up and then spread out and dried for identification. Identification in many instances would be difficult. Another example could be cited that is probably more pertinent—the similarity of appearance between certain heterophils and eosinophils. This similarity will be discussed more fully later but it may be said here that these cell types also could be arranged in a structural series from heterophil to eosinophil, and the literature on avian blood reflects this confusion; yet at present there are no suggestions that the mature form of one develops into the other. From what has been said it is apparent that inability to catalog without question, or the mere existence of a structural series, is not in itself proof of genetic continuity. Having applied this reasoning to lymphocytes and monocytes, it must be pointed out at once that studies made on spleen, bone marrow, and early embryonic blood make use of a structural series of cells to trace developmental stages. On the basis of such series one is led to an opinion, but the diversity of opinions on hematologic principles of cell relationships is evidence enough that such an approach falls short of carrying the weight often assigned to it.

The most convincing evidence that lymphocytes and monocytes are as distinctly different as are any other two cell types came from their treatment with X-rays (Lucas and Denington, 1957). Single total body irradiation from 50r to 300r applied once to chickens at different ages has clearly demonstrated that lymphocytes are highly susceptible to this treatment, and by 1 to 3 days after irradiation had reached a maximum degree of depression in which the normal value of 20,000 to 30,000 cells had dropped to about 2,000 to 3,000 cells. The recovery was rapid and, depending upon age of the bird and severity of treatment, was half to fully completed by the 15th day after irradiation. The monocytes reacted entirely differently; only the higher doses gave any indication that these cells had been affected at all, and the drop in number reached its maximum between the third and eighth days.

The typical lymphocyte and the typical monocyte are easily distinguished but to describe and illustrate merely the typical cells would defeat an important function of an atlas on blood, that of showing variability so that questionable and unidentified cells in differential counts are reduced to a minimum. As Lucas and Denington (1956) noted in a study on the morphology of the liver, the "typical" is very rare. On the other hand, what is normal may include a wide variability as was shown to be true for the avian erythrocyte. In the case of lymphocytes and monocytes there is overlapping in respect to the various characteristics commonly associated with each of these cells.

It is simple and convenient to classify cells on the basis of a chief and supporting characteristic as was done for polychromatic erythrocytes. Unfortunately, this method will not work on lymphocytes and monocytes because their variability ranges overlap, and one is forced to use multiple characteristics with the confusion that often results. Characteristics of monocytes and lymphocytes have been presented in table 3. Relatively few cells will show all the characteristics listed under each cell type. The confusion comes when cells show characteristics partly of one cell type and partly of the other. Examples will be pointed out when individual figures are discussed (pp. 50–73).

In table 3 the characteristics are set up on the basis that all mature lymphocytes are either small or medium in size. A group referred to as "large lymphocytes" has not been considered in the preparation of criteria for the table for several reasons. It is only rarely that cells of this type have been seen in the circulating blood of normal adult birds. Four of them are illustrated (figs. 121–124) but it is misleading to call them lymphocytes when obviously it is much more probable that they are immature cells in the process of development toward some other particular cell type. To make the term "lymphocyte" so inclusive that it designates both a fully mature functional cell of circulating blood and also the other extreme, a stem or blast cell from which other cell types arise, may be entirely justifiable when propounding a unitarian theory of blood-cell interrelationships.[4] However, this is not workable when the term is used merely to identify a definite structural cell type without reference to any hematopoietic theory. It is for this reason that the "large lymphocyte" is treated separately from the small and medium-sized cell. To do this will not change the values obtained for differential counts since, as already pointed out, the "large lymphocyte" occurs so rarely in the

[4] The unitarian point of view has been clearly stated by Dantschakoff (1909a, p. 157): ". . . Speziell ist der kleine Lymphozyt im erwachsenen Organismus nicht eine reife Zellform, sondern, im Gegenteil, es ist eine ganz differente junge Zelle mit sehr mannigfaltiger, prospektiver Entwicklungspotenz. Gewiss entstehen die kleinen Lymphozyten in den Keimzentren durch Wucherung der grossen, aber sie können sich dann später, vielleicht nach einer längeren oder kürzeren Ruheperiode wieder durch Hypertrophie in typische grosse Lymphozyten zurückverwandeln und zum Ausgangspunkte der Hämatopoese werden."

Translation: In particular, the small lymphocyte in the mature organism is not a mature cell form, but on the contrary it is a quite distinct youthful cell with most manifold prospective developmental potential. Certainly the small lymphocytes arise in the germinal center through proliferation of the large, but they can later change back again through hypertrophy into typical large lymphocytes, perhaps after a short or long period of rest, and become the point of emergence of hematopoiesis.

Table 3.—Characteristics of lymphocytes and monocytes [1]

Characteristic	Lymphocyte (small and medium)	Monocyte
Cell size	Size is continuous from a small cell with almost no cytoplasm to one that is as large as the average heterophil.	A few cells are smaller than the average heterophil but most monocytes are larger.
Cell shape	Lymphocytes may be round and regular or have a contour made irregular by projecting blebs of protoplasm or broad protoplasmic lobes.	Mature monocytes are often round with a smooth contour. Monocytes with a hyaline mantle are usually irregular. Immature cells may show lobes. Mature monocytes often acquire an irregular shape if squeezed between other cells at the time the smear is made. This distorts the cell and its contents and makes it difficult to identify.
Nuclear position	The nucleus is centrally placed or nearly so in many cases but is eccentric sufficiently often to offer a point of confusion with monocytes.	The nucleus is usually eccentric.
Nucleocytosomal ratio	The nucleus relative to the cytoplasm is large. The latter may vary from a narrow to a rather broad rim. A larger proportion of cytoplasm associated with an eccentric nucleus may make the cell appear to be a monocyte.	The monocyte nucleus occupies a proportionately smaller area of the cell than does the lymphocyte nucleus. The difference in nucleocytosomal ratio appears to be greater than it actually is because the monocyte nucleus has an eccentric position.
Cytoplasmic structure	The cytoplasm may be relatively homogeneous or contain closely packed irregular basophilic masses. Under pathologic conditions the cytoplasm may become conspicuously and extensively alveolar.	The cytoplasm contains uniform alveolar spaces, especially well developed in the region of the *Hof*. In the literature the cytoplasm is often described as having a ground-glass appearance. Many monocytes show two structural regions in the cytosome—a hyaline mantle forming the distal end of broad protoplasmic lobes and a denser, darker staining, granular portion adjacent to the nucleus.
Hof and orange-staining spheres.	There usually are no *Hof*-like areas in the cytoplasm even when the nucleus is eccentrically placed.	Most monocytes show a rarefied area of alveolar cytoplasm adjacent to the indentation of the nucleus. This *Hof* sometimes contains an orange-staining substance filling the alveolar spaces. A well-defined *Hof* is not common in the wild species studied.
Specific cell inclusions	Intensely stained magenta granules are frequently found in the cytoplasm of lymphocytes. Cells containing them are regarded as abnormal, even though these bodies are probably the counterpart of the azurophilic granules reported for mammalian lymphocytes. They are very different structurally and tinctorially from the azurophilic granules of monocytes. In some wild species of birds they are so conspicuous as to cause the cell to superficially resemble a basophil.	The dark magenta bodies of lymphocytes are rare in monocytes. Instead the azurophilic substance in these cells stains a delicate pinkish orange and are dustlike flecks in the cytoplasm. Usually the color appears at the denser interstices of the protoplasmic ground substance and merges into the blue color of the reticulum. Occasionally these pinkish-orange bodies are punctate and discrete.
Nuclear shape	The nucleus of the lymphocyte is round, or nearly so. It rarely shows an indentation and when it does it is the sort of constriction that comes from folding the nucleus on itself.	Nearly all monocyte nuclei are either flat on one side or show a broadly curved depression in which lies the *Hof*. Round nuclei are more frequently found in small monocytes than in large ones.
Nuclear structure	Small lymphocytes and some medium lymphocytes show large blocks of basichromatin that occupy most of the nuclear space. In many medium lymphocytes, the nucleus shows a mixture of chromatin clumps and a delicate reticulum. The nucleoplasm is tinged with dissolved basichromatin.	Monocytes show chromatin clumps that are small and an integral part of the nuclear reticulum. The nucleoplasm is usually more nearly colorless than in lymphocytes.
Cell division	Division of lymphocytes in the circulating blood is by mitosis.	Division of the monocyte nucleus in circulating blood is by constriction.

---

[1] The characteristics chosen are those that can be seen after using Wright's stain and they do not include mitochondria, neutral red bodies or other cell structures that are revealed with vital stains.

49

circulating blood of a normal chicken that differential counts would have to be based on one or two thousand cells, instead of one or two hundred, to find any to count. Of course, if monocytes are included with lymphocytes, as has been done sometimes in the literature, the total agranulocyte count would be 3 to 10 percent higher than the lymphocyte count alone. Large lymphocytes are present in fowl leukemias or after cell transplants of lymphocytomas, but these blast cells usually identify themselves by their association with some particular cell line.

LYMPHOCYTES

Normal mature lymphocytes (figs. 90–101)

Cell size.—These 12 cells illustrate the various characteristics of lymphocytes presented in table 3. No one cell shows them all, and some of them reveal structures that are usually ascribed to monocytes. Figure 90 is probably as close to a typical lymphocyte as any; it is average in size, it has a fairly round and regular contour, the nucleus lies in the center of the cell, the cytoplasm forms a narrow rim that has neither a distinctly granular nor a hyaline texture, and the nucleus contains large dense clumps of chromatin and a tinged nucleoplasm. This cell comes from the same slide that produced the reactive thrombocytes, figures 80, 82, and 83. Lymphocytes are usually classified as small, medium, and large, but too often the subjective impression is based on nuclear size rather than the whole cell, or, stated differently, by what is left of the cell after the cytoplasm has lobulated and broken off. Thus, if a medium-size cell with its medium-size nucleus loses its cytoplasm it is counted as a small lymphocyte. Since lymphocytes often throw off blebs of cytoplasm, perhaps they should be classified by size of nucleus rather than by size of cell; errors in estimating would certainly be less.

The cells shown in figures 92, 102, 103, and 104 are considered as small lymphocytes. In figure 102 all cytoplasm is gone except for barely perceptible bits on one side of the cell and several lightly stained magenta granules. The cell in figure 92 is somewhat larger, but after it has lost the blebs that are in the process of pinching off, it will be about the same size. The cells of figures 93–95 and 99–101, and others are medium in size. Whether a cell such as shown in figure 92 can reconstitute its cytosome is not known.

The range in size of lymphocytes is illustrated also in the outline drawings (fig. 150) and by the graph (fig. 152). None of the cells in these examples are as large as blast cells. More on the subject of size will be given in chapter 6. The variations in size and shape shown in the colored illustrations are further extended in figure 150. Each row represents samples of lymphocytes taken from a different breed or source, but there were no obvious differences; however, it has often been noted that on a slide from a particular bird a small cell may be dominant and that in another bird the medium size may be more abundant; or in one, blebs may be common and in another a hyalin cytoplasm may appear frequently. It is these points of difference, when their significance becomes known, that will make for critical studies on avian blood.

Blast cells may be found occasionally in the circulating blood and four are illustrated here (figs. 121–124), and in the legends suggestions are given as to the line that each represents, but there is much room for error. The cells of figures 121 and 124 have nucleoli and show a coarse nuclear pattern; the erythrocyte relationship is moderately certain for figure 121 but is questionable for 124, and the intensely stained nucleus and cytosome are indications that it belongs to the thrombocyte line. The general appearance of figure 122, particularly the tendency of the cytoplasm to be frothy or vacuolated, and the vagueness of nuclear pattern are suggestive of the early lymphocyte as seen in the thymus (figs. 335 and 336). The narrow rim of dense blue cytoplasm of figure 123 with its moderately uniform meshlike nuclear structure suggests a granuloblast, but this cell is not as typical as those seen in the spleen and the bone marrow.

Cell shape.—Avian lymphocytes may have a regular contour but in certain slides from apparently normal birds the lymphocytes will exhibit many protoplasmic blebs (figs. 92–94). This reaction in mammals has been identified as stimulation of the blood toward antibody formation by pathogenic agents or other causes. In view of this, the history of the three individuals in which these cells were found is interesting. Figure 94, which shows a few small lobes, was taken from a bird killed at 619 days of age, at which time it had a wryneck but no lesions of lymphomatosis or other diseases to account for the condition. The cell represented in figure 93 has several broad lobes with restricted bases, as if the cell had been taken just at the moment the cytoplasm was being pinched off. The smear was taken when the pullet was 113 days old, and when killed at 151 days she showed severe gasping and emaciation. At gross necropsy there was atonicity of the crop and a slightly irregular pupil, suggestive of ocular lymphomatosis. In figure 92 the lobes are numerous. At their tips are basophilic granules that in size and shape look as if they were intracellular organisms, but this is incorrect; instead, they are some of the basophilic masses that are commonly found throughout the cytoplasm of most lymphocytes (figs. 90 and 96–98). The smear from which figure 92 was made was taken from a hen at 113 days. At 288 days she showed a prolapsed uterus from which an unexpelled egg was removed. She recovered and then was killed at 312 days because of lack of holding space. The bird was still in production and apparently normal.

When the lobes are discharged into the plasma of the blood, there remain cells that look like figure 102, in which there is barely enough cytoplasm around the nucleus to exclude it from being a naked nucleus. This cell came from a smear taken at 108 days. When the hen was killed at 668 days she was a strong vigorous bird. At gross necropsy some urates in the kidney and white spots in the air sacs were found.

The evidence furnished by these few examples is certainly not sufficient to permit us to draw any generalizations concerning the association of blebs and the health of the bird. No extensive quantitative study has ever been made along these lines; yet, obviously, this should be done and it might lead to some interesting and important information concerning the actual health of birds that seem normal. In any study of this sort it would be necessary to take blood samples at closely spaced intervals in order to catch the rise and fall of bleb formation. The discharge of blebs probably occurs quickly.

Johnson and Conner (1933) sought to associate budding in lymphocytes with manifestations of the avian leukosis complex. They state:

"In 14 birds of the 31 studied with symptoms of paralysis of the limbs but no gross lesions no-ticed on autopsy, budding of lymphocytes occurred. In 10 of the 14 studied with symptoms of paralysis of the limbs and lymphatic hyperplasia of visceral organs, budding of lymphocytes was marked. In only three of the 15 paralyzed birds with tumors found on autopsy was budding of lymphocytes noted. Three of the 12 birds with iritis or gray eyes also had numerous lymphocytes."

For comparison, a study of budding phenomenon in normal birds and in birds with various types of diseased conditions is needed.

Frank and Dougherty (1953) were able to produce budding in lymphocytes of man *in vitro* by treatment of the buffy coat with cortisone and hydrocortisone. The mean percentage of lymphocytes showing budding in normal controls was 1.2 ± 4 percent, and for those treated with hydrocortisone it was 11.63 ± 1.25 percent.

The outline drawings in figure 150 have already been mentioned. In some it appears that lymphocytes are capable of locomotion by throwing out broad pseudopodia, and many of the cells look as if they had been caught during amoeboid movement. Others, however, have small protrusions more or less equally distributed around the cell. These are probably blebs of protoplasm pinching off. Many others, with almost no cytoplasm left, look as if they had already lost the blebs.

Nuclear position.—The nucleus lies at one side of the cell (figs. 91, 94, 99, 101, and some of the cells in fig. 150) almost as often as it does at the center (figs. 90 and 104). Sometimes the amount of cytoplasm is so small that the nucleus can only be in the center (figs. 92, 102, and 150 *D, c* and *F, b* and *e*).

Nucleocytosomal ratio.—Nucleocytosomal ratio is influenced not only by the pinching off of lobes, which is a regressive type of change, but also by a change in character of the cytoplasm in which it takes on a hyaline appearance and flows out like a thin fluid in all directions (fig. 100). This was found quite frequently in chicks about 5 weeks old. The cytoplasm was pale and as seen in the microscope gave an impression of fluidity without adequate framework. These lobes are different from the type where the cytoplasm is pinched off. Often it spreads out between the boundaries of nearby cells, and it was difficult to find examples for drawing that were not misshapen beyond recognition. Even in figure 100 two of the projections were flattened against adjacent erythrocytes. The example shown is large enough to be a monocyte but its structure is quite different from that of monocytes taken from the same slide, an example of which is shown in figure 125.

In general there is less cytoplasm relative to the nuclear area than in monocytes, but again there is overlapping of their ranges, as may be seen by comparing figures 150 and 151 and graphs on figures 152 and 153. If the outline drawings on these two plates were cut apart and and shuffled it would be impossible to separate them correctly in many cases into the two cell types; this fact emphasizes the point that separation of lymphocytes and monocytes is based on more than just size, shape, nuclear position, and nucleocytosomal ratio.

Cytoplasmic structure.—The cytoplasm may stain intensely or faintly. It may be granular or nearly homogeneous. The granular condition is quite common and appears as a flocculation of basophilic material (figs. 95–99). These figures illustrate variations in the size of the basophilic masses and in the intensity of staining. In figure 98 the granules near the edge of the cell are large and dark, those near the nucleus are smaller. In figure 96 the basophilic material gives texture to the cytoplasm but there are no distinct basophilic masses. The flocculent appearance of the cytoplasm lies at the limit of microscopic visibility and sometimes the cytoplasm appears to be a reticulum with denser masses at the interstices, such as shown in figures 95, 99, and 101.

All the cells mentioned so far have been stained with Wright's stain. The cell in figure 91 was stained with May-Grünwald Giemsa, which accounts for a coloration different from the rest of the cells. It also shows the basophilic masses in the cytoplasm but here they are more nearly spherical and are more definite than in the previous examples.

The cytoplasm in figure 90 is nearly homogeneous with only slight irregularities in density. Further change toward a hyaline structure is shown in figure 100. When the cytoplasm reaches this hyaline condition it tends to flow out away from the nucleus. In the hyaline type, the

quantity of cytoplasm is great enough in relation to nuclear size to establish the cell as a monocyte, if only the one character of nucleocytosomal ratio is used for identification.

Sometimes a lightly stained area is present in the cytoplasm adjacent to the nucleus. The cell in which this is illustrated (fig. 97) is classed as a lymphocyte, although in the table on lymphocyte and monocyte characteristics, such a light area is more typical of a monocyte (see, for example, figs. 126, 127, 129, and 144). This is another example illustrating the point that the presence or absence of only a single characteristic is insufficient basis for a satisfactory separation of these two cell types. Looking over the entire group of lymphocytes from figure 90 to figure 101, there is little question that the cytoplasmic structure of these cells is highly diverse and that no narrow characterization will cover them all.

Hof and orange-stained spheres.—These are characteristic of monocytes and so will be discussed later. Specific cytoplasmic inclusions are not normally present in lymphocytes but in cells, considered to be abnormal, they do exist as magenta bodies (figs. 102–116); therefore the details of their structure will be deferred until abnormal cells are discussed. These magenta bodies are almost specifically associated with lymphocytes and thus are useful for identification purposes.

Nuclear shape.—The lymphocyte nucleus is approximately round, as shown in figures 90, 93, 105, and in many of the cells in figure 150. Deviations from that shape are common and, as would be expected, they occur by imperceptible structural differences in various directions. When the nucleus is eccentrically placed, the contour of the portion adjacent to the mass of cytoplasm is more flattened than the remainder, which is adjacent to the outside wall (figs. 97, 101, and 107). If the cytosome of the cell is lobulated, often the contour of the nucleus is irregular also but not necessarily concentric with the cell outline.

Indentation of the nucleus is not common in lymphocytes but does occur sometimes (figs. 91, 94, 111, and 114). Usually the depression is not deep and the margins curve inward to a sharp angle (⌣) instead of forming a depression with a rounded base as often occurs in monocytes (⌣). In lymphocytes there is usually no *Hof* opposite the depression; the cytoplasm appears the same opposite the depression as in the more lateral areas, but sometimes the nucleus shows an indentation and there is a rarefied area opposite. In figure 131 there is such a cell and it has been classed as a monocyte, but some might be of the opinion that this cell should be included with the lymphocytes because of its small size and high nucleocytoplasmic ratio. Fortunately, borderline examples of this type are not numerous.

Nuclear structure.—The nuclei of lymphocytes are typically described as filled with dense chromatin clumps. Probably figure 102 fits the usual description best and a similar effect is given in figure 90. Dense clumps of basichromatin are common in small lymphocytes but rare in larger cells. In lymphocytes of medium size the reticular network with small chromatin masses at the interstices is the usual arrangement (figs. 95–99 and 101). As we study the change in cell size from the larger to the smaller, it is easy to find all corresponding degrees of change in chromatin clumping. Figure 98 shows two phases of the process in the same nucleus—on one side there is the reticular appearance of the larger cell and on the opposite side are dense clumps commonly associated with the smaller cell.

When there is a delicate reticular pattern in the nucleus the spaces between are clear and transparent—the nucleoplasm is colorless (figs. 97–99 and 101). When the nuclear pattern takes the form of dense clumps there is some dissolution of basichromatin, which gives to the nuclear sap a color almost as dense as the chromatin itself (figs. 100 and 104). The wide variation in size of chromatin clumps and density of nuclear pattern is clearly demonstrated when a smear containing lymphocytes of small and medium sizes has been fixed in Petrunkevitch No. 2 and stained in May-Grünwald Giemsa (figs. 199 and 200). When this technic is used the nucleus of the medium-sized lymphocyte may resemble closely the nucleus of the monocyte (compare figs. 200 and 201).

Cell division.—Cell division is rare in circulating blood and in fact its occurrence in lymphocytes has been questioned. One of the arguments against the lymphocyte as an undifferentiated blast cell has been the absence of mitosis, a process that has been observed only a few times and then in birds that had been irradiated. Cells undergoing mitosis are usually difficult to name because identifying characteristics are lost in the process; however, in the case of figure 108, magenta bodies were present that have a high specificity for lymphocytes. Blood stains and air-dried fixation do not give a sharp delineation of the individual chromosomes but there is no question that the cell is dividing mitotically. It is interesting that the magenta bodies should arrange themselves approximately midway between the poles. The division of lymphocytes by mitosis is in contrast to that of monocytes that divide by nuclear constriction.

Developmental stages found in circulating blood

Probably less is known about the cytomorphosis of lymphocytes than about any other leukocyte. Immature lymphocytes have been identified in the thymus where they are developed in large numbers, and it has been suggested that figure 122 represents a young lymphocyte, but in general they are difficult to identify. There are identifying structural features, it is true, but fitting them into a maturation series is not easy. The developmental series of lymphocytes depicted in atlases of mammalian hematology are usually derived from cases of lymphoblastic leukemia. Here the association with many other cells, all developing in the same direction, makes a kind of pure culture, as it were, from which a developmental series can be constructed. After it has been put together there still is not much in the way of specific cell identification by which an occasional immature lymphocyte, which one might find in the circulating blood, can be satisfactorily distinguished from various types of blast cells.

The curve for the sizes of avian lymphocytes shows approximately a normal distribution (fig. 152). It is generally recognized that specific criteria useful for the identification of age and maturation are generally lacking in the lymphocyte series. Wiseman (1931b and 1932) considered that the degree of basophilia of the cytoplasm could be used as such a measure and under stress that there could be a shift toward greater basophilia among the cells counted. This would have the same significance for the lymphocytes that Arneth found for nuclear changes in granulocytes. In a study of lymphocytogenesis in the thymus (chap. 4) it was concluded that lymphoblasts are larger than the next stage in maturation and that mature lymphocytes were relatively small. With increasing age there was a loss of mitochondria and a change from delicate reticular pattern in the nucleus to dense chromatin clumps.

It is true that there are certain examples suggestive of nuclear change from an open, lightly stained reticular type (fig. 99) to one showing dense clumps of chromatin. Some nuclei, such as the one shown in figure 98, show a transitional condition from reticulum to clumps. It is a question whether this nuclear variability is a measure of increasing cellular differentiation or an inseparable accompaniment of decreasing cell size. There is no evasion of the fact that cell size and nuclear structure are very closely associated; and if chromatin clumping is a mark of cytomorphosis, decreasing cell and nuclear size must carry the same connotation.

Abnormal lymphocytes (figs. 102–120)

It is anticipated that a number of hematologists will question the accuracy of cataloging as abnormal all the cells included in this section. It is admitted that the evidence is not extensive but it seems sufficient to tip the balance of opinion toward the abnormal. It will be noted that all cells from figures 102–116 show various kinds of granules; in table 3 these have been called magenta bodies and they probably are equivalent to what has been called azurophilic granules in mammalian lymphocytes. "Magenta body" is a new term that does not carry any implication of function or origin. A new expression has been devised to replace the term "azurophilic granules" because the colors and affinities for the stain of these granules in lymphocytes and in monocytes of birds are so different that to give both the same name would be confusing. This confusion does not occur in the mammalian agranulocyte because in both cell types the azurophilic granules appear similar. It is not the presence of these granules that led to designating these cells as abnormal but rather their frequent association with nuclei that are degenerating and with cells whose cytoplasm is blown up and vacuolated. The magenta bodies stain intensely, whereas the azurophilic granules of the monocytes are small, stain rather faintly, and have an orange color.

About the largest magenta bodies observed, as well as some small ones, are shown in figure 104. All of them are spherical, which is the usual shape, but not infrequently they appear diploid or crescent shaped as in figures 105 and 106.

FIGURES 90–108.—Normal and abnormal lymphocytes. 2,470×.

FIGURES 90–101: *Normal lymphocytes.*

90   A typical lymphocyte.
91   Lymphocyte stained with May-Grünwald Giemsa.
92   Lymphocyte pinching off cytoplasmic blebs containing basophilic granules.
93   Lymphocyte with hyaline cytoplasm like figure 100, in the process of pinching off cytoplasmic blebs.
94   Lymphocyte with finely granular nucleus.
95   Typical lymphocyte with nucleus less dense than in figure 90.

FIGURES 96–99: *Four cells that show stages between pachychromatic and leptochromatic nuclei.*

96   Basichromatin of lower half of nucleus coarsely and finely granular, upper half in clumps.
97   Granular and slightly clumped basichromatin intermingled.
98   Slightly clumped basichromatin in the right side and granular basichromatin in the left side of the nucleus.

99   Nucleus largely filled with granular basichromatin.
100   Normal lymphocyte with hyaline cytoplasm.
101   Nearly maximum size for a normal lymphocyte.

FIGURES 102–108: *Abnormal lymphocytes with magenta bodies in the cytosome.*

102   Small amount of cytoplasm remaining after bleb formation. Several small magenta bodies are present.
103   Magenta bodies often in pairs. Slight autolysis of the nucleus.
104   Large magenta bodies.
105   Some of the magenta bodies are arranged in pairs. Nucleus partially autolysed.
106   Nucleus almost completely autolysed.
107   Magenta bodies in a reactive lymphocyte. For the rest of this series, see figures 109-112.
108   Lymphocyte in telephase of mitotic division. Magenta bodies between poles in spindle region.

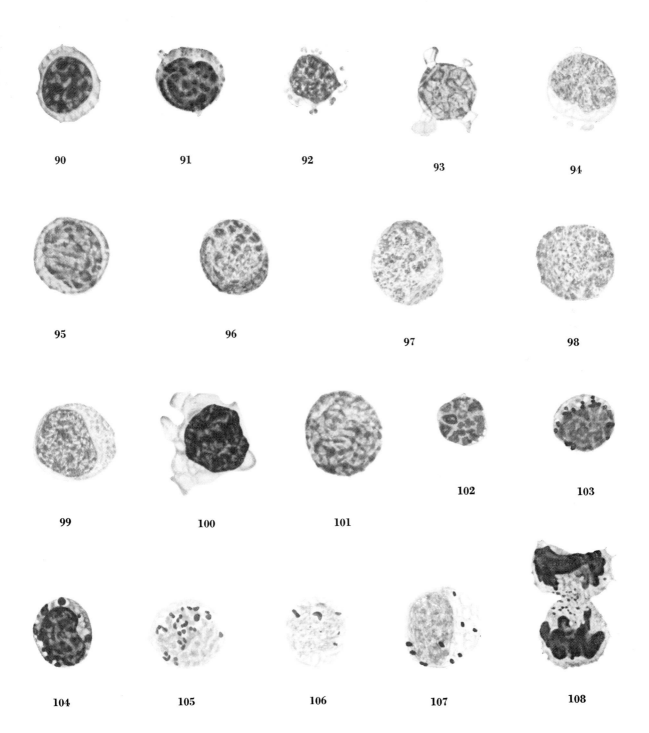

90   91   92   93   94

95   96   97   98

99   100   101   102   103

104   105   106   107   108

FIGURES 109–124.—Abnormal and so-called large lymphocytes. 2,470×.

FIGURES 109–112: *Reactive lymphocytes with magenta bodies and vacuolization of cytoplasm.*

109 Vacuolization has begun but nucleo-cytoplasmic ratio is about like that of a normal lymphocyte.
110 Lymphocyte with leptochromatic type nucleus; slight hypertrophy of nucleus and cytosome.
111 Reactive lymphocyte. Typical lymphocyte nucleus. Magenta bodies and cytoplasmic vacuoles relatively few.
112 Typical reactive lymphocyte; hypertrophy of the cell cytoplasm, frayed and vacuolated and containing abundant magenta bodies.

FIGURES 113–116: *Questionable abnormal and reactive lymphocytes. These may be monocytes.*

113 Azurophilic granules, concentrated mostly above the nucleus; lymphocyte type nucleus.
114 Mixture of azurophilic and magenta bodies.
115 Magenta bodies and vacuolated and frayed cytoplasm.
116 Lymphocyte with a few pale magenta bodies. From same slide as the preceding three cells.

FIGURES 117–120: *Abnormal lymphocytes that show varying degrees of chromophobia of the basichromatin. Same set of slides from which figures 3 and 44–49 were taken.*

117 Lymphocyte with two chromophobic fractures.
118 Chromophobic areas surrounded by normal basichromatin.
119 Normal basichromatin restricted to about one-third of the nucleus.
120 An almost completely chromophobic nucleus.

FIGURES 121–124: *So-called large lymphocytes, which are early immature blood cells (blast cells). All found in circulating blood of chickens 4 months to 5 years old.*

121 Delicate reticular nucleus type with nucleolus probably belongs to the erythrocyte or thrombocyte series.
122 Blast cell; probably belongs to the lymphocyte series.
123 Blast cell; probably belongs to the myelocyte series, although nucleolus is faintly visible.
124 Blast cell; probably belongs to the erythrocyte or thrombocyte series.

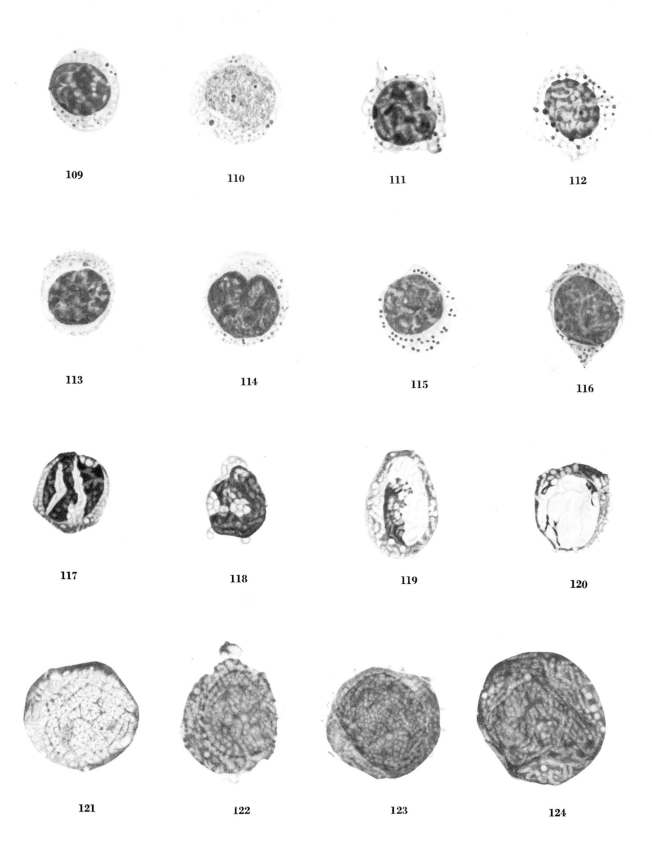

109 110 111 112

113 114 115 116

117 118 119 120

121 122 123 124

57

FIGURES 125–138.—Normal monocytes. 2,470×.

FIGURES 125–131: *Variations in size and appearance of normal monocytes.*

125 A typical monocyte. A hyaline mantle extends beyond the reticular portion of the endoplasm. The cytoplasm is a mixture of azurophilic and basophilic substances.

126 Monocyte with well-developed *Hof*, or clear area, filling the nuclear indentation.

127 Monocyte nucleus but with a nucleocytoplasmic ratio of the lymphocyte.

128 Deeply indented monocyte nucleus but no *Hof*.

129 A type of monocyte frequently seen in smears of avian blood.

130 A monocyte that shows the polychromasia of the cytoplasmic reticulum.

131 A monocyte having the size and nucleocytoplasmic ratio of the lymphocyte. See table 5, page 71.

FIGURES 132–135: *Monocytes with numerous azurophilic granules.*

132 Azurophilic granules concentrated on the side of the nucleus opposite the *Hof*.

133 *Hof* absent. Azurophilic bodies filling most of the cell.

134 Bilobed nucleus. Azurophilic granules conspicuous against the blue-stained cytoplasm.

135 Azurophilic granules larger and more abundant than normal.

FIGURES 136–138: *Bilobed and double nuclei in monocytes.*

136 Slightly constricted nucleus, similar to the one in figure 134, which is a larger cell. No *Hof* present in either of these cells.

137 Nucleus nearly completely constricted. Metachromatic cytoplasm. A small questionable *Hof* present.

138 A binucleated monocyte. A definite *Hof* on the upper side in the angle between the nuclei.

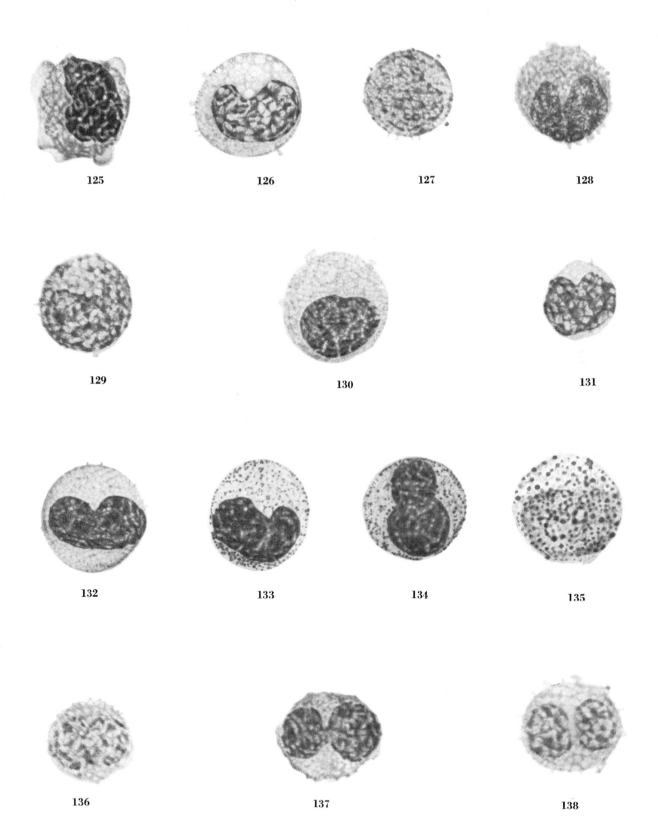

125 126 127 128

129 130 131

132 133 134 135

136 137 138

FIGURES 139–149.—Developmental stages of monocytes as found in the circulating blood, also abnormal cells and artifacts. 2,470×.

FIGURES 139–142: *Developmental stages with intensely stained nuclei, ranging from leptochromatic to pachychromatic type.*

139 The young amoeboid cell of the monocyte series; possibly a monoblast. A nucleolus is faintly shown.
140 Amoeboid monocyte with both azurophilic granules and magenta bodies.
141 A round young monocyte.
142 A young monocyte with a rounded nucleus. The cell has a well-developed *Hof*, and a concentration of azurophilic granules around the periphery.

FIGURES 143, 144: *Developmental stages with lightly stained nuclei.*

143 Amoeboid monocyte, more differentiated than the blast stage.
144 Nearly mature monocyte. The contents of the *Hof* vacuoles are slightly stained.

FIGURES 145–147: *Abnormal monocytes.*

145 The accumulation of basophilic granules around the periphery of the cell is not typical. The faint reddish tinge of the cytoplasm is suggestive of early autolysis.
146 A monocyte definitely undergoing autolysis.
147 Some *Hof* vacuoles have become abnormally large. Vacuolar content stains a light orange color.

FIGURES 148, 149: *Technic artifacts. Smudged monocytes.*

148 A monocyte in which the cytosome, but not the nucleus, has broken.
149 Identification of this as a squashed monocyte nucleus is based on the fact that this slide contained many such cells with transitional stages from normal intact monocytes to this type of large basophilic mass.

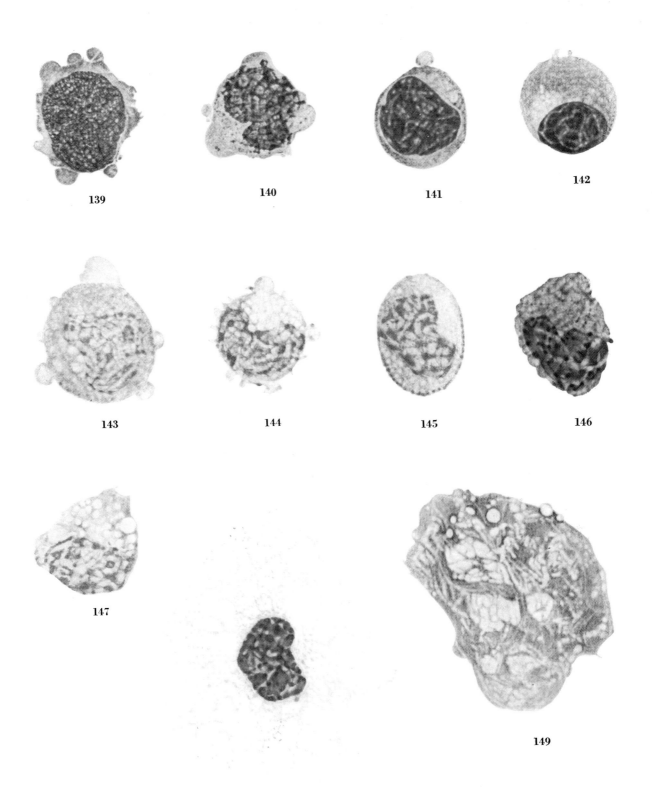

139

140

141

142

143

144

145

146

147

148

149

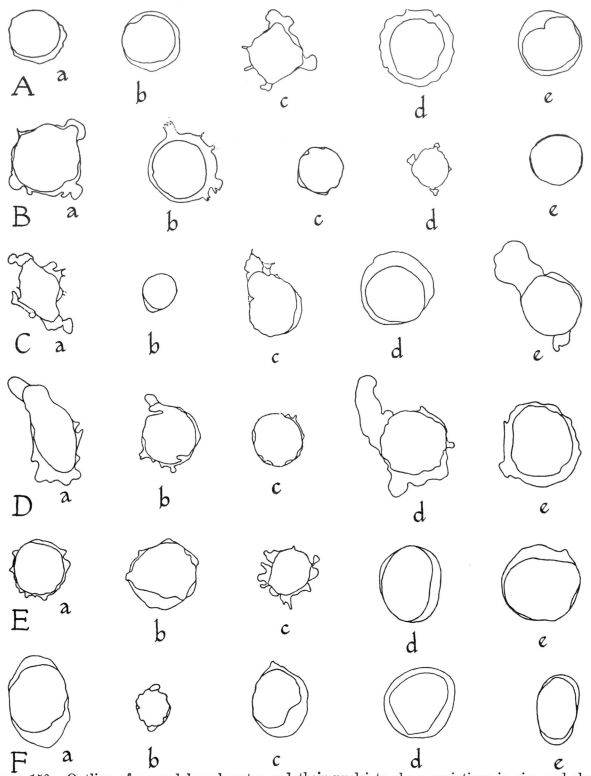

FIGURE 150.—Outline of normal lymphocytes and their nuclei to show variations in size and shape within and between breeds or stocks of chickens.   2,470×.

A, a–e   Ancona, from Hy-Line Poultry Farms, Iowa.

B, a–e   Barred Plymouth Rock, from Hy-Line Poultry Farms, Iowa.

C, a–e   New Hampshire, from Hy-Line Poultry Farms, Iowa.

D, a–e   Single Comb White Leghorn, from Iowa State College, Genetics Department.

E, a–e   Single Comb White Leghorn, from Hamilton Farm Bureau, Michigan.

F, a–e   Rhode Island Red, from Hamilton Farm Bureau, Michigan.

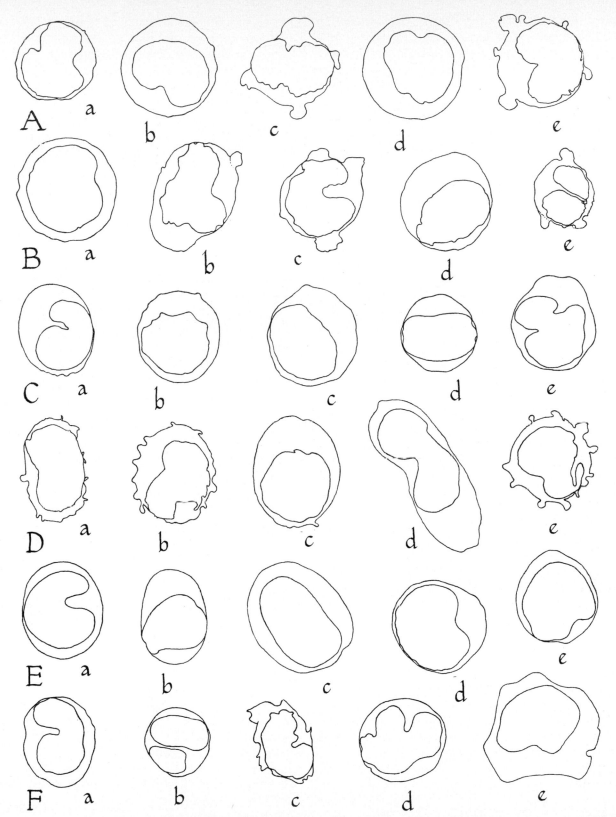

FIGURE 151.—Outlines of normal monocytes and their nuclei to show variations in size and shape within and between breeds and stocks of chickens. 2,470×.

Same slides and presented in the same order as in figure 150.

When the nucleus stains darkly, the overlying magenta bodies that have the same staining affinities are not clearly visible (figs. 104 and 109). When the nucleus is extensively lysed as in figures 105–107 the overlying magenta bodies are usually conspicuous.

No one has yet associated the presence of magenta bodies with any particular pathological condition in birds, but the impression has been gained that they are often associated with birds that have a disposition toward early mortality. Olson (1952) noted them in lymphocytes taken from cases of avian leukosis but he does not say that they are specifically associated with the disease. There is much speculation concerning the presence of a lymphomatosis agent of viral size that, by acting upon the lymphocyte, ultimately stimulates the cell into a neoplastic condition. These magenta bodies may have no relationship to lymphomatosis infection but their sporadic appearance in lymphocytes of chickens would seem to justify further study in an effort to find out what they are and what they are doing in the cell. Their presence does not necessarily indicate a dying cell; mitosis can occur (fig. 108).

Michaelis and Wolfe (1902) are said by Doan (1932) to be the first to describe azurophilic granules in lymphocytes. They used blood from man. Their description agrees closely with the observations made on avian blood. They established the fact that it was actually a lymphocyte that contained the granules. In circulating blood about one-third of the lymphocytes contained these granules, but they were absent from the lymphocytes of lymph nodes. The significance of these granules is still not adequately established.

Another type of cell response that produces atypical lymphocytes is hypertrophy with vacuolization of the cytoplasm (figs. 109–112). The stain taken by the cytoplasm is faint compared with that of the typical normal lymphocyte. The vacuoles may be small as in figure 109, irregular in size as in figure 111, and large as in figure 112. There may be few or many magenta bodies and these may show considerable variation in size; they may lie either in the vacuoles or between them or at their margin. From the appearance of the cytoplasm in which many vacuoles are present, a transformation toward a macrophage might be suggested. The nuclei of such vacuolated cells as seen in figures 109–112 show a closer resemblance to those of lymphocytes than to those of macrophages. The nucleus of the macrophage was studied in blood spots (Lucas, 1946) and in cardiac punctures of the embryo (figs. 309–317) where the typical chromatin pattern was a uniform reticulum with evenly distributed, dotlike bodies of chromatin at the interstices of the network. This punctate appearance of the macrophage nucleus is quite different from the delicate reticulum or massive irregular clumps of the typical lymphocyte.

Downey and McKinlay (1923), and Blackfan, Diamond and Leister (1944) illustrated and described the lymphocytes found in cases of infectious mononucleosis. The azurophilic bodies and the vacuolated cytoplasm of human lymphocytes in infectious mononucleosis simulate, in part, the magenta bodies and hypertrophied, vacuolated cytoplasm of avian lymphocytes, which may be seen in some seemingly normal birds. Although chickens do not carry the virus of infectious mononucleosis, as far as we know, the fact should not be ignored that lymphomatosis is also an infectious disease, and that it has a stimulating effect on the mononuclear cells accumulating within the tissues of the avian body (Lucas, 1949; Lucas, Craig, and Oakberg, 1949; Lucas and Oakberg, 1950; Lucas, Denington, Cottral and Burmester, 1954; Oakberg, 1949, 1951).

Osgood (1935) described fenestration in lymphocytes from cases of mononucleosis. He observed a vacuolization and canaliculization of the nucleus somewhat similar to, yet different from, the clefts of nuclei of avian cells.

A further variant of the magenta bodies is shown in figures 113–116, in which the colors range from a pale orange to the typical magenta color. Some of these cells show the slight nuclear lysis that already has been mentioned as occurring in lymphocytes with magenta bodies. The cytoplasmic inclusions in figure 114 show gradation from the light to the dark type of granule but the direction in which the reaction is going is not known. Cells of this type are rare and it should be noted that these cells came from birds having the same parents. In these same slides monocytes were present that seemed to have an unusually large quantity of azurophilic granules. The history of this family of nine birds is interesting. All were hatched June 19, 1944. The blood smears were taken at 112 days of age, except from F205C5.

F205W4—Female. At 66 and 115 days reactions were normal but at 163 days there was a slight loss of weight. Died at 166 days. Questionable visceral lymphomatosis.

F205X4—Male. Showed gasping at 163 days. Died at 339 days. Extreme emaciation and atrophy of the musculature.

F205Y4—Male. At 115 and 163 days bird showed vigorous reactions. Died at 518 days. Bird appeared to be in good condition. Cause of death undetermined (figs. 113–115 and 134).

F205Z4—Female. At 163 days reactions fair. At 253 days ill and put in a separate cage. Died at 292 days. Emaciation and impaction of crop (fig. 133).

F205A5—Female. At 110 days showed poor reactions and at 151 days ill and put in separate cage. In moribund condition and killed at 157 days. Neural and questionable visceral lymphomatosis.

F205B5—Male. At 163 days reaction fair. Died at 658 days. Cause of death undetermined.

F205C5—Female. Moribund at 75 days. Killed at 77 days. Lymphomatosis, neural.

F205D5—Male. At 115 days reaction was fair. Unsteady on feet at 155 days and moribund at 165 days. Killed. Lymphomatosis, neural and ocular.

F205E5—Female. At 65 days reactions were fair. At 126 days atonicity of crop. Moribund at 151 days and killed. Emaciation and dehydration (figs. 93, 116, 130, 132, and 142).

Various conditions were shown by the nine birds, both clinically and at necropsy, and all died before they were 2 years of age. At the time the smears were made the birds seemed to be reasonably healthy but in their subsequent history their performance was poor; thus it would seem inadvisable to represent some of these as normal cells from normal birds. It certainly should be determined, however, whether cellular reactions of this type have any value in understanding the causes of death in birds that die from tumors or in a generally unhealthy condition.

Another type of abnormal cellular reaction was found in the slides that showed, in the nuclei of erthyrocytes, chromophobic bands that usually had a uniform width. In lymphocytes these spaces were quite irregular (figs. 117–120). The clefts in figure 117 are irregular; yet, as in the erythrocytes, there is no actual break in the cell membrane but rather a sharply demarked transition from a densely stained area to one that did not take the stain; in the latter, a very faint reticulum can be seen. The lack of staining can affect small lymphocytes with lobes (fig. 118) as well as larger cells (figs. 119 and 120). Whatever the reaction may be, it can cause complete disappearance of basichromatin. Figures 117–120 show a transitional series leading to an "empty" nucleus.

The cytoplasm of erythrocytes was not affected when the nuclei showed chromophobic bands; about the only difference noted in lymphocytes was a somewhat more vacuolar organization than is generally found in lymphocytes. The possibility that these nonstaining effects are due to technic is not excluded but for the present it seems more likely that they represent some abnormal disturbance of the cell. If technic produces the defect, we have the question of how it alone could cause the chromatin to disappear and yet leave so sharp a boundary with the basichromatin that remains. If the defect truly represents cell pathology, tracing it back to the disease condition that is producing it should be relatively simple.

MONOCYTES

Normal mature monocytes (figs. 125–138)

The monocyte cytoplasm has been described in the literature as having the appearance of glass beads, and this effect is given as an important characteristic for separating monocytes from lymphocytes. This cytoplasmic quality probably does aid in the identification of these cells but actually it is of little value as a sole point of reference. The necessity of using multiple characteristics has already been emphasized. Owing to the overlapping of characteristics of lymphocytes and monocytes, it is necessary to consider each of their 10 points of difference. These will be taken up in the same order as they were for lymphocytes.

Cell size.—The ranges in size of lymphocytes and monocytes overlap as already seen in the comparisons from outline drawings and graphs. It is obvious that on the average the monocyte is larger than the lymphocyte; in fact, the average area of the whole lymphocyte is slightly smaller than the average area of the monocyte nucleus.

The maximum, minimum, and average values in table 4 are based on 300 planimeter measurements of cells projected and traced with a camera lucida. Half of these were from our Laboratory chickens and half from two different breeds from a commercial laboratory. The possibility of breed or inbred line differences is discussed in chapter 6. These curves indicate that nuclear size is much less variable than the area of nucleus plus cytosome (fig. 153). For the nucleus of both lymphocytes and monocytes the size is symmetrically distributed on each side of the mean; whereas, when cytoplasm is added, there is a definite tendency toward skewness with relatively few low values, but a trailing off in incidence of the high values. Approximately 25 percent of the lymphocyte nuclei overlap 22 percent of the monocyte nuclei in size, whereas only about 15 percent of the lymphocyte total cell area overlaps 7 percent of the monocyte cell area.

Another interesting point brought out by table 4 is the broad range from minimum to maximum areas, which for lymphocytes is 9.2-fold and for monocytes is 3.8-fold. In terms of diameters one could expect, therefore, a 3-fold range for lymphocytes and about a 2-fold range for monocytes. Since there is a 3-fold range in diameters, one may separate lymphocytes arbitrarily into 3 categories—small, medium, and large. Cells with a diameter up to 7.8μ would be classed as small, those from 7.9 to 10.3μ as medium, and those above 10.4μ as large. Of the 300 lymphocytes measured and plotted, 55 percent would be classed as small, 36 percent as medium, and 9 percent as large.[5] Blast cells have not been in-

---

[5] Wiseman (1932) reported that in dried blood smears from man the range for small lymphocytes is considered to be from 6μ to 9μ; for medium, from 9μ to 12μ; and for large, $12\mu+$.

Table 4.—**Nuclear and cell areas and diameters for lymphocytes and monocytes**

Cell measurement	Lympho-cytes	Monocytes
Nuclear size:		
Area (in square microns):		
Minimum...............	10. 3	23. 1
Maximum..............	88. 6	97. 6
Average................	33. 5	54. 2
Diameter, average (in microns).	6. 5	8. 3
Total cell size:		
Area (in square microns):		
Minimum...............	12. 8	59. 1
Maximum..............	118. 1	226. 0
Average................	49. 3	114. 8
Diameter, average (in microns).	7. 9	12. 1
Nucleocytosomal ratio.............	1: 0. 47	1 :1. 12

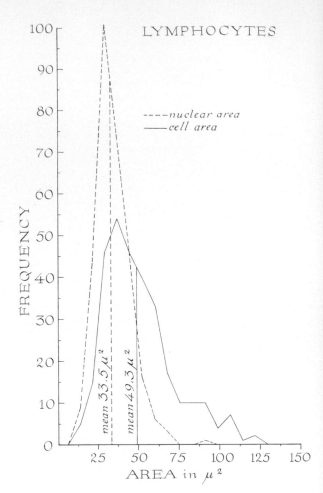

FIGURE 152.—Frequency distribution curves of cell area and nuclear area for 300 lymphocytes chosen at random.

cluded in these data—the term "large," therefore, merely indicates the upper end of the range. For practical purposes, two divisions of lymphocytes are about as many as one can judge accurately from mental impression. From an examination of the two curves for lymphocytes and monocytes, there would seem to be no reason for separating either lymphocytes or monocytes into groups of various sizes; yet, for convenience, lymphocytes are so separated; monocytes are not. Cell size may have functional significance and certainly one bird will show a higher average of one cell size than will another bird; but until there is some clue concerning the physiologic significance of cell size, there is little point in recording it in the data. If it should be established that diminishing cell size is a corollary of aging, perhaps a record of size would serve the

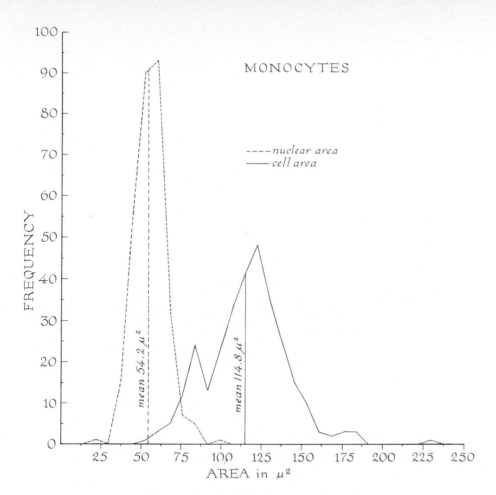

FIGURE 153.—Frequency distribution curves of cell area and nuclear area for 300 monocytes chosen at random.

same usefulness for the agranulocytes that the Arneth counts do for the granulocytes.

Mainland et al. (1935) studied statistically the significance of lymphocyte size in the human species and concluded that cell size was a unimodal curve, but with skewness in most cases, and that a small and a large lymphocyte did not exist as classes. From their data, there was no indication that age, sex, or state of health were factors influencing the size of lymphocytes in man.

These opinions on size are in agreement with those of Magath and Higgins (1934), who measured the diameters of lymphocytes from each of eight ducks and concluded that they all belong to one series with a size range from 4.0 to 8.1μ and that all attempts to classify them into small, medium, and large were futile. Cul-

len (1903) finds that monocyte diameters range from 6.7 to 9.3μ; both of these values are below the average given in table 4. Magath and Higgins found the average to be between 11 and 13.5.

Cell shape.—The variety of shapes exhibited by the monocyte can be appreciated best by glancing over figures 125–138 and the cells outlined in figure 151. In general, the monocyte has a round shape. Occasionally there may be small bleb projections such as seen in figures 126, 127, and 138. Whether they serve the same function in monocytes that they are said to serve in lymphocytes, namely, contributing globulins to the plasma, is not known.

There is another type of cytosomal protrusion that occurs rather frequently. It is a hyaline mantle that extends in irregular fashion beyond the denser endoplasmic portion of the cell (figs. 125 and 143). The hyaline mantle in the latter figure is somewhat more lightly stained. In contrast to the mantle, the central reticulum retains an approximately round shape.

Weiss and Fawcett (1953) mention the existence of a mantle in avian monocytes when grown in tissue culture. The mantle was found to be visible when cells were examined under the phase microscope. It is not altogether clear that the type of mantle (thin undulating membrane) they observed, and the type we have described are identical. Weiss and Fawcett believed that mantle formation is part of the process whereby monocytes become macrophages. Additional support for the idea that monocytes may become macrophages comes from Dawson's (1933a) study of blood cell reactions to lead poisoning in *Necturus*.

Since monocytes are large cells they are distorted more readily during the process of making dried smears than are small cells. The cytosome and even the nucleus often are squeezed between other cells, and so take various angular shapes, or they may overlap other cells. These variations occur most readily when there is a hyaline mantle. If, however, they happen to fall in an open space free from other cells, they usually show a round contour and cells such as these are the ones usually selected for drawing.

Nuclear position.—The nucleus in many monocytes is eccentrically placed, as may be seen in figures 126–133 and 135; sometimes it forms a bridge across the middle of the cell (figs. 134 and 136). The wide diversity of position is shown in the outline drawings. In the first row only 1 of 5 could be said to have the typical or eccentric position. The proportion is about the same in the other rows. The ratio of 1 eccentric nucleus to 5 centrally placed is probably not a true one because a disproportionate number of cells selected for making the outline drawings were atypical but were selected to show as wide a range of morphologic expression as possible. The eccentric position of the nucleus is of considerable value in distinguishing between a monocyte and a lymphocyte but it must be borne in mind that a monocyte can have a centrally-placed nucleus (fig. 151, *A, b* and *B, a*), as do many lymphocytes.

Nucleocytosomal ratio.—Not only are monocytes larger than lymphocytes on the average but the cytosome is proportionately larger than it is in lymphocytes. This difference is not so great, however, as superficial examination of cells might lead one to believe. The eccentric position of the nucleus gives the impression that there is a large mass of cytoplasm; but when the same quantity of cytoplasm is uniformly distributed around a centrally placed nucleus there seems to be only a narrow rim. This false impression is magnified by the indentation of the monocyte nucleus. The nucleocytosomal ratios for the two cell types are given in table 4. They average 1: 0.47 for lymphocytes and 1:1.12 for monocytes. In other words, the cytosomal area in relation to nuclear area in monocytes is 58 percent greater than in lymphocytes. In terms of nucleocell diameters the ratio is 1:1.22 for lymphocytes and 1:1.46 for monocytes.

Cytoplasmic structure.—The descriptive term "ground-glass effect" has been used by numerous writers on avian blood. It is important to try to understand what the structural elements are that create the ground-glass illusion. Actually, we have failed to see what others call the "ground-glass effect." Any one of the following three elements within the cell might be responsible for the optical effect:

(1) The open reticular framework such as seen in figures 138 and 143, where there exist numerous uniform spaces bounded by a delicate reticulum. These spaces, however, have low refractility; the term "ground-glass" suggests rather conspicuous refractility.

(2) The delicate orange-stained substance that sometimes fills the vacuolar spaces in the *Hof* (fig. 144). Figure 126 shows similar spaces in the *Hof* but the material that fills them has not taken an orange color. When the orange-stained substance is present, it increases the contrast with the reticulum and thus gives the illusion of greater refractility. This may be what has been called the ground-glass appearance of the monocyte cytoplasm.

(3) The polychromatic reaction of the protoplasmic network (figs. 130 and 137), which gives a textural effect to the cytoplasm. The interstices of the network that in the previous figures took either a light or a dense basophilic stain show in the last two cells mentioned a shift in

staining of this substance in an azurophilic direction. Because of the mixture of salmon and blue colors, the cytoplasm has been given a textural effect that does not occur when the same structure shows a uniform single hue. Dual coloration of the reticulum gives the optical effect of thickness and density. Of the three structural elements listed, this is the one that offers the best explanation of the "ground-glass effect."

There is only one other possibility—the presence of definite azurophilic granules. They, however, are relatively rare (figs. 132–135) and thus would not be mentioned as typical for monocytes. Some of the cells shown in the drawings came from the same parents that produced the reactive lymphocytes, as has already been stated. The azurophilic bodies may give to the monocyte a tinged margin (fig. 142). The only other cell type that shows a tinged border of this sort is an immature thrombocyte (figs. 296–299 and 303). This particular monocyte shows a well-defined *Hof* that helps to identify it as a monocyte. In other examples drawn from the same family of birds (fig. 132, 134, and p. 65), there is an increasing number of azurophilic granules in the cytoplasm. Sometimes they are on the side of the nucleus opposite the *Hof;* at other times they are on the same side; and they may be more or less uniformly scattered over the whole cell. Figure 135 is an extreme example. Here the azurophilic bodies are larger than normal. They show considerable variability in staining intensity, and in some respects resemble an early heterophil myelocyte. This type of azurophilic granule is so atypical for monocytes in general that only rarely indeed would a cell of this appearance be picked up in a differential count.

Hof and orange-staining spheres.—The *Hof* has been mentioned a number of times as a lightly stained, vacuolated area in the cytosome that has considerable value in the identification of monocytes. It may or may not contain orange-stained material. The meaning of the term as used here is slightly different from that stated in the broad definition given in Dorland's Medical Dictionary—"The area of the cytoplasm of a cell encircled by the concavity of the nucleus." This definition may fit quite well in some cases. Typical examples of a *Hof* are shown in figures 126, 138, and 144. The clear space in figure

142 is called a *Hof* also, although it is obviously not encircled or even bounded by an indentation of the nucleus. The area, nevertheless, is clearly demarked from the rest of the cytoplasm. Figures 128 and 133 are good examples of cells that show indented nuclei but there is no *Hof* in the sense in which the term is used here. The *Hof* shown in figure 129 is rather indistinct, and in figure 132 it is present as a broad space that fills most of the cytosome on one side of the nucleus. The next three figures contain none. The vacuolar space opposite the indentation of the nucleus in figure 131 could be called a *Hof*, as could the clear space in the lymphocyte (fig. 97). The *Hof* is nearly always found in monocytes but there may be exceptions, as already mentioned.

Just how closely associated are the *Hof* and the rosette obtained with neutral red vital stain is not known. It is assumed that they are closely associated but it has not been determined whether cells that fail to show a *Hof*, in the sense in which the term is used here, would also fail to show a rosette.

Specific cell inclusions.—The vacuolar spaces of the *Hof* often contain a homogeneous substance that takes a very faint orange color with Wright's stain, a stain that is better for this purpose than May-Grünwald Giemsa. Perhaps the orange spheres could be classed as an azurophilic substance also, although the coloration is distinctly more yellowish than in the small azurophilic granules described under the heading "Cytoplasmic structure." It takes an excellent light source and microscope correctly used to show any tinge of color in the *Hof;* yet it is a real substance, as may be demonstrated in the abnormal cell, figure 147, where the *Hof* substance has become concentrated into large spheres.

All three substances—(1) the azurophilic granules, (2) the azurophilic tinge of the reticulum, and (3) the orange spheres of the *Hof*— are useful in the identification of the monocyte and carry much weight in separating monocytes from lymphocytes. The only specific cell inclusions found in lymphocytes are the magenta bodies, which are nearly always darker and more intensely colored than any of the three listed for monocytes.

Nuclear shape.—Nuclear shape needs very little additional discussion. The difference between the shape of the indentation in lymphocytes and in monocytes has been mentioned, and the examples shown in the various figures of monocytes bear out the observation that the nuclear depression is usually broad with a rounded bottom, as diagramed on page 53.

The presence of this type of indentation is helpful in identifying monocytes but certainly it cannot be relied upon entirely; many monocytes have round or elongated nuclei without any depression (figs. 151, *B, d, C, c, D, c,* and *E, c*). Some have irregularly shaped nuclei (figs. 151, *A, d, B, b, D, b* and *e,* and *F, d*) or double indentations (figs. 136, 137, and 151, *C, e*), and sometimes the indentation cuts the nucleus into two equal or unequal parts (figs. 138, 151, *B, e* and *F, b*). This variability must be kept in mind when a differential count is being made so that some monocytes will not be omitted from the count because they have atypical nuclei.

Nuclear structure.—Nuclear structure is a pattern that is often viewed impressionistically without giving deliberate attention to the parts. When the pattern is carefully studied, it breaks down into a complex of interrelated details such as size, shape, and distribution of chromatin clumps, the character of the reticulum and its relation to the basichromatin and the tinctorial reactions of the nucleoplasm. When viewed superficially the monocyte nucleus gives the impression that it has a delicate lacelike reticular pattern of chromatin and a transparency that is not generally observed in the lymphocyte nucleus.

Upon close examination, it may be observed that the clumps of chromatin at the interstices of the network are often small, as in figure 127. Sometimes they may be relatively large and dense, as in figure 125, which has a highly colored nucleoplasm and thus would not give a transparent effect. In lymphocytes a reticular appearance was often found associated with larger nuclei. Whether the more open reticulum and smaller chromatin clumps commonly found in monocytes represent a characteristic difference between the two cell types, or are nothing more than a reflection of the larger nuclear size, is undetermined. Nuclear pattern carries relatively little weight in the separation of the two cell types, chiefly because a definite type of chromatin organization cannot be considered specific for

each of these cells. Yet any survey involving hundreds of monocytes and lymphocytes will clearly reveal that each type has its own general pattern. It will also reveal that monocyte nuclei fall into two groups—those with a delicate open reticulum and those with coarse blocks. The same differences may be found in the immature stages (figs. 139–144).

Cell division.—The indentation of the nucleus so common in monocytes is often carried further, leading to various degrees of constriction that may approach the center from two sides (figs. 136–138) or cut the nucleus from one side only (fig. 151, *B, e*). This may lead to complete division of the nucleus into two parts. When they are equal in size, they suggest cell division by amitosis; but the occurrence of unequal nuclei (fig. 151, *F, b*) raises the question of whether this type of nuclear duplication has any more relationship to amitosis than has the lobulation of the granulocyte nucleus. No actual pulling apart of the cystosome to form two cell bodies has ever been observed. Constriction of the nucleus is much more frequently found in monocytes than in lymphocytes, and this is a useful morphologic feature that aids in separating these two leukocytes.

Conclusions derived from use of table 3.—Frequent mention has been made of the fact that one cannot decide whether a particular cell is a monocyte or a lymphocyte without considering numerous characteristics, which must be balanced against one another. A few cells, questionable ones as well as those that are obviously of one type or the other, have been presented in tabular form in table 5 to show how the various characteristics given in table 3 have been applied. Table 5 should make clear why some questionable cells have been classed as monocytes instead of lymphocytes and vice versa and it brings out that oftentimes a cell will show a characteristic that is just as frequently found in monocytes as in lymphocytes, and there may be a "+" in both rows of the table.

Developmental stages found in circulating blood (figs. 139–144)

Lymphocytogenesis and monocytogenesis are vague and controversial subjects, chiefly because

Table 5.—Classification of individual cells into lymphocytes and m onocytes [1]

Figure	Cell type [2]	Characteristic										Conclusion
		Cell size	Cell shape	Nuclear position	Nucleo-cytosomal ratio	Cyto-plasmic struc-ture	*Hof* and orange-staining spheres	Specific cell inclu-sions	Nuclear shape	Nuclear struc-ture	Cell division	
94.....	L.....	+	+	–	+	+	+	–	+	+	–	Lympho-cyte.
	M.....	–	+	+	–	–	–	–	±	+	–	
99.....	L.....	+	+	–	+	+	+	–	+	–	–	Lympho-cyte.
	M.....	+	+	+	–	–	–	–	–	+	–	
125....	L.....	–	–	–	–	–	–	–	–	+	–	Monocyte
	M.....	+	+	+	+	+	+	–	+	+	–	
126....	L.....	–	+	–	–	–	–	–	–	+	–	Monocyte
	M.....	+	+	+	+	+	+	–	+	+	–	
127....	L.....	±	+	–	+	–	–	–	+	–	–	Monocyte
	M.....	+	+	+	–	+	+	–	+	+	–	
131....	L.....	+	+	–	+	–	–	–	–	+	–	Monocyte
	M.....	–	+	+	–	+	+	+	+	+	–	

[1] See table 3, p. 49.   [2] L=lymphocyte; M=monocyte.

the cells lack a sufficient number of cell features by which differentiation can be followed. In contrast, erythrocytes have hemoglobin; granulocytes and thrombocytes their various types of specific granules. All these aids are lacking in lymphocytes and monocytes. One must resort to less reliable criteria such as lobulations, nuclear structure, and cytoplasmic texture and color. Three cells in the process of monocytogenesis have been shown in the spleen of a chick 35 days of age (fig. 331, *16–19*). The immature cells have lobulated cytosomes with a uniform basophilic granulation and nuclei with small clumps of chromatin, which are generally uniformly scattered. The immature monocytes of figures 139–144, found in the circulating blood, have two types of nuclei—those with a fine reticulum in which the chromatin stains a pale purple color, and those in which the nucleus takes an overall magenta color, including the nucleoplasm. None of the cells in the first row (figs. 139–142) came from the birds that gave figures 143–145; therefore, the difference in coloration may be due either to technic or to the bird, and we should probably guard against overemphasizing this difference.

Two early immature cells have been drawn (figs. 139 and 140) but these are seen very rarely in circulating blood; they may be found in blood dyscrasias. The fine, highly dispersed pattern of nuclear chromatin and the few remaining mito-chondrial spaces in the cytosome all indicate immaturity, and lobulation when combined with the nuclear pattern, points to the same thing. Young primary erythroblasts in the circulating blood of the 48-hour chick embryo are another example of cells showing lobulations as an indication of their immaturity. The azurophilic granules in the cytosome of figure 140 aid in identifying it as a monocyte, and the lobulation and nuclear pattern identify it as a young cell. A few of these granules take a magenta stain like the nucleus and the specific granules of lymphocytes; a pair of them, along the lower edge of the nucleus, actually appear to be connected with the nuclear membrane by delicate strands. If it could be established that magenta bodies actually arise as extruded nuclear substance, it would go far toward establishing that the usual type of azurophilic material of the monocyte, and the magenta bodies found in a few monocytes and in many abnormal and reactive lymphocytes, are not the same.

The amoeboid cell (fig. 143) is also a young monocyte but it shows more extensive vacuolization of the cytoplasm than figures 139 and 140. In some cells, blebs project that appear to be pinching off. Later immature monocytes are illustrated in figures 141, 142, and 144. Some blebs are still present, the nucleus may be round or nearly so, and a clear *Hof* has appeared.

Abnormal monocytes (figs. 145–147)

The two cells shown in figures 145 and 146 are classed as abnormal because they are undergoing early autolysis. In the former there are only early manifestations of cell breakdown, the vacuolization in the region of the *Hof* has become amorphous, and the remainder of the cytosome has an atypical tinge of color. The concentration of basophilic bodies at the cell margin is probably not indicative of abnormality.

A somewhat later stage in autolysis is shown in figure 146, in which the cytoplasm has taken on an overall reddish color and there is a decreased color difference between nucleus and cytosome. Otherwise the structural breakdown has not been extensive. There is no indication whether the nucleus will go in the direction of lysis or of chromatin clumping.

Abnormality has been expressed in still another way (fig. 147). The orange spheres of the *Hof* increased in size whereas ordinarily they are relatively uniform. The increase might be due either to an abnormal growth of a sphere or to the coalescence of adjoining spheres accompanied by changes in the reticulum. Aside from this one point there is very little indication that the cell is abnormal.

Technic artifacts (figs. 148, 149)

Only one type of technic artifact has been found thus far in monocytes—a squashing of the cell when the smear is made. A squashed monocyte is rarely identified with certainty. In figure 148 the large size and the indented nucleus aided in the exclusion of other cells. The monocytes, for some reason, were the only cells in the slide from which figure 149 was taken that showed fragility. This slide gave an excellent series of stages from a slightly squashed monocyte to the extreme condition shown in figure 149. When it reaches the last condition there is nothing by which the squashed cell may be identified as a monocyte. Its size so far exceeds the size of the normal monocyte nucleus that it has very little meaning. The significance of the configuration of such cells has been discussed in mammalian literature, where they are called basket cells and disintegrating cells when they have the appearance shown in figure 149. Osgood and Ashworth (1937) in speaking of them say (p. 20), "These cells are probably not artifacts made in smearing but remnants of dead cells."

Kracke and Garver (1937) mention (p. 84) that in mammalian literature smudged cells have been divided into two types: "It has been stated that smudge forms are degenerating lymphocytes and that basket cells . . . are degenerating granulocytes. . . . Nevertheless, it seems more probable that the smudge cell is an early stage and the basket cell a late stage of the same process.

"Crushing and rupturing of monocytes, neutrophils, eosinophils and basophils . . . occur in improperly made smears, especially when too much pressure is applied to the drop of blood. These cellular remnants are found in various abnormal states where there is excessive destruction of leukocytes. In these cases their occurrence is probably the result of toxic agents or of an increased fragility of the cellular elements." This point of view is in agreement with our opinion that the actual production of smudged cells comes at the time the smear is made and that it is not a record of *in vivo* degeneration of leukocytes. The basis for this opinion is the conspicuous difference between smears made from the same bird at the same time and also the fact that large numbers of smudged cells often occur at thinned-out portions of the smear where presumably the pressure is greater. This point of view is not in conflict with the idea that there are differences in cell fragility and that increased fragility may accompany diseased conditions.

Osgood and Ashworth (1937) say (p. 20) that, "One should not, however, make the error of omitting to include the disintegrated cells in the differential count as a large number of disintegrated cells is strongly suggestive of a diagnosis of leukemia and failure to include them may give an erroneous impression of the true incidence of other cell types."

We have not found at this Laboratory that the presence of smudged cells aids in the diagnosis of the avian leukosis complex, but it is agreed that smudged cells can influence the differential count. A good example is the slide from which figure 149 was made. Smudged monocyte nuclei similar to the one illustrated were found in abundance; yet intact monocytes were scarce and were actually fewer than the smudged nuclei. Should they be counted? It has been our experience with avian blood that it is impractical. In mammalian blood only the leukocytes have nuclei, and so any smudged nucleus must at least be a leukocyte. But in avian blood where the erythrocytes and thrombocytes are nucleated also, the possibility of error in identification of a smudged nucleus becomes so great that any possible value of its addition to a count is nullified by the increased source of error; and if some cannot be properly classified, those that can be identified, such as the three granulocytes, should not be included either. On the other hand, if in a particular bird the smudging affects only one of the types of white cells, some account must be taken of the fact, or the differential values will be biased.

Granular Leukocytes

There are three granular leukocytes in birds as in mammals—heterophils, eosinophils, and basophils. Eosinophils and basophils received their names because the cells contain granules that have an affinity for eosin and for basic dyes. The term "heterophil," which was suggested by Kyes (1929), applies to the third granulocyte cell type, in which the specific inclusions of homologous cells among the various classes of vertebrates show great diversity in reaction to stains. The heterophil of birds and reptiles is the equivalent of the neutrophil in man. The term "neutrophil" is based on the staining reactions; the term "heterophil" is not.

Ryerson (1943), f r o m his comparative studies, suggests that the morphology of heterophils and eosinophils has been influenced by two lines of evolution through the vertebrate classes (p. 44), " . . . one line contains the selachians, reptiles, and birds; the other contains the cyclostomes, teleosts, amphibians, and mammals."

HETEROPHILS

Normal mature heterophils (figs. 154–167)

Heterophils as usually seen in the circulating blood show a low variability in size. Some indication of range may be obtained by comparing the various drawings and, particularly, the graph (fig. 197). Kennedy and Climenko (1928) gave a range of 4.2 to 9.0μ with an average of 6.35μ, which is nearly 2.3μ less than the average of 8.7μ from these data. Under stimulation such as replacement after irradiation, a shower of smaller cells may be liberated. Perhaps this reflects a factor of cytoplasmic growth, independent of seeming maturity that is indicated by nuclear lobulation, in that smears made from bone marrow show many more small heterophils than are found in circulating blood, and yet these cells show multilobed nuclei and in this respect are considered to be mature. This fluctuation in size of heterophils, and also of eosinophils, is a factor that may account for differences in size reported by different investigators for these cells. If one emphasized the size of heterophils as some have emphasized the size of lymphocytes, it might be that cell size would prove to be a criterion as useful as number of nuclear lobes in indicating the condition of health of the bird.

From these figures of heterophils it can be seen that the dominant shape is a circle, which is surprising in view of the fact that in life heterophils are actively amoeboid.

In a strict sense practically none of the heterophils from circulating blood should be regarded as representing their true structure and appearance. Nearly all these cells reveal an artifact involving the nucleus, and many reveal a second artifact that involves the rods. The artifact in the nucleus is so constant with Wright's stain that it is of considerable value in identifying the cell type, but the one in the rods is an ever-present cause of confusion between heterophils and eosinophils.

The rods, which are the specific inclusions for heterophils, have typically the appearance shown in figures 154 and 155. They are long fusiform bodies, they are pointed at each end, and they take the eosin stain brilliantly. Both Dantschakoff (1909a and b and 1916b) and Hamre (personal communication) have observed that in some cells the rods are grouped in a fanlike cluster. This arrangement has never been observed in mature cells in any of our smears; instead the rods are always scattered like a pile of short straws with pointed ends. Ryerson (1943), in his study of heterophils in turtles, shows a radial arrangement of the rods in the myelocytes but not in the mature cells. There may be considerable variability among cells in the length of these rods. Some are long and narrow (fig. 154) and others short and relatively broad (fig. 2, *1*). In some cases these differences can be characteristic of a species (figs. 400, 401, 403, and 406.)

In many heterophils some rods may contain central granules. Hamre is of the opinion that each rod contains a central granule that is revealed when Wright-Giemsa is used (p. 230).

The research necessary to prove or disprove the point has never been undertaken but the results obtained with Wright's stain gave no indication that every rod has a central granule and the same opinion is supported by evidence from a study of developmental stages in bone marrow and spleen stained with May-Grünwald Giemsa. Even in squashed cells where the individual rods are thrown apart from each other, central granules may be absent in one case (fig. 175) and present in another (fig. 176). Additional evidence on this point comes from the fact that in cells where the rods have disappeared there may remain numerous central granules (fig. 161) or they may be absent (fig. 165).

Sometimes instead of a granule there may be a vacuole or at least a nonstaining clear space in the center of each rod (figs. 166 and 167). In the second figure most of the rod substance has

---

FIGURES 154–176.—Heterophils from circulating blood—mature, immature, and smudged cells. Some evidence of technic artifact is apparent in practically all normal mature heterophils. (The terms "central bodies" and "central granules" as applied to heterophils are synonymous.) 2,470✕.

FIGURES 154–167: *Normal mature heterophils selected to show variability in structure and size of cells and in staining defects.*

154 Well-preserved rods, without central granules. Nuclear lobes are poorly stained.
155 Rods with a few central bodies. Variable staining of the nuclear lobes.
156 Approximately one central granule per rod. Nuclear lobes are fully stained.
157 Partial dissolution of rods; central bodies are large and do not disappear. Variable staining of the nuclear lobes.
158 Nearly complete dissolution of rods; the rod substance gives to the cytoplasm an overall pink color with Wright's stain. Central bodies are small.
159 Nearly complete dissolution of rods, which gives an intense color to the entire cytosome. The outer portions of the nuclear lobes are well stained; inner parts are poorly stained.
160 Small heterophil showing only central bodies of varying size.
161 Heterophil with only central bodies visible. The large central bodies of this and the preceding cells cause these cells to resemble the eosinophils, but they can be separated by the difference in color of the cytoplasmic ground substance. Compare with figures 177–180.
162 Completely dissolved rods with only relatively few small central bodies. Nuclear lobes are weakly stained.
163 Central bodies few, with a range in size varying from small to large.
164 Heterophil with but few central bodies and no rods.
165 Heterophil without rods or central bodies.

166 Heterophil in which the central bodies appear as vacuoles within the rods.
167 Heterophil in which the rods have contracted around the vacuolar-type central bodies.

FIGURES 168–173: *Developmental stages of heterophils found in circulating blood.*

168 Heterophil granuloblast. No nucleolus visible. Found on same slide with heterophil myelocytes, figures 169–172.
169 Heterophil promyelocyte. Nucleus in lower two-thirds of cell appears to merge with the cytosome. Magenta granules and rings identify this as a heterophil.
170 Heterophil promyelocyte. Approximately the same stage of development as preceding cell, but smaller.
171 Heterophil promyelocyte.
172 Heterophil promyelocyte. Greater vacuolization of cytoplasm than in preceding cells. Nucleus is not yet clearly separated from cytosome.
173 Heterophil mesomyelocyte. Early stage in the differentiation of the specific heterophil rods.

FIGURES 174–176: *Technic artifacts.*

174 Mature heterophil. M. G. G.; the central bodies were retained as they are following Wright's stain but the rod substance was almost completely dissolved. Nucleus poorly stained.
175 Smudged heterophil with two nuclear lobes. Rods retained their form.
176 Smudged heterophil with rods dissolved. The large spheres are the central granules and the small ones are serum granules.

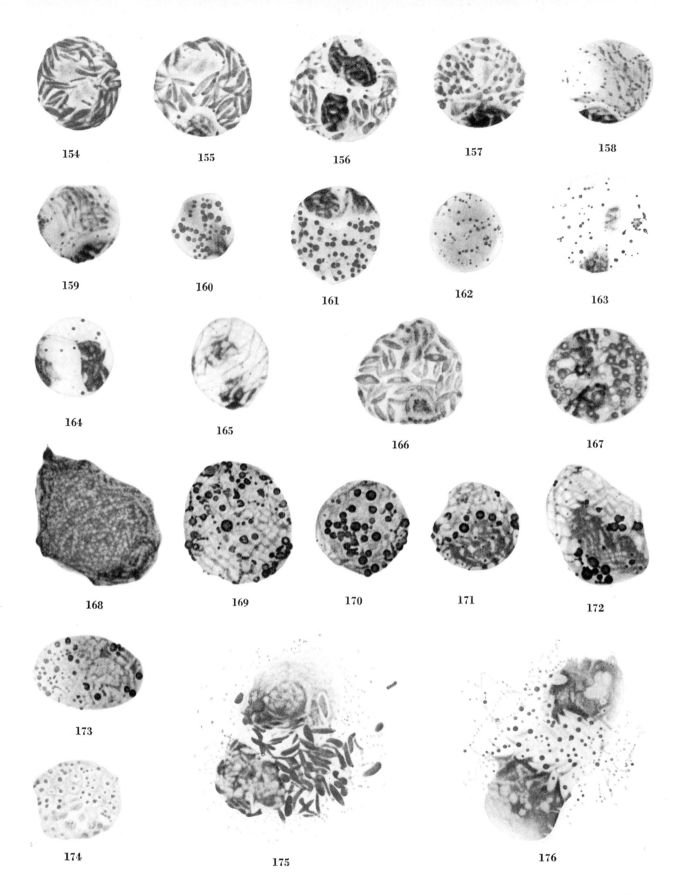

154

155

156

157

158

159

160

161

162

163

164

165

166

167

168

169

170

171

172

173

174

175

176

FIGURES 177–187.—Eosinophils from circulating blood—mature, immature, and smudged cells. 2,470×.

FIGURES 177–183: *Normal mature eosinophils that show size range.*

FIGURES 177–180: *Typical eosinophils. The light blue-staining cytoplasmic background is an identifying characteristic of these cells; so is the full staining of the nucleus.*

177   The eosinophilic granules can be composed of 4 smaller granules in a square.
178   The eosinophilic granules can appear as scattered small granules on a reticulum.
179   The eosinophilic granules can have a size range of large to small and be intermingled.
180   The eosinophilic granules can appear as large spheres with a clear space in the center, with little or no indication that they are made up of 4 smaller granules.

FIGURES 181–183: *Small normal mature eosinophils, not so common as the larger size.*

181   Eosinophilic granules, closely aggregated. Cell might be confused with a heterophil.

182   Eosinophilic granules, small and closely aggregated.

183   Small eosinophil with a high nucleocytoplasmic ratio.

FIGURES 184–186: *Developmental stages of eosinophils found in circulating blood.*

184   Eosinophilic mesomyelocyte. Strong basophilic cytoplasm with specific granules in early stages of development.

185   Eosinophilic metamyelocyte. Later stage of development than the preceding cell.

186   Late eosinophilic metamyelocyte, almost fully differentiated.

FIGURE 187: *Technic artifact.*

187   Smudged eosinophil. The grouping of small granules to form large granules duplicates what was observed in the intact cell, figure 177.

 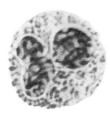 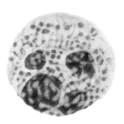 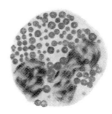

177   178   179   180

181   182   183

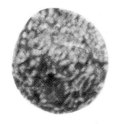 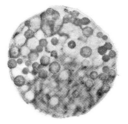 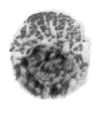

184   185   186

187

77

FIGURES 188–196.—Basophils from circulating blood—mature, immature, and smudged cells. 2,470×.

FIGURES 188–192: *Normal mature basophils, all of which show slight to extensive artifacts due to the water used with Wright's staining technic.*

188 Basophil having an appearance approaching that following methyl alcohol fixation, figure 390.
189 Basophil showing early artifact of coalescence and dispersion of granules.
190 Basophil showing moderate artifact of coalescence of granules above the nucleus and discharge from the cell surface.
191 Basophil showing extensive artifact. Complete loss of cytoplasmic granules except for two pairs on the cell margin and those above the nucleus that coalesced when the cell dried.
192 Basophil showing extensive artifact. Magenta masses above the nucleus represent basophilic granules of the cytosome, not basochromatin of the nucleus.
193 Basophil promyelocyte.

FIGURES 194–196: *Technic artifacts, smudged cells.*

194 Slightly smudged basophil.
195 Moderately smudged basophil.
196 Extensively smudged basophil.

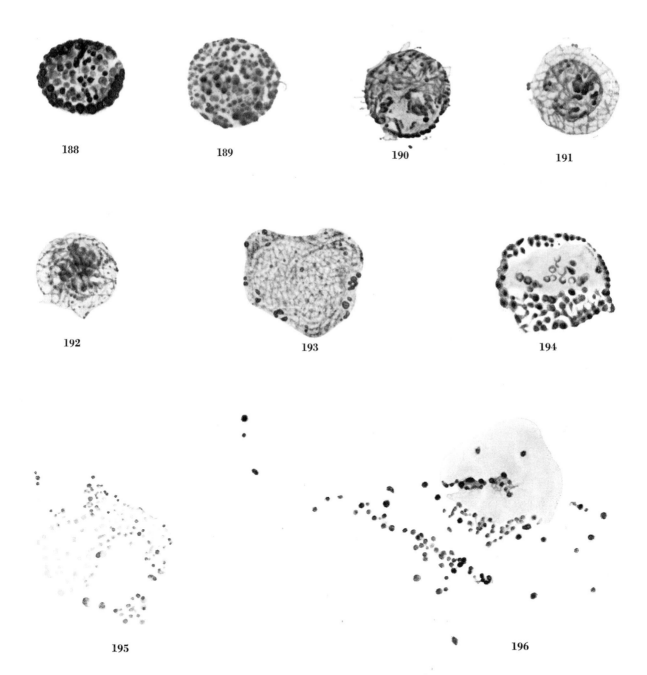

188   189   190   191

192   193   194

195   196

79

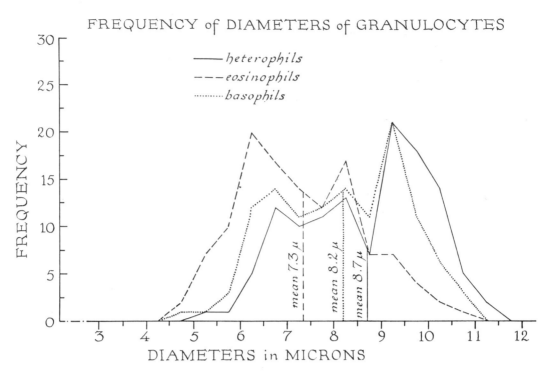

FIGURE 197.—Frequency distribution curves for cell diameter of heterophils, eosinophils, and basophils.

FIGURES 198–223.—Effect of Petrunkevitch No. 2 fixation and M. G. G. stain. Granulocytes arranged to give a series of nuclear lobes for Arneth counts. 2,470×.

198 Erythrocyte nucleus with this technic almost a solid dark blue.
199 Small lymphocyte with cytoplasmic blebs and pachychromatic type nucleus.
200 Average lymphocyte with leptochromatic type nucleus. Perinuclear space in this and the preceding cell.
201 Monocyte. This technic shows the stainability of the substance filling the vacuoles of the *Hof.*
202 Thrombocyte. The specific granule of the thrombocyte lies within a vacuole.
203 Heterophil, 3 nuclear lobes. This technic dissolved out completely all rods and granules, leaving only a cytoplasmic framework.
204 Heterophil, 1 nuclear lobe.
205 Heterophil, 1 nuclear lobe.
206 Heterophil, 2 nuclear lobes.
207 Heterophil, 2 nuclear lobes.

208 Heterophil, 3 nuclear lobes.
209 Heterophil, 3 nuclear lobes.
210 Heterophil, 4 nuclear lobes.
211 Heterophil, 4 nuclear lobes.
212 Heterophil, 4 nuclear lobes.
213 Heterophil, 5 nuclear lobes.
214 Heterophil, 5 nuclear lobes.
215 Eosinophil, 2 nuclear lobes. Specific granules are not destroyed by this technic in the chicken.
216 Eosinophil, 1 nuclear lobe.
217 Eosinophil, 3 nuclear lobes.
218 Eosinophil, 3 nuclear lobes.
219 Eosinophil, 3 nuclear lobes.
220 Eosinophil, 4 nuclear lobes.
221 Basophil, 1 nuclear lobe. Specific granules well preserved.
222 Basophil, 1 nuclear lobe.
223 Basophil, 2 nuclear lobes.

80

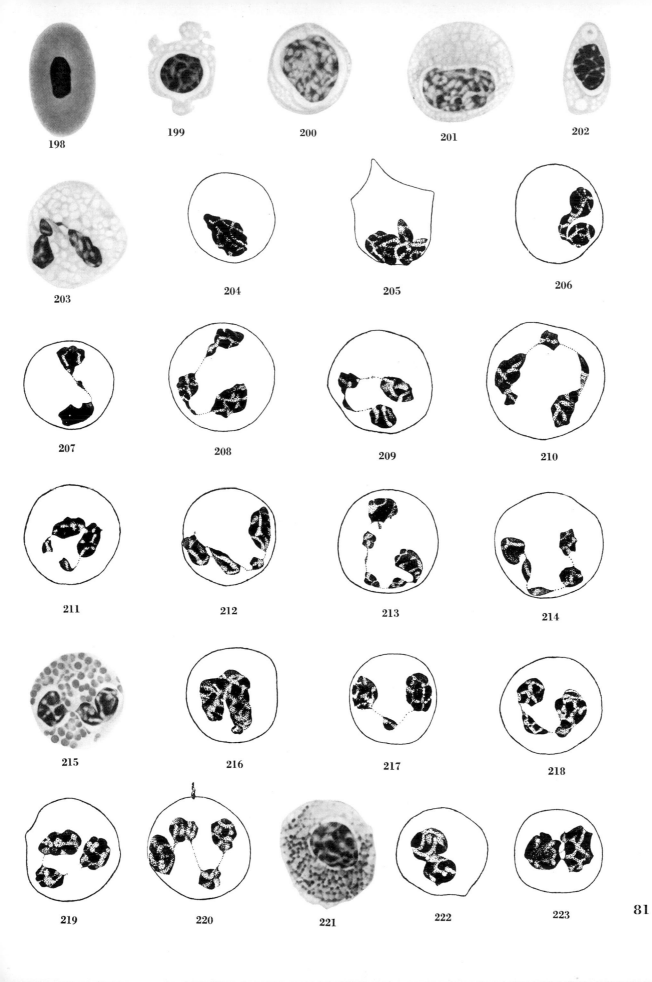

198

199

200

201

202

203

204

205

206

207

208

209

210

211

212

213

214

215

216

217

218

219

220

221

222

223

81

disappeared, leaving vacuoles with a narrow rim of stainable material. The significance of different types of rods, some with granules, some with vacuoles, and some with neither, is not known. Are they nothing more than differences between individuals or are they handles that can be used to gain an insight into the bird's condition of health and disease?

Information is needed also on the chemical nature of the rods and their granules. Whatever may be the significance of the granules, they are part of the apparently normal development and may be found in heterophil myelocytes. Weidenreich (1911) according to Lundquist and Hedlung (1925) concluded that the uncolored spots within the rods are merely optical phenomena. Lundquist and Hedlung found central granules in vital preparations but not in stained smears and agreed with Weidenreich that the central granules are not definite organelles. Burckhardt (1912) expressed essentially the same point of view: ". . . In der Mitte der Spindel wird oft ein ungefärbter Punkt sichtbar, der je nach der Stellung der Mikrometerschraube bald aufblitzt, bald Schwarz erscheint. Ueber die Zusammensetzung dieses Punktes wurde schon mehrfach diskutiert, mir scheint er am einfachsten als Lichtbrechungsphänomen zu erklären."[6]

Anyone studying avian blood soon recognizes the fact that the rods show varying degrees of dissolution. Figures 154–165 show a progressive series from clearly defined and well-developed rods to no trace of rods, but the story does not read in quite this sequence. The granules are more resistant to the processes of dissolution than are the rods. If the rods without granules disappear from figure 154 there is left a cell like that shown in figure 165, but if a cell like that shown in figure 155 loses its rods there remains a cell like figure 164. Figure 156 would result in something like figure 163, and figure 157 would result in something like figure 161. In each case of the loss of rod substance, the cell has come to look more like an eosinophil; in some instances the resemblance is quite close (fig. 161). However, there is no implication in what

has been said that heterophils become eosinophils. This similarity of appearance under some conditions is probably the basis for more confusion in making accurate differential counts than any other single factor.

How are such heterophils and eosinophils to be distinguished? This will be discussed more fully after the eosinophils have been described, but the most important fact is that the rods as they break down or go into solution give the cytoplasm an orange or pinkish color such as is readily seen in figures 158–162. The background color of the true eosinophil is practically always light blue. That difference, combined with the fact that in most cases some part of the heterophil nucleus is pale and poorly stained, makes it relatively simple to distinguish the two granulocytes. This characteristic difference in background color was observed in the heterophils and eosinophils of reptiles by Ryerson (1943).

Nuclear staining is extremely variable, as may be seen in the series of figures 2, *1* and 154–167. Sometimes the staining is vigorous as in figure 2, *1*, where the nuclear lobes are clearly defined. In other examples the nuclei vary in their receptivity to stain from those moderately well stained as in figures 156 and 167 to those in which there is no trace of chromatin pattern or a distinct nuclear boundary. In the same cell (figs. 157 and 158) one lobe of the nucleus may be stained and the more central ones may not be stained. Often there will be a difference in staining of the same lobe, the more central portion being faint and the part adjacent to the cell wall fairly dark. Failure of the nucleus to stain is not a mark of degeneration as indicated by Emmel (1936) but merely means that Wright's stain failed to penetrate the cell and color the nucleus properly.

The normality of the heterophil nucleus can be quite easily and convincingly demonstrated if, after the smear is made on the slide, the blood is allowed to acquire a dull sheen and is then dipped immediately into Petrunkevitch No. 2 (see ch. 7). If stained with May-Grünwald Giemsa the nucleus appears as shown in figure 203. The treatment destroys the rods or distorts them so that they run together as a network but reveals the nuclear structure in all its detail. In none of these slides was there any indication of nuclear degeneration. It is obvious that an Arneth index could not be obtained from a dry fixed Wright's or a May-Grünwald Giemsa

---

[6] Translation: In the middle of the spindle there can often be seen an unstained dot, and after the adjustment of the micrometric screw this often shows up as light, sometimes as dark. There has been much discussion already over the composition of this dot: it seems to me simplest to explain it as a phenomenon of light diffraction.

stained slide. Two slides are necessary for bird's blood—one processed to show the structure of the cytosome and its inclusions, and the other to show the nucleus. This may be the reason why so few counts thus far have been published for birds on the number of lobes in heterophils.

Avian blood has not as yet received the same critical study as human and mammalian bloods nor have avian diseases been approached with the idea of closely correlating the physiology of the diseased condition with the hematologic response, although from the reviews given by Olson (1937 and 1952) it is indicated that many workers have made important contributions to blood diseases of birds.

Differential counts serve a useful purpose but actually hold only a small place in the total of blood reactions. The Arneth or Cook-Ponder counts can contribute additional information. Figures 203–214 show the range of variation in number of nuclear lobes in heterophils. It is obvious that a single nucleus will be separated into two lobes by a gradual process. Thus all stages will be found, and it becomes necessary to decide arbitrarily when one nuclear mass has been sufficiently separated from another to be called a second lobe. Figures 204 and 205 would each be considered to have a single nucleus. In mammalian work cells of this type are often called juveniles, nonsegmenters, and band cells.

There may be some question as to the proper designation for figure 206 but since there is a deep constriction, rather than a broad band, it has been called two-lobed. In chicken blood, a small particle of nuclear material may be retained more frequently along the length of the desmos as the lobes pull apart than in mammalian blood. An example of this is seen in figure 207; it meets the requirements of a distinct lobe in that it is separated from adjacent lobes by a complete constriction but, to be arbitrary, and to give some meaning to the Arneth count, it seems inadvisable to count these small nuclear masses as lobes. On this basis the figure referred to has 2 instead of 3 lobes. Three lobes are shown in figure 203.

Three lobes are shown in figure 208, and if the small spatulate portion still attached to the upper lobe were completely separated by a constriction, it would be counted as a fourth lobe.

The spatulate portion is somewhat larger than the small mass discussed for figure 207.

Four lobes would be counted in figures 210–212. The fourth lobe in figure 210 is the long narrow structure that is separated from the lower lobe by a complete constriction; no connecting thread has yet been formed. The constriction near the tip of the left lobe is not sufficient to warrant counting this body as 2 lobes. Figures 211 and 212 have 4 lobes each, and figures 213 and 214 have 5 each. Sometimes the lobes break apart and no trace of a connecting line between is visible (fig. 213, upper lobe).

Judgment in counting lobes of eosinophils and of basophils is based on the same criteria already described for heterophils. The eosinophil, figure 216, is counted as one lobe. In this particular cell, there actually may be two lobes, one overlying the other, but it is less confusing and probably sufficiently accurate to include this in the single-lobe class. Figure 215 is an example of a nucleus belonging to class II. Figures 217–219 are examples of nuclei belonging to class III. In figure 217, the middle lobe, although small, is sufficiently large and definite to be counted as one lobe. Figure 220 is an example of a nucleus belonging to class IV. No examples of class V were found among the eosinophils.

Basophils usually have but a single nuclear lobe (figs. 221 and 222). Rarely the nucleus may be divided into two lobes (fig. 223).

The Arneth index gives a useful statistic that measures the rate at which old cells are being replaced. There are 5 classes. Class I includes all cells in which the nucleus is composed of one lobe. The remaining classes—II, III, IV, and V—include cells that have the corresponding number of nuclear lobes; class V includes, also, those of over 5 lobes. Cells with more than 5 lobes are rare; none were found in a sample of 1,500 cells counted. The results of one Arneth count on 1,500 heterophils, 142 eosinophils, and 295 basophils are given in table 6. Arneth used nuclear lobe counts on eosinophils and basophils but they have never been found as useful as the counts made on the heterophils. In the literature it is stated that heterophils have more lobes than eosinophils. This observation is supported by the data in table 6 where the index for the former is 2.44 and for the latter 1.97. However, the presence of more lobes is definitely not a characteristic by which the two cell types can be separated. It should be noted that the largest class for both of these cell types is II. In some counts on a Canada goose the index for the eosinophils was considerably greater than for the heterophils (table 24).

Since but few had previously used nuclear lobe indices of this sort on birds, it was considered desirable to make a sample count to determine the index variability and to find any possible suggestion of a relationship to livability or to infection with the agent of lymphomatosis (table 7). Of the 13 cases that showed values above the mean of 2.44 (a shift to the right) there were 2, or 15 percent, that were grossly diagnosed as lymphomatosis and 12 of 17 cases, or 70 percent, with index value below the mean (a shift to the left) were diagnosed as lymphomatosis. A correlation was run between age at death and index value. It resulted in an r value of $+0.423$, significant between the 2- and 1-percent level. One test made on another group of birds did not give the same results. Obviously this type of test should be repeated and carried out on a much larger scale.

Table 6.—Arneth counts on granulocytes of chickens

Cells	Class (nuclear lobes)					Index
	I	II	III	IV	V	
	Per-cent	Per-cent	Per-cent	Per-cent	Per-cent	
Heterophils.....	8.7	45.9	38.8	6.0	0.7	2.44
Eosinophils.....	17.5	69.8	11.2	1.5	0	1.97
Basophils.......	99.0	1.0	0	0	0	1.01

In an Arneth count, the classes are arranged so that the first lies to the left and the fifth to the right, and thus, in relation to the average or index value, the youngest cells are to the left and the oldest to the right. The shifting of the index either to the right or to the left has significance in the evaluation of the extent of morbidity of the individual.

Arneth subdivided each class several times, which added cytologic criteria to the classification based on lobe number. Schilling (1929)

Table 7.—The heterophil Arneth index

[Count taken for each bird at 70 days of age.]

Arneth index	Bird No.	Age at death	Cause of death
		Days	
2.96	F6 B 3	315	Termination, negative
2.82	1112 J 5	652	Termination, negative
2.80	6 C 3	511	Undetermined
2.74	205 B 5	658	Undetermined (in good flesh)
2.70	1111 M 4	638	Termination, negative
2.70	54 O 3	640	Undetermined
2.62	1104 K 4	665	Termination, negative
2.62	67 T 3	651	LO
2.60	216 O 2	312	Prolapsed uterus
2.58	69 P 3	450	LN, LV, and muscular atrophy
2.56	205 Y 4	518	Undetermined
2.52	205 E 5	151	Emaciation, dehydration
2.52	11 J 2	376	Emaciation, dehydration
Avg. 2.44			
2.40	204 K 3	574	Accumulation of ascitic fluid (410 cc.), enlarged heart
2.38	216 P 2	193	LN
2.36	65 L 3	486	LN
2.36	75 U 3	326	Blood poisoning
2.34	205 C 5	77	LN
2.34	1102 N 4	568	LV
2.32	204 J 3	292	LO, prolapsed uterus
2.32	205 D 5	165	LN, LO
2.32	1114 M 4	666	Termination, negative
2.30	71 Z 3	88	Emaciation, dehydration
2.28	203 B 3	610	LN
2.26	72 E 4	454	Emaciation and dehydration
2.26	75 V 3	326	LN
2.26	204 F 3	342	LV, LN
2.24	204 G 3	542	LN
2.24	205 A 5	157	LN
2.12	205 W 4	166	LV, cannibalism

(Left column marked "Shift to right" for the upper portion and "Shift to left" for the lower portion.)

LV, LN, LO=Visceral, neural, and ocular lymphomatosis.

criticized the basic principles of an Arneth count and index as follows (p. 148):

"While Arneth's theory takes into account only a juvenile shift to the left, we distinguish two classes, (a) regenerative shift, (b) degenerative shift."

Many others have prepared systems of classifying heterophils and other granulocytes. Their contributions have been reviewed by Richter (1938) and by Sugiyama (1938). The latter author has presented a table of nuclear types for representative fish, amphibia, reptiles, birds, and mammals. For the heterophils of the domestic fowl, he gave class I, 12.0 percent; class II, 62.0 percent; class III, 22.5 percent; class IV, 2.3 percent. These values calculate to an index of 2.17.

Examination of table 7 raises the question of whether the mean value of 2.44 is a normal one for birds. When the smears were taken at 70 days of age, all the chickens were seemingly normal; yet the average index for the 4 that went to the termination date and were found grossly negative was 2.65. Perhaps this is a more nearly normal index than the lower value. A group of chickens known to be free from the agent of lymphomatosis and other diseases is needed in order to arrive at a set of normal standard blood values. The question also arises, Are the birds that are destined to develop grossly visible tumors infected and fighting against the disease during the several hundred days before neoplasia appears?

Before leaving the subject of the normal heterophil, the fact should be mentioned that the French veterinarian, Lesbouyries, (1941) described a sixth type of white blood cell in chickens. He listed a neutrophil in addition to a heterophil. In his descriptions they are not synonymous. His sixth cell is the type shown in figure 165 and it does resemble superficially a mammalian neutrophil. Our own studies have shown it to be a heterophil from which the rods (without granules) have dissolved, and there is no justification for giving it a different name and creating a separate class for it. Breusch (1928) listed 4 types of granulocytes—eosinophilic leukocytes, amphophilic or pseudoeosinophilic leukocytes, basophilic leukocytes, and neutrophilic leukocytes—but described only the first 3, and includes only these 3 in his tables of differential counts. The application of terminology whereby heterophils and eosinophils are correctly identified has not been a simple matter. Magath and Higgins (1934) have listed the various synonyms that have been used from 1880 to 1931. Even separation of these cells on the basis of those with eosinophilic rods and those with eosinophilic granules leads to difficulty in identifying these 2 cell types in ducks (see p. 207). Loewenthal (1930) also found what he called neutrophiloid cells, which in his opinion were derived from rods by a process of dedifferentiation; he suggested that in the course of evolution it was this type of cell that produced the mammalian neutrophil.

Developmental stages found in circulating blood (figs. 168–173)

Immature cells of the heterophil series are rare in normal blood, but probably not more so than are the immature stages of red cells when the difference in relative numbers is taken into ac-count. If the heterophil count is recovering after destructive irradiation, the immature heterophils may be quite numerous.

A granuloblast found in the circulating blood is shown in figure 168. There may be some question of whether it is destined to be a heterophil or a basophil, but the large size of the cell, the rim of basophilic cytoplasm broken by many mitochondrial spaces, and the uniform reticular pattern of the nucleus, all identify it as a blast cell. When compared with the granuloblasts of figures 330, 1 and 2, 366, and 367, little doubt remains as to its identification as a granuloblast.

The metagranuloblast stage of development has not been seen as yet in the circulating blood, but is found in bone marrow (figs. 368 and 369).

Four examples of promyelocytes (figs. 169–172) have been illustrated. The nuclear boundary in the earlier phase of development (figs. 169 and 170) is even less distinct than in the bone marrow, and the number and density of magenta rings and granules are greater. Figures 171 and 172 are not good examples of late promyelocytes, because the contents of the vacuoles did not take the stain. It is assumed that the same stage, had it been taken from the bone marrow, would have looked like figures 370–372.

These immature heterophils in circulating blood have a different appearance from those in bone marrow. Perhaps this is due to the fact that different stains were used in the two situations, or it may be due to the effects of these environments on the penetrability or selectivity of the stains. Whatever the cause, the difference in appearance should be kept in mind and not be allowed to hamper identification.

A typical mesomyelocyte (fig. 173) has less than half of the definitive granules. Many of the precursor orange spheres have attained a dense coloration but none of them have elongated as in figure 373. Two sizes of granules are present, and there is a possibility that the small ones become the central bodies for the rods that develop out of the large ones. The carryover of magenta rings and granules from the early to the late stages sometimes occurs as it has in figure 173. The whole process of myelopoiesis will not be discussed at this time since a rather critical and detailed comparison, which is presented later, is necessary in order to relate what is found in birds to the named stages given for mammals. See also the discussion by Lucas (1959).

Abnormal heterophils

The only cell defect recognized thus far is the fractured nuclei such as shown in figure 3, *1*. In this case, 2 of the 3 lobes showed a nonstaining band. It is apparent that the same type of nuclear chromophobia occurring in the erythrocytes, lymphocytes, and other cells can also occur in heterophils. The possibility that these fracture lines and empty nuclei represent pathologic conditions, rather than technic defects, has been discussed (pp. 32 and 65).

Undoubtedly other abnormal heterophils exist in birds as they do in mammals but up to this time sufficient knowledge of the normal by which identification of the abnormal can be made is lacking. Toxic granules in human neutrophils are considered abnormal and play an important role in prognosis. Osgood and Ashworth (1937) note three points of difference from normal cells—color of cytoplasm, presence of vacuoles, and coarse granulation. Osgood goes on to say (p. 51), "The author predicted death of more than 100 consecutive patients from a three or four plus change in two of these factors. Ninety percent of these died within a week after the prediction was made. These patients died of a wide variety of conditions, including malignant tumors and leukemias as well as infections." In view of its value in human hematology, it would seem desirable to further study avian blood in search of this mammalian counterpart. Thus far, however, nothing has been observed that could be identified in avian blood as toxic granules. Perhaps this is because most of these studies have been on birds that showed no obvious disease.

Technic artifacts (fig. 174)

The effect of water on the rods was emphasized by soaking the slide for 20 minutes after methyl alcohol fixation and before staining in May-Grünwald Giemsa. The result of such treatment is shown in figure 174. All trace of rods has disappeared; instead there is a cytoplasmic network with a granule in the center of each space. The technic used in figures 154–165 was Wright's stain but it was applied by the bulk method (p. 229) instead of to individual slides on a rack. Since the bulk method requires somewhat longer staining and slower drying, it involves longer ex-

posure to aqueous solutions. Hence one finds in this series of slides more examples in which rods have disappeared than one usually finds in normal birds by using the staining rack technic. No technical method has yet been found that will hold the rods well enough to insure confidence that the appearance of the heterophil is really due to the bird and not to technic. Such a method is urgently needed. Even the Petrunkevitch fixed smears show dissolution of the rods (fig. 203) and in this case neither rods nor granules were visible. Petrunkevitch No. 2 (p. 230) is an alcoholic solution with copper, ether, and other substances, and it would not be expected to act like an aqueous fixative. Bradley (1937), quoted on p. 88, observed that adequate fixation would not hold the rods if followed by aqueous stains.

In view of the high lability of the rods, it seems appropriate to raise the question, How faithfully has the heterophil rod been preserved in tissue section? If rods disappear but granules remain, a heterophil can look like an eosinophil. Thus, the descriptions of tissue infiltration or of myelopoiesis as worked out on tissue sections may be open to question until it has been demonstrated that the technics used do not destroy the rods. Dantschakoff (1909a and b) in her study on the bone marrow of birds follows the processes of myelopoiesis through the stages showing rods, and her beautiful colored plates show them well preserved. Our sections of hematopoietic embryo tissues failed to show these rods.

Much that is seen in the dried smear from circulating blood may be artifact; yet the opinion is maintained that bird differences are in part responsible for some of the deviations from the typical. Although all slides are handled alike in bulk staining, some birds show rods and in others hardly a rod can be found. It would go far toward solving some of these problems if fresh blood preparations were carefully studied under the phase microscope. The variability due to technic and that due to bird differences could be separated. Additional evidence that rods of heterophils can come to look like granules of true eosinophils *in vivo* is indicated in the examination of smears from blood spots of eggs. Here every heterophil simulated an eosinophil (Lucas, 1946). Natt and Herrick (1954) have reaffirmed what others have demonstrated, that loss of rod substance leaves a central granule that gives to the heterophil an appearance similar to that of the eosinophil.

The literature on the subject of heterophils and eosinophils reflects some of our present uncertainties. The observation that aqueous solution causes a degradation of rods is not new. Bizzozero and Torre (1881) stated that if one treats a blood preparation with water the white corpuscles in question swell; the same thing happens to the rods themselves, which become pale and at last disappear. They also found that upon treatment with dilute citric acid the protoplasm of the white corpuscles becomes swollen and pale. The rods first draw together so that there is formed a shining heap that hides the nucleus. This heap very suddenly becomes pale and finally disappears. Although Bizzozero and Torre recognized only four kinds of white blood cells, they did include the true granular eosinophil as distinct from the rod eosinophil. Denys (1887) writing on the bone marrow of pigeons is less definite about the number of types of white blood cells, does not distinguish between the two eosinophils, and says it seems probable that most, if not all, of those seen as dots are simply rods viewed from the axis.

Lundquist and Hedlung (1925) have presented a review of the subject and mention those who believe the eosinophils in birds represent two distinct types and those who consider that there are only four kinds of leukocytes in birds. They quote S. Henschen, who concludes that there are two distinct types but who also mentions that post mortem processes can cause the rods to go over into granules. Lundquist and Hedlung's own investigations led them to the unique opinion that the granular eosinophil cell represents the true condition and that the rods are artifacts, produced at the time the smears are made. They point out that the inclusions have the form of granules after methyl alcohol fixation and of rods after formalin or trichloracetic. In order to follow the transformation from granules to rods they diluted the blood in a white cell pipette with 0.9-percent sodium chloride solution, which was considered to be isotonic with chicken blood. The diluent was allowed to act for 2 minutes before the blood mixture was put into a counting chamber, then an eosinophil was observed in order to note the form of granulation present. After this, a solution of higher or lower concentration was added to the side canal of the counting chamber and the changes in the cells were followed. Usually filter paper was touched to the fluid layer on the opposite side in order to hasten the exchange. When the preparation was diluted with water they found large, clear cells with large, clear, scarcely visible round granulations; when it was diluted with 0.7-percent NaCl solution, all the granulations were round and were larger than in the previous solution. Preparations treated with 0.9-percent NaCl produced mostly round granulations in the cells, but in a few cells these bodies took the rod form. At 1½-percent NaCl concentration, the cells contained rod-form granulations, and now and then spherical granules. They summarize by saying that in water the cells and granules swell and become faint, but in 1.5-percent salt solution the cells shrink and the round granulations are transformed into the rod form. If not carried too far these are reversible reactions, and thus the rod eosinophil is an artifact brought about by osmotic conditions.

The chief reason why the interesting conclusions of Lundquist and Hedlung have relatively little value is that their study of cellular change was made at the relatively low magnification required in using a counting chamber, and, although they mention these changes in the same cell, it would seem rather difficult to keep a particular cell in the field during a rapid exchange of fluids.

Bradley (1937) examined the blood of numerous birds and made observations similar to our own. He reports (p. 995) that, "When the color of the rod bodies has been partially removed, . . . demonstration is made of darker or lighter parts, giving the impression of deeply stained granules along the paler length of the body." In regard to technic he says (p. 997), "Avian (fowl) blood is best stained by a method which applies the eosin or related acid stain in alcoholic solution and when the use of water or saline solution forms no part of the process until after the alcoholic stain has acted.

"Adequate fixation before treating with water or watery stain is no preventive for the destructive action of the latter on the rods. Water applied in moderation after staining is not detrimental to the result, and when left in contact with the stained preparation for a longer time is the means of showing up details of structure of the rod bodies not otherwise appreciated."

Interpretation of the loss of rods is sometimes influenced by the type of problem involved. Hewitt (1940) attributes this loss to degeneration or phagocytosis due to the malarial parasite. Difficulty in the identification of eosinophils and heterophils is not limited to the older literature; for example, Diesem (1956) found it difficult to separate these two cell types, and combined them in his cell counts.

The most recent opinion on the subject of rod degradation has been expressed by Dr. Hamre (personal communication). The opinion is that the rods themselves remain unchanged when acted upon by various stains and aqueous solutions but that the capacity of the rod substances to absorb the stain does change, and that if Wright-Giemsa is used as he has modified it (the technic he recommends is given on p. 230) rods will always stain and each rod will contain a central granule.

One additional cellular defect remains to be described—squashed cells. Squashed or smudged heterophils are probably the easiest cells to recognize because the specific cellular inclusions are preserved. Squashing takes place at the time the smear is made; yet the same variability is to be found in the rods broken out of the cell as was found in the intact cell (figs. 175 and 176). Figure 175 shows rods without central granules and figure 176 shows central granules with dissolved and almost completely faded rods. These were taken from different birds but both smears were made the same day. The birds were exactly the same age and the slides were stained together. Both cells show many fine magenta-colored granules, partly among the broken fragments of the cell but mostly surrounding the cell. These small, darkly stained bodies are serum granules. Something is liberated from the broken cell that acts as a mordant on the serum granules and causes those in the immediate vicinity to take the stain. As may be seen from figure 176 their color and size differ from even the smallest of the central granules of the rods. The central granules show a variability in size among themselves similar to that found in the intact cell.

EOSINOPHILS

The fact that both heterophils and eosinophils stain with eosin has led to the use of numerous terms for designating these two cell types, such as "rod eosinophils," "granular eosinophils," "pseudoeosinophils," and "true eosinophils." Some have reversed the last two terms so that "true eosinophil" applies to the heterophils. For this reason, the use of "true" and "pseudo" can lead to confusion. The terms "rod" and "granular" are not good either because rods often change to spheres. Therefore, the terms "heterophil" and "eosinophil" have been chosen. These have the added advantage that the cells are each designated by one word instead of two. The eosinophil of birds is homologous with the cell receiving the same name in other classes of vertebrates.

Normal mature eosinophils (figs. 177–183)

The eosinophil shows a rather wide range in size; some are large, like figures 177–180, and some small, like figures 181–183. Usually they are about the size shown in figure 177. The range for size (fig. 197) is shown by a frequency distribution curve in which there is a minimum of a little over 4μ to slightly over 11μ. The average size of 7.3μ is approximately 1 micron less than for heterophils or basophils, and probably was brought about by the occurrence of small eosinophils in circulating blood; whereas, cells of the size shown in figures 181–183 are rare for heterophils or basophils. The cell is nearly round as may be seen from the figures.

The cytoplasm stains a pale, clear blue color, which, of course, shows best when the granules are not crowded together. The granules are often crowded and there is not much cytoplasm to be seen; yet the background blue color is one of the best means of separating the two types of eosin-staining cells when the rods of heterophils have been degraded to granules. The blue-staining ground substance is readily apparent among the granules of large eosinophils, but the blue color is often obscured in small cells. Small cells, such as those shown in figures 181–183, are relatively rare. Their identification is aided by the strong affinity of the nucleus for stain.

There is some variation in the structures of the granules. Often they appear as homogeneous bodies, but sometimes when they are larger and not so crowded, the structure of each granule is revealed. It is made up of 3 or 4 smaller bodies held together in a ring. This is shown especially well in figure 177. The small granules that make up the ring give it an angular contour and in the center is a clear space. Sometimes one may have an impression of a clear space in the center of the sphere (fig. 180) and yet the individual particles that go to make up the ring cannot be separated.

A knowledge of the detailed structure of the eosinophil granule (or ring) in the chicken is necessary for the identification of the eosinophil in various species of wild birds, especially the ducks. The space may be responsible for the general report that the eosinophil granules are refractile. In formalin-fixed cells that are stained with phloxine and floated on a slide, as they are in the counting chamber when Wiseman's method has been used in preparing the material, they can readily be distinguished from heterophils by their strong refractility. Had these differences been observed by Lundquist and Hedlung (1925) they probably would not have concluded that these two eosin-staining cells belong to the same type.

Usually, granules are uniformly stained but it is fairly common, especially in medium to large cells, to find that some of the granules stain faintly, as shown in figures 178 and 179. Quite often in association with this variation there are differences in concentration of granules in different parts of the cell, as shown in the two examples. It may be that these deficiencies represent immaturity of the cell; yet the fact that there are four nuclear lobes is evidence that the cell in figure 179 is not an immature cell; perhaps the cytoplasm continued to increase in volume after the process of granule formation had ceased. Further discussion of the problem of variation in the size and arrangement of eosinophil granules appears later (ch. 6 and fig. 411).

One characteristic of the granules in the eosinophils that aids in separating them from heterophils containing granules is the imperviousness to aqueous solutions; the granules of the eosinophil are never affected in the chicken and the same difference is shown following Petrunkevitch No. 2 fixation (compare figs. 203 and 215).

The nucleus always stains well in the eosinophil. Except for the masking of lobes by the granules, it would be possible to count the nuclei quite accurately. No cell with more than 4 nuclear lobes has been illustrated, and the data for eosinophils in table 6, based on 142 cells counted, also indicate that an eosinophil with 5 or more lobes would be rare in the chicken. The Arneth index for eosinophils, 1.97, is lower than for heterophils.

To point up the differences between these two cell types for purposes of identification, table 8 was prepared.

Table 8.—**Characteristics of heterophils and eosinophils**

Characteristic	*Heterophil*	*Eosinophil*
Cell size.............	Usually a relatively small range of variation in circulating blood but a large range of variation in the bone marrow.	Wide range in size but usually not in the same slide.
Cytoplasm...........	When rods are well formed the cytoplasm is colorless. If there is any degradation of rods to spheres, the cytoplasm is tinged with the eosinophilic material.	The cytoplasm maintains a pale blue background color for the red-staining granules. Only rarely is there an exception to this.
Specific granules......	Contain eosinophilic rods that may be long and narrow, or short and plump, or even spherical. Rods disintegrate in aqueous solutions and the central body may be all that remains. Central bodies are variable in number and size; they may be absent or may be represented by a vacuole.	Contain eosinophilic bodies that are uniform in size in the same cell and usually uniformly distributed. Eosinophilic bodies may be homogeneous spheres or rings, often with 4 granules in the ring, or scattered separate small granules. Resistant to aqueous solutions. In some species the rings may be flattened and elongated to give the superficial appearance of a rod.
Nuclear lobes........	The average Arneth index is 2.44 or higher for chickens.	The average Arneth index is slightly less than 2.00. Cells with class V nuclei are rare in chickens, if they exist at all.
Nuclear staining......	Wright's stain usually fails to stain the nucleus completely or well.	Wright's stain shows a strong affinity for the nucleus and brings out the details of chromatin pattern.

Developmental stages found in circulating blood (figs. 184–186)

The low percentage of eosinophils in the differential count makes it difficult to find developmental stages of eosinophils in the circulating blood of normal birds. The youngest observed thus far is shown in figure 184—a mesomyelocyte in which there are fewer than half the number of granules found in the mature stage. The cytoplasm is still strongly basophilic. The range in coloration of the specific granules is not so great as has been observed in these cells in the bone marrow (fig. 379). The large size of the granules in the metamyelocyte (fig. 185) stands in contrast to the groups of small granules in figure 186. These granules in figure 185 give the cell an appearance similar to that of the mesomyelocyte stage of the heterophil (fig. 374) and it is possible that this cell has been misplaced, especially since small granules are mixed with the large ones. Difference in granule size is a characteristic found in heterophil, but not in eosinophil, myelocytes. There is no question about the identity of the cell in figure 186; the strongly stained nucleus and the small uniform granulations establish it as an eosinophil.

Abnormal cells

No cells belonging to this classification have been seen.

Technic artifacts (fig. 187)

This is an example of a smudged eosinophil. The characteristic of a strong affinity for stain by the nucleus of the eosinophil, in contrast to the tendency toward defective staining in the heterophil, is still retained in the squashed cells. The scattered contents of the broken cell (fig. 187) demonstrate again that the large eosinophil granule is composed of smaller granular units.

BASOPHILS

Specific granules for these cells have an affinity for basic dyes and show metachromasia. In chickens this cell is more abundant than the eosinophil, averaging about 2 percent in a differential count. There is no confusion in terminology for this cell and basophils are homologous through various classes of vertebrates. The only confusion comes in the theoretical relationship between the blood basophil and the tissue mast cell.

Aqueous solutions have a severe detrimental effect here, as they have on heterophils; therefore, all basophils in a dried smear show technic artifacts in varying degrees. This same reaction exists in mammalian cells and has been discussed by Michels (1938). Because of this fact, abnormal cells have not been identified.

Normal mature basophils (figs. 188–192)

Basophils are only slightly smaller than heterophils, as shown in the graph (fig. 197). This slight difference would not be apparent visually. The impression has been gained during the routine examination of many slides that when the technic defects are minimal the cell is relatively small; whereas, when there has been extensive washing out of granules the cell seems larger. Not only is the size of the cell less but even the granules are smaller when they are well preserved. See, for example, figures 389 and 390, which show basophils from bone marrow; the cells were fixed in methyl alcohol and stained with thionin in alcohol. Basophils are round, as are the other two granulocyte types, and they are not severely deformed when other cells press against them. Sometimes the cell membrane becomes irregular in contour owing to the extrusion of particles (fig. 190).

The cytoplasm of basophils is colorless. Usually it is masked by the granules but when they are washed out there is very little residual color (figs. 191 and 192). More convincing, perhaps, are the small breaks seen between the granules when they have not been severely disturbed (figs. 188 and 189). In the Petrunkevitch No. 2 fixed smear there is a basophilic tinge to the cytoplasm (fig. 221). The spaces between the granules seem larger than normal because the granules are either shrunken or partially dissolved.

The granules in the dried smear are basophilic and metachromatic; that is, they have an affinity for basic dyes and the resulting color produced in the stained object is different from the color of the dye in solution. Even with a group of slides that receive the same treatment, there is considerable variability between birds in the resistance of the granules to water. This may in part reflect differences in age of the cells but it has not been proved that the granules developing in basophil myelocytes are more resistant to water than they are in older cells.

The nucleus of basophils is usually masked by granules, but occasionally it may be visible as a structureless, pale blue staining body lying in the center of the cell. The penetration of Wright's stain, found to be poor in the heterophil nucleus is practically nil in basophils. Sometimes it appears as if chromatin clumps of the nucleus were being stained (figs. 190, 191, and 192), but this is due to the basophilic bodies of the cytoplasm that are trapped above or below the nucleus when the cells are flattened in drying. For some reason the pressing of the nuclear membrane against the cell membrane protects the granules to some extent from the action of water. Failure of the nucleus to stain is not evidence of degeneration—when fixed with Petrunkevitch No. 2, they stain as strongly as any normal nucleus (fig. 221).

Variations in shape of nuclei and number of lobes are seen in figures 222 and 223. Usually the nucleus is centrally placed and has a round shape. Constricted nuclei may be seen, but only rarely. A nucleus in the condition shown in figure 222 is counted as one lobe; only when the isthmus between is reduced to one or more delicate strands is the nucleus regarded as bilobed (fig. 223). A trilobed nucleus has never been observed in a basophil, and from the Arneth counts on these cells (table 6), the bilobed condition occurs only about once in one hundred cells.

After one has seen a representative collection of basophils, this cell type becomes the most easily recognized leukocyte of the blood. Yet errors have been made in the literature; Emmel (1936) labeled as "normal premyelocyte" (his fig. 6E) a cell that is a typical basophil of circulating blood, as nearly as can be determined from his black-and-white drawing. This would help to explain why he found only two basophils in differential counts made on 50 chickens. In normal chickens tested at this Laboratory, these cells run about 2 percent of the differential count, and in pheasants it may be 10 percent (table 20).

Developmental stages found in circulating blood (fig. 193)

This is the only immature basophil that has been seen in the circulating blood. It closely resembles in cellular and nuclear detail the heterophil granuloblast (fig. 168); but resemblance is lacking in one respect—the cytoplasm contains numerous magenta granules. These bodies are equivalent to the granules and rings found in heterophils at this same stage of development, and often the two cells are hard to separate. Usually the magenta rings of the heterophil are larger than those of the basophil, and in the latter there is less vacuolization of the cytoplasm and the nucleus tends to remain in the center of the cell more frequently than in the heterophil. These points are made evident by a comparison of immature granulocytes from bone marrow shown in figures 370–372, 382, and 383. The magenta body in the basophil promyelocyte is not the definitive basophilic granule and is not affected by aqueous solutions.

Technic artifacts (figs. 194–196)

Since aqueous staining methods dissolve the basophilic granules, every cell illustrated as typical of the normal is, in reality, an example of a technic artifact, and the same can be said for the failure of the nucleus to take the stain. In addition to these artifacts, squashed cells may be found. Figures 194–196 show three degrees of severity. In figure 194 the cell is only slightly squashed; the granules are separated and they are larger than normal, and the nucleus of the cell shows early autolysis. In figure 195 the cell membrane wall is definitely broken and some of the granules are scattered. In this particular cell there is considerable variation in the way the granules take the stain. This, however, may have existed in the cell before it was broken. The granules from the cell shown in figure 196 have been widely scattered and for some reason retain a strong affinity for stain. Obviously, all the factors responsible for dissolution of granules are not yet fully known. The clefts in the autolysing nucleus are probably the spaces between the blocks of chromatin.

Hemokonia and Serum Granules

Hemokonia, or blood dust (the English equivalent), refers to the cell fragments, debris, and minute bodies floating in the serum. Most of these lie near the limits of microscopic visibility When cell fragments are large they are called plastids, but when small they are called hemokonia.

Little has been written about cell debris. Downey does not have "hemokonia," "blood dust," or "serum granules" in the index of his 4-volume work on hematology. This is true for some of the atlases on blood. Kracke and Garver (1937) give one paragraph on the subject in which they say (p. 107), "These particles do not stain and their nature is unknown. They appear similar in size to the granules in the cytoplasm of granular leukocytes. This has led to the supposition that they are extruded granules but no conclusive proof has been given for this identity."

In avian blood occasional small fragments from broken cells may be found. These are chiefly heterophil rods or myelocyte rings and granules. Their presence is due to the breaking of cells that occurs when a smear is made. They appear in practically any smear of bone marrow; and recognizable rods from granulocytes, especially heterophils, can be found here and there over most slides. Since granulocytes are so much more abundant in bone marrow than in circulating blood, it is not surprising that debris of this sort is also more abundant.

What should be included under the term "hemokonia" has never been well defined; thus it is not possible to decide whether serum granules should be included under the term. For the present they are considered to be different from hemokonia. They are found in great abundance in the blood of birds. Usually they do not take the stain but when they do, they produce a stippled mask over the cells (figs. 72 and 322). Even when they do not stain, they can be seen by reducing the diaphragm of the microscope to increase the apparent refractility. In embryo smears and in bone-marrow and thymus smears of the embryo, they are especially abundant (figs. 329 and 332). The typical appearance is shown in figure 322. Among the serum granules of this field are fragments of broken cells also. Most low-power drawings from hematopoietic organs of both adults and embryos have been made without including the serum granules. Cell identifications cannot be made accurately where the granules lie on top of the cells in large numbers. As may be seen in figure 322, the serum itself may take up the stain as well as the granules in it.

Two other granules should be mentioned—(1) definite yolk granules found when blood is taken from the early embryo at 48 to 72 hours, and (2) chylomicrons, which Gage and Fish (1924) describe. Yolk granules are larger than serum granules and sometimes a whole yolk sphere is seen. Yolk is not present in adult circulating blood.

Whether chylomicrons are present in birds has never been determined. As the term was first used it referred to the submicroscopic spheres found in lacteal drainage from the small intestine of mammals. It has a broader meaning than this and in general refers to lipid spheres found in blood, chyle, or lymph. Dark field is required to see them. It would be interesting and useful to determine whether chylomicrons of mammals and serum granules of birds are the same thing. There is considerable difference in size, the serum granule being larger.

The serums of pigeons and chickens are said to contain a lipochrome pigment (Halliburton, 1886) that gives to them a color identical with that found in fat cells of these birds.

ADDENDUM

The irregularity in the shape of erythrocyte nuclei is described in the early part of chapter 2 and is illustrated in figure 29. The cause is not known, but Bessis (1956, fig. 195) photographed similar irregularly shaped nuclei in chickens after treatment with folic acid antagonists.

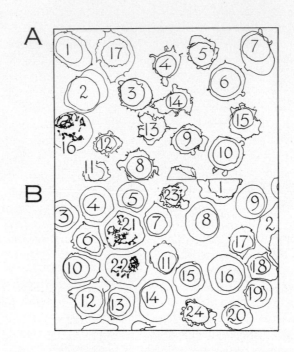

FIGURE 224.—Blood from dorsal aorta of early chick embryo.   1,370×.

Slides of embryo blood stained with May-Grünwald Giemsa.

A   Incubation age, 1 day 22 hours.

1–10   Typical early primary erythroblasts with lobulated basophilic cytosome and 1 or 2 nucleoli.

11–15   Small shrunken primary erythroblasts.   Frayed and shrunken appearance of some cells probably due to delay in drying the cells; especially true of 11 and 12.

16   Primary erythroblast in mitotic division.

17   Slightly smudged erythroblast.

B   Incubation age, 1 day 23 hours.

1– 2   Large primary erythroblasts, similar to the stage shown in A or younger.

3–20   Late primary erythroblasts of various sizes from large (14 and 16) to small (18 and 19).

21–22   Large primary erythroblasts in mitotic division.

23–24   Small cells with lobulated cytosomes.   Probably early embryonic thrombocytes.

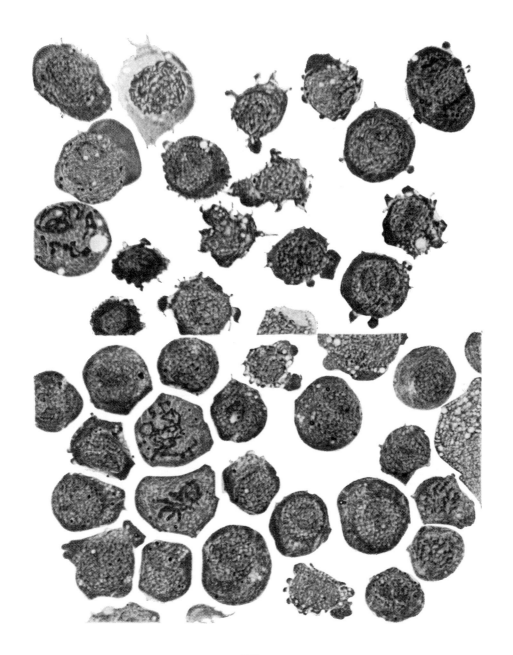

224

FIGURE 225.—Blood from dorsal aorta of early chick embryo. Incubation age, 2 days 17 hours.
1,370×.

1–11 Early polychromatic primary erythrocytes.
12–19 Mid-polychromatic primary erythrocytes.
20 Mitotic telophase of early polychromatic primary erythrocyte.
21 Mitotic metaphase of early or mid-polychromatic primary erythrocyte.
22 Mitotic telophase of early or mid-polychromatic primary erythrocyte.

23 A mid-polychromatic primary erythroplastid.
24 Large embryonic thrombocyte.
25 Embryonic thromboblast.
26 Medium embryonic thrombocyte.
27 A group of 4 small embryonic thrombocytes clumped together but fixed before disintegration set in.

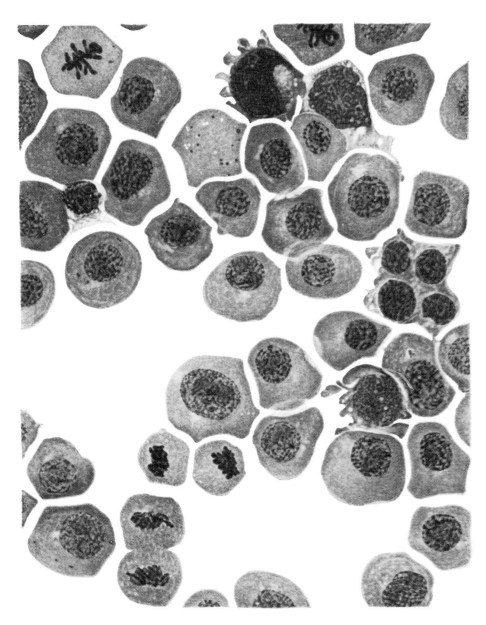

225

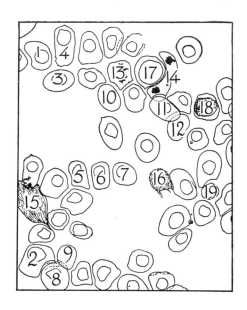

FIGURE 226.—Blood from heart of chick embryo. Incubation age, 4 days 12 hours. 1,370×.

1–2 Mid-polychromatic primary erythrocytes.
3–9 Late polychromatic primary erythrocytes.
10–12 Late polychromatic erythrocytes showing early stages of cytosomal fracturing, an artifact.
13 Late polychromatic primary erythrocyte near the metaphase stage.

14 Late polychromatic primary erythrocyte in the late telophase stage.
15–16 Smudged primary erythrocytes.
17 An erythroblast of later embryonic generation, or an embryonic thromboblast.
18 A medium embryonic thrombocyte.
19 A small embryonic thrombocyte.

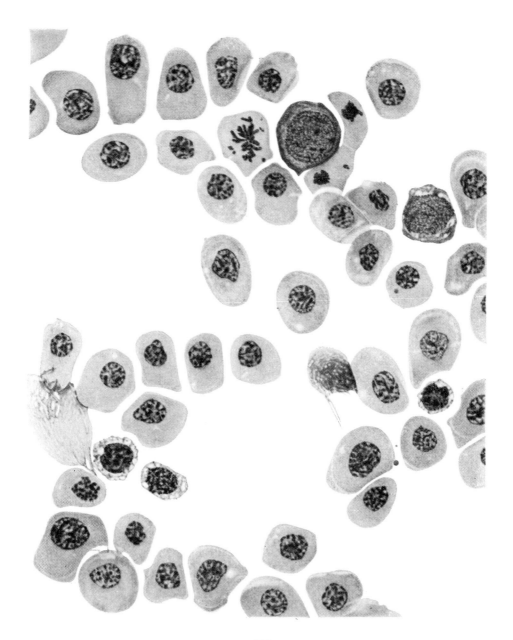

226

FIGURE 227.—Blood from heart of chick embryo. Incubation age, 5 days 21 hours. 1,370×.

1–12 Mature primary erythrocytes ranging in size from large (5) to small (9 and 10).

13–15 Mid-polychromatic erythrocytes of later embryonic red-cell generations.

16–18 Late polychromatic erythrocytes of later embryonic red-cell generations. Cell 17 is at the transition between mid- and late polychromatic stages.

19–24 Late polychromatic erythrocytes in which the artifacts of cytosomal fracturing are present.

25 Early polychromatic erythrocyte in mitosis, probably an early anaphase.

26 Erythroblast of later embryonic cell generations.

27 Medium embryonic thrombocyte.

28 Small embryonic thrombocyte.

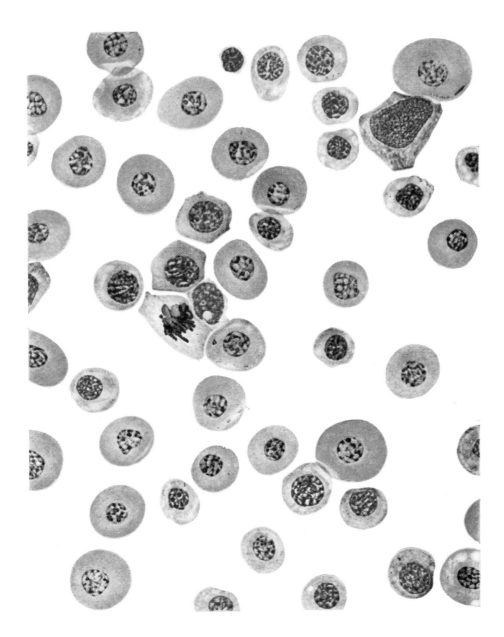

227

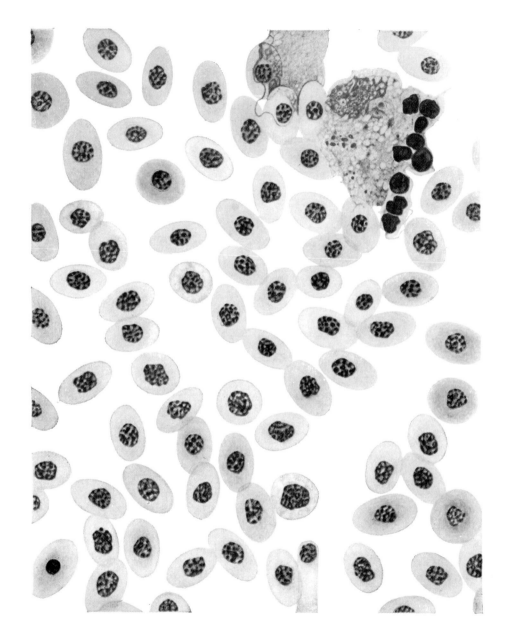

228

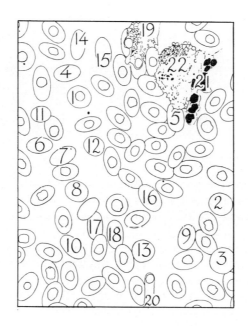

FIGURE 228.—Blood from heart of chick embryo.   Incubation age, 9 days 15 hours.   1,370✕.

1–3   Mature primary erythrocytes.
4, 6–10   Late polychromatic erythrocytes from later embryonic red-cell generations.
11–13   Late polychromatic erythrocytes in which the artifacts of cytosomal fracturing are present.
5, 14–18   Mature erythrocytes from later embryonic red-cell generations.

19, 20   Smudged erythrocytes.
21   Small embryonic thrombocytes that have clumped, accompanied by degeneration as shown by loss of cytoplasm and by pyknosis of the nucleus.
22   Embryonic macrophage.

CHAPTER 3

Circulating Blood of the Embryo

ERYTHROCYTE CHANGES DURING INCUBATION

Early in the process of blood development, mesenchyme transforms into angioblasts or into primitive erythroblasts. The red blood cells—in the first generation, at least—develop from the walls and within the lumen of the newly formed vessels (Sabin, 1920). This process of development is well under way before the first circulatory arc through the embryo has been completed. As soon as afferent and efferent channels have been joined, the heart pumps through them the cells that previously had accumulated in the yolk sac. This event begins at 33 to 36 hours and is well established by 48 hours incubation, which is the age when the first smears were made in this study. Before this, the development of hemoglobin has caused the blood to take on a red color. In the primary generation of red cells, the hemoglobin is acquired much more rapidly than in the later generations, with the result that, although the cell has a red color as seen with the unaided eye, the stained cytoplasm retains a strong affinity for basophilic dyes. It is this fact that leads to misunderstanding in cell terminology and to error in identification of the stage of development. As successive generations appear this source of error becomes less and less.

Dantschakoff's (1907 and 1908a and b) observations of the early transformation of mesenchyme into blood islands and thence into intravascular and extravascular blood elements were based on celloidin-sectioned material. The statements agree closely with those of Sabin (1920) but the names and interpretations are different. Both authors agree that blood cells can be produced from the endothelium of the blood islands of yolk sac and the dorsal aorta of the early embryo.

Dantschakoff (1907) summarized her basic hematologic theory as follows (p. 166):

"Auf Grund des Erorterten konnen wir also eine vollstandige Analogie zwischen der ersten Blutbildung ausserhalb und innerhalb des embryonalen Korpers annehem. Die ersten Blutzellen treten hier wie dort zuerst als *Lymphozyten* kleinerer und grosserer Form auf,—*diese mussen also als die Stammzellen aller Blutelemente betrachtet werden* und erzeugen durch Proliferation und Differenzierung in verschiedenen Richungen die mannigfaltigen Formen der roten und weissen Blutkorperchen, die wir im erwachsenen Organismus finden." [1]

Murray (1932) analyzed the observations of Sabin and of Dantschakoff by studying early blood formation in tissue culture. He used parts of the primitive streak of the chick embryo before the head fold developed. From these undifferentiated cells, he obtained cultures that went through all the early stages of blood island formation, with angioblasts enclosed within an endothelial boundary. These early stages agreed very closely with the observations made by Sabin on the living chick. Murray observed in tissue culture all the steps in primary erythrocyte differentiation up to cells that had an oval shape and contained hemoglobin, even up to a fully mature cell. This entire process took place in his cultures within 24 hours.

It has been pointed out by Dantschakoff (1908b and 1909b) that whereas Maximow (1909) found but two generation types in the development of red blood cells in mammals—primary and definitive—she found that in chickens there was a succession of generations by which the transition from the primary to the definitive type was accomplished. Each generation of cells attained maturity within its life span.

The primary generation of red blood cells in the chick embryo is so conspicuously different

---

[1] Translation: On the basis of the discussion we can assume a complete analogy between the first blood formation outside and inside the embryonal body. The first blood cells in both places first appear as *lymphocytes* of large or small size,—*these must be considered the parent cells of all the blood elements*, and through proliferation and differentiation in different directions they make the numerous forms of red and white blood corpuscles such as we find in the mature organism.

from all subsequent generations that the occurrence of slight differences in these later generations is often overlooked. The existence of a succession of generations brings our terminology into question. In both birds and mammals the term "primary" for the first generation of red cells is satisfactory, but in the chick the cells that follow cannot be called definitive generations since actually it is not until near the end of the embryonic life that the definitive type of red blood cells appears. Probably the term "embryo erythrocytes" or "embryonic erythrocytes" would more accurately designate these cells in the chick. In the embryonic span there are numerous generations beginning with the primary, so that first, second, third (and so on) generations could be designated. Actually, the term "generations" in reference to red blood cells is somewhat misleading since the cells are being produced continuously and not periodically. The term is applied in the same sense as it is used for human populations in that one speaks of different generations; whereas, in fact, there is a complete and unbroken frequency distribution in age from youngest to oldest. Even the mitotic periodicity known to exist in adult birds and mammals is not present in the embryo.

Evidence for the existence of successive generations of red cells following the primary generation is based almost entirely on the appearance of the mature cell, the shade and hue of the cytoplasm, the shape of the nucleus and cell, the nucleocytoplasmic ratio, and the tendency of the nucleus to become dense and pyknotic. Realization that there are successive generations is one thing, but saying that a particular cell belongs to a particular generation—such as the third or fifth—is another. It has not been possible to say this. Moreover, it has not been possible to say for sure how many generations there are during embryonic life. We know that there are more than 2, and the total is probably about 4.

Embryonic erythrocyte generations can be followed quite well in *Amblystoma*. Cameron (1941) demonstrated that cells of the first generation contained 128 yolk plates and each succeeding generation held half the number contained in the parent cell from which it arose by division. After eight generations the yolk plates were reduced to one per cell and then the plates degenerated. At the time of hatching, definitive erythrocytes appeared that lacked yolk plates.

The early generations of embryonic erythrocytes retained round forms, whereas later generations took on elliptical forms. Yolk plates are absent from avian embryonic erythrocytes but the possibility exists that the pattern of reproduction in amphibians may be carried over to some extent in birds.

Figure 232 was prepared so as to show the succession of forms. For the sake of simplicity, the embryonic erythrocytes have been divided into only two groups—the primary generation and succeeding generations. Under the age baseline the hours given are 3 less than the actual duration of the egg in the incubator. This period of time was estimated to be required for the egg to become warm and for developmental processes to get under way. All embryonic ages given in captions or text are estimated on this basis. Incubation age is given either in hours or in days and hours. Table 9 has been included because it is useful in converting from one kind of time scale to the other.

Dawson (1936a) made a similar statistical and cytological study on the shift of erythrocyte stages during embryonic development. His table 1 should be compared with our figure 232, and his photographs of smears from embryos that ranged between the age of 4 days of incubation and hatching age should be compared with figures 226–230, which cover essentially the same range. Under each group of erythrocytes, whether primary or later generations, there are five subdivisions—erythroblasts; early, mid-, and late polychromatic erythrocytes; and mature erythrocytes. The data included in the differential counts included all these stages but the only stages selected for illustration in figure 232 were those that during embryonic life became dominant cells. Each curve was plotted as a hand-drawn average from a large number of differential counts made from closely spaced ages. Sometimes, among the differential counts for a particular cell type at a particular age, the range of variability would run almost 100 percent, but in other cases all the values would be closely clustered.

The first samples of blood were taken from the dorsal aorta of 46- and 47-hour embryos. The technic employed for obtaining intraembryonic blood at this early age is given in chapter 7. Low-power drawings from such embryos are shown in figure 224, *A* and *B*. Although these

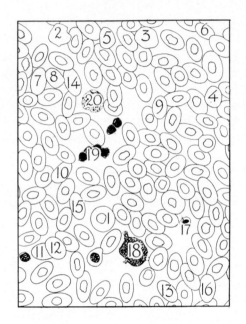

FIGURE 229.—Blood from heart of chick embryo.   Incubation age, 13 days 16 hours.   1,370×.

1 Mature primary erythrocyte.	17 Microcyte.
2–4 Mid-polychromatic erythrocytes, all of which show artifacts of cytosomal fracturing.	18 Erythroblast or thromboblast.
5–13 Late polychromatic erythrocytes; some show artifacts of cytosomal fracturing. Two cells, 7 and 13, are nearly mature.	19 Small embryonic thrombocytes that have clumped and disintegrated the cytoplasm.
14–16 Mature erythrocytes.	20 Basophil mesomyelocyte. The presence of any granulocyte in the circulating blood of the embryo is rare.

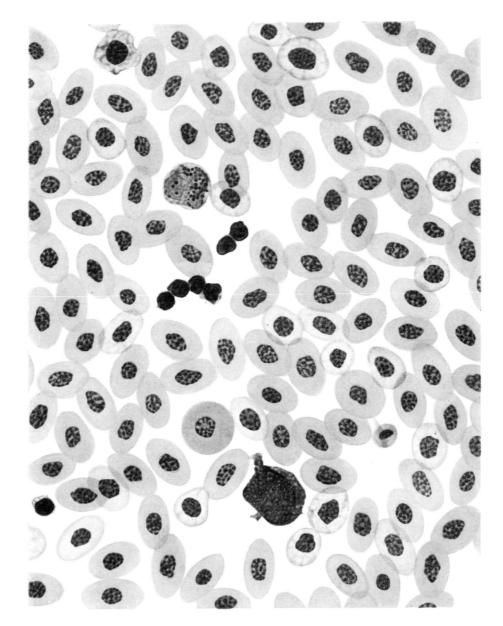

229

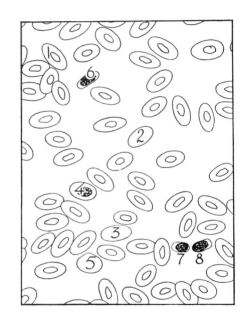

FIGURE 230.—Circulating blood taken from basilic (cubital) vein of the chick about 4 hours after hatching. 1,370×.

1–3   Mature erythrocytes.
4, 5   Late polychromatic erythrocytes.

6–8   Mature thrombocytes of varying size and shape.

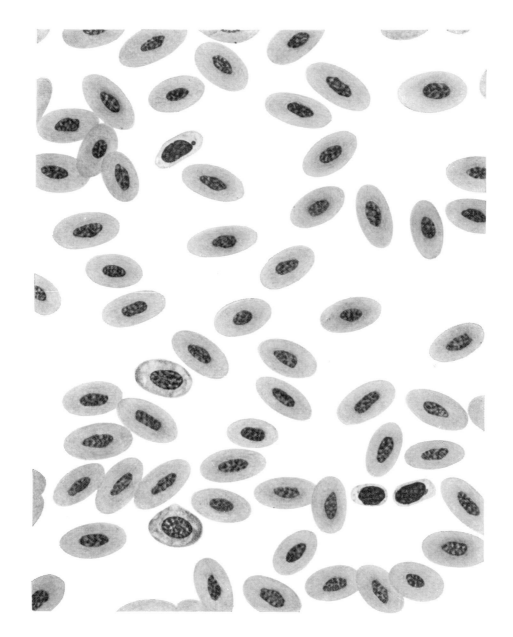

230

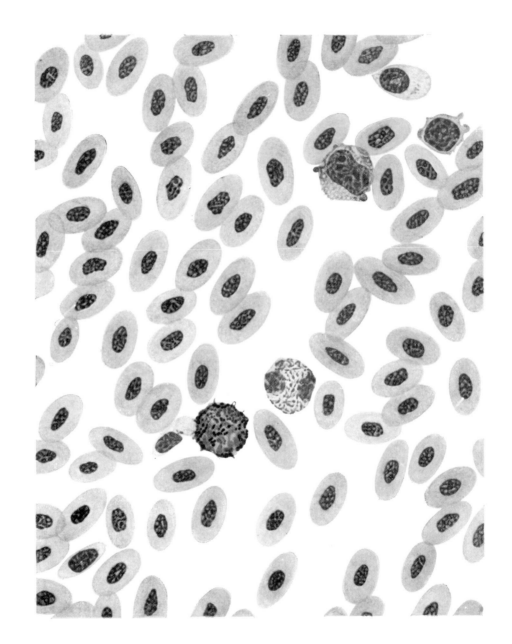

331

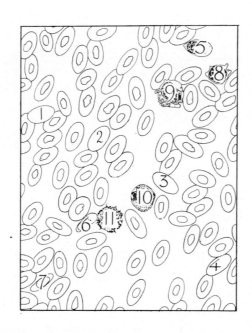

FIGURE 231.—Blood from basilic (cubital) vein of a 7-day-old chick.   1,370×.

A region was selected for drawing that had more than the average number of leukocytes for this number of erythrocytes.

1–4   Mature erythrocytes.
  5   Slightly immature thrombocyte.
6, 7   Mature thrombocyte.
  8   Mature lymphocyte.
  9   Mature monocyte.
 10   Mature heterophil.
 11   Mature basophil.

Table 9.—**Time table—chick incubation**

Total hours	Days	Hours	Total hours	Days	Hours
6	0	6	258	10	18
12	0	12	264	11	0
18	0	18	270	11	6
24	1	0	276	11	12
30	1	6	282	11	18
36	1	12	288	12	0
42	1	18	294	12	6
48	2	0	300	12	12
54	2	6	306	12	18
60	2	12	312	13	0
66	2	18	318	13	6
72	3	0	324	13	12
78	3	6	330	13	18
84	3	12	336	14	0
90	3	18	342	14	6
96	4	0	348	14	12
102	4	6	354	14	18
108	4	12	360	15	0
114	4	18	366	15	6
120	5	0	372	15	12
126	5	6	378	15	18
132	5	12	384	16	0
138	5	18	390	16	6
144	6	0	396	16	12
150	6	6	402	16	18
156	6	12	408	17	0
162	6	18	414	17	6
168	7	0	420	17	12
174	7	6	426	17	18
180	7	12	432	18	0
186	7	18	438	18	6
192	8	0	444	18	12
198	8	6	450	18	18
204	8	12	456	19	0
210	8	18	462	19	6
216	9	0	468	19	12
222	9	6	474	19	18
228	9	12	480	20	0
234	9	18	486	20	6
240	10	0	492	20	12
246	10	6	498	20	18
252	10	12	504	21	0

cells are known to carry hemoglobin, they fill the requirements of an erythroblast in that they have a strongly basophilic cytoplasm and contain nucleoli. At this age practically all cells show an almost identical stage of development, and yet there is a wide range of size as a result of cell division.

A digression for discussion of the implications of these facts may be desirable. Sabin (1920) has shown that the first erythroblasts appeared even before 24 hours of incubation. She also indicated that new erythroblasts continuously developed from their stem cells and that while this was taking place there was a rapid multiplication of cells that had already begun differentiation. This information might lead to the conjecture that, at a later time, when these cells were thrown into the circulation, there would be a wide range of developmental stages present. Instead, one actually finds a remarkable degree of uniformity in the level of differentiation. Therefore, it is suggested that antecedent to the completion of the embryonic and yolk sac circulatory arcs the erythroblasts lie dormant within the vitelline channels and that cytoplasmic and nuclear differentiation is inhibited, although mitosis continues at a rapid rate. Only one phase of differentiation is taking place—that in which the synthesis of hemoglobin is involved—but the nuclear and cytoplasmic changes that ordinarily accompany this process are lacking in these cells. Once circulation is established and the cells begin to move with the flowing blood that has now created a new environment, differentiation proceeds, and about a day and a half later (at 65 to 69 hours, fig. 225) the erythroblasts are transformed into the early, mid-, and late polychromatic erythrocytes of the primary generation. At 48 hours practically all the cells are erythroblasts, but at 65 hours only a few erythroblasts are present, and after that they disappear from the circulating blood. From this time on there is an ever-increasing tendency for immature stages of erythrocyte development to be retained at the loci of their origin.

Apparently blood cells in themselves are not fully equipped to bring about their complete differentiation but something is added while they are being circulated that enhances differentiation. Moreover, as development of the embryo proceeds it is no longer necessary for the immature cells to enter the circulation in order to receive the chemical stimulus that is to be found there. It is no longer necessary because the circulating blood is brought into intimate contact with the areas where the cells are being produced and thus more and more of the immature stages are almost completely differentiated before being released into the circulation. (See Gordon, 1959.)

It is obvious that the suggestions made need the support of additional evidence obtained from experimentation. The effort required to sort out the factors involved in stimulating differentiation would be justified since it is apparent that the same problems of differentiation that have been solved by the embryo are unsolved in cases of leukemia. The cells seen in leukemia of birds and mammals often closely resemble those of figure 224 and may have the large size and conspicuous nucleoli of figure 251. It is generally believed that some change has taken place in the cell metabolism that prevents the normal process of differentiation. The great mass of data on the cytology and propagation of leukemic and other neoplastic cells amply substantiates the idea that an intracellular change can and does occur; but this does not exclude the presence in the plasma of a "differentiating" factor, and the sequence of events observed in embryonic blood before and after circulation is established suggests that such a factor does exist. Whether such a factor is sufficiently potent to force the differentiation of a leukemic cell to the point where it performs the equivalent function of the normal cell is, of course, unknown.

Dantschakoff (1909a) made an interesting observation on erythropoiesis. The phenomenon she saw is undoubtedly an expression of the difference between intravascular and extravascular environment. In the early chick embryo, primary erythroblasts are being rapidly produced both inside and outside the vessels of the vitelline membrane and of the embryo. In both environments, differentiation to the extent of taking up hemoglobin is started but only inside the ves-

sels does the process go to completion. The cells of the primary erythrocyte series in the mesenchyme tissue outside the vessels are destroyed, either by disintegration or by phagocytosis.

Let us return to a description of the changing picture of the circulating blood. The rapid shift between 48 and 65 hours has already been indicated. The mid-polychromatic primary erythrocytes are present at a higher percentage level at 65 hours than are the early polychromatic erythrocytes and, with variations, remain high after the latter have declined to a low level. The maximum reached in the differential counts was 71 percent at 93 hours. There is an irregular decline in mid-polychromatic primary erythrocytes at 97 to 120 hours, and there is a tapering off at 120 to 142 hours. Late primary polychromatic erythrocytes are present only in small numbers at 65 hours, and the number increases gradually until it reaches a peak at about 120 hours (fig. 226). Beyond that age there is a rather rapid diminution in number for this stage of development and by 160 hours (fig. 227) all have disappeared. It is not until after 100 hours that the primary generation of erythrocytes

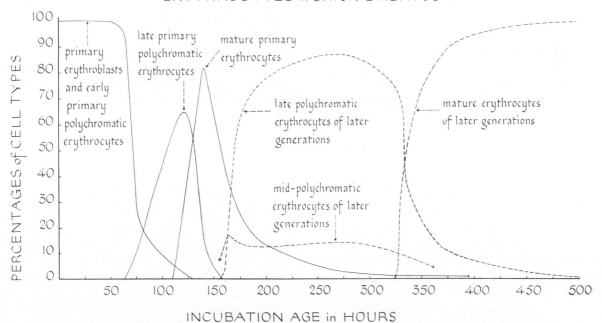

ERYTHROCYTES in CHICK EMBRYOS

FIGURE 232.—Curves showing the percentage rise and fall of three stages of maturity in the primary and later embryo erythrocytes. Solid line—primary erythrocyte. Dotted line—combined later generations of embryo erythrocytes.

reaches maturity; then they differentiate rapidly to become dominant cells at 140 to 142 hours; from that time on these cells may be found in the circulating blood in considerable numbers up to 16 days of incubation. Occasionally they have been seen after hatching.

The tabulation shown in figure 232 gives us some information about the processes of intravascular differentiation, but the picture of decline is always masked by the rise of the next higher stage of development. Undoubtedly much of the apparent decline in mature primary erythrocytes is due to the increase in the proportion of subsequent generations since the data for these curves have been collected as percentage values. A study is definitely needed in which the absolute number of each cell type is obtained, as Kindred (1940) has done with the rat. Then the true picture of the rise and decline of cell types can be visualized; in addition, rate of differentiation and the true life span of the cells during embryonic life will be known.

Following the primary generation there is a succession of generations—secondary, tertiary, and others. Since it is practically impossible to separate them except in the fully differentiated cell, and then only in a general way, all generations after the first have been grouped together. Graphically this produces long low curves instead of a succession of sharp peaks.

Erythroblasts with nucleoli and basophilic cytoplasm are picked up occasionally at between 141 and 214 hours (fig. 227). They may be seen even later but would not constitute a significant percentage in a differential count. Early polychromatic erythrocytes are never abundant; between 160 and 243 hours they vary from 0 to 11 percent, and occasionally cells may be found up through the second week of embryonic life. Most of the cells of these two stages are retained at the site of origin in the yolk sac. Differentiation processes within the circulating blood are limited largely to development from the mid-polychromatic erythrocyte on to the mature form.

The percentage of mid-polychromatic erythrocytes of the later generations never reaches a high level—38 percent at 160 hours is the maximum in our data. The tabular data from which the graphs of figure 232 were constructed suggested that there was a sharp rise in percentage level at about 160 hours, followed by a sharp decline that does not continue downward because

the later embryo generations of mid-polychromatic erythrocytes continue to be present at a low but fairly constant level until about 285 hours of incubation and then drop off gradually.

The frequency distribution curve for the late polychromatic erythrocytes of later embryo generations does not show a sharp peak. Late polychromatic erythrocytes are present in the blood at a high level throughout the period from 212 to 312 hours, after which they decline rapidly at first but later continue to be present at a lower percentage level. The course for these cells trails out up to the time of hatching. They are still present in variable numbers after hatching and practically any slide, even from older birds, will always show a few.

Mature late embryo erythrocytes do not appear until after 210 hours. Later they rise rapidly and from about 375 hours until hatching maintain a high level in the blood. On about the 16th day of incubation, they constitute about 90 percent of the cells present. On the day before hatching close to 100 percent of the erythrocytes present belong to this stage of development and this, of course, is the condition that continues after hatching (fig. 230).

No one, to our knowledge, has as yet attempted to prepare a table of hematologic values for the chick embryo at various ages. The data presented by Flemister and Cunningham (1940) are at least a beginning. They found that in the allantoic circulation at 8 days incubation there were 1,210,000 erythrocytes/mm^3, and at 10 days, 1,880,000. The hemoglobin at 8 days was 9.3 grams/100 cc. and at 10 days, it was 14.7. Their percentage values for the types of leukocytes listed are such as to indicate that they did not identify the nonhemoglobin containing cells the same way we have in this study.

Data for each day of the last week of incubation were given by Roberts, Severens and Card (1939). They presented erythrocyte, total white cell, heterophil, and lymphocyte counts for two lines of chicks. Up to the time of hatching, 75 to 96 percent of the white cells were heterophils. The total white cell counts were generally below 10,000 per cubic millimeter from the 15th through the 19th day of incubation. On the 20th day the count reached about 11,000 and on the 21st day about 16,000 cells. It has been our impression that heterophils were not such a constant constituent of embryo blood, and that lymphocytes appeared only sporadically in the circulating blood, even up through hatching.

It is apparent that additional studies on the number of cellular elements in the circulating blood of the embryo are needed to give us a more firmly established baseline.

DESCRIPTION OF THE CELLS

A great deal can be learned concerning blood-cell lineage and morphogenesis from a study of the circulating blood in embryos at various ages. When this is supplemented by studies on hematopoietic tissues, spleen, bone marrow, and thymus, a fairly complete picture can be obtained of the interrelationship of cells. Without this background the various circulating blood and hematopoietic tissues of the adult fall into numerous unrelated series of cells.

Primary erythrocytes

Satisfactory preparation of the primary erythrocytes at 2 days incubation requires careful attention to technic. Most of the early smears gave shrunken cells that carried numerous protoplasmic processes around their periphery. They looked like cells *A, 11–15,* of figure 224 but most of them were worse. Any contamination of the pipette with saline used to float the embryo or with albumen or yolk would produce this effect, and if there was any delay in getting the cells on the slide, spreading them out into a thin layer, and drying them, they would be greatly distorted.

At all early incubation stages, satisfactory preparation was found to depend greatly on speed in making the smears. With a few refinements in technic, blood could be taken from the dorsal aorta of the embryo as soon as circulation begins, or it could be taken from vitelline vessels without contaminating it with other fluids.

A considerable difference in degree of differentiation exists between *A* and *B* of figure 224; yet there is only 1 hour of difference in incubation age. It is suspected that the development of the embryo represented by *A* was retarded. Practically all the cells at this age, according to the terminology of Doan, Cunningham, and Sabin (1925), are megaloblasts and are destined to produce erythrocytes.

The structure of the early primary erythroblast is shown in cells *1–10* of figure 224 *A.* Probably the least differentiated cell is *2,* which has a cytoplasm of uniform texture quite different from that of the other cells. This cell was added to the drawing from another part of the same slide, as were also *5, 11–14,* and *17.* Consideration of the significance of this cell is helped by looking ahead to figure 225. Within less than 24 hours of additional incubation these will have differentiated in the blood into two distinct cell lines—the dominant primary erythrocytes and the embryo thrombocytes. The latter are said to come from the same precursor cells as the erythrocytes. Therefore, it is quite possible that these are early embryonic thromboblasts. Had Ralph's benzidine technic been applied (p. 231), the point in question could have been settled easily; with this technic the cytoplasm of primary erythrocyte cells gives a positive yellow color when hemoglobin is present, while the cytoplasm of the thrombocytes is negative. The appearance of the cell differs also from that of the early primary erythroblast shown in figure 233. The latter has a cytosome filled with mitochondrial spaces [2] surrounded by granular cytoplasm that has a type of texture characteristic of primary erythroblasts. The primary erythroblasts in which this texture is found include those undergoing mitosis (fig. 224, *A 16, B 21,* and *22.* [3]

In the cytosome of the primary erythroblast are three types of spherical bodies. One of these is probably an artifact. It appears in the cells of figure 224 *A* as clear spherical spaces. The spaces may be small as in *2* and *5* or large as in *15* and *16.* Although they appear to lie within the nucleus this is an artifact. A vacuole or other

[2] Takagi (1931) showed that rod and filamentous mitochondria are present in the blood cells of the yolk sac of the early embryo, but he was not concerned with the specific problem of the identity of mitochondria with cytoplasmic spaces. Jones (1947), who was interested in the structure of primitive erythroblasts, concluded that (p. 317):
"Light areas in basophilic cytoplasm previously described as hyaloplasm or paraplasm represent, for the most part, the negative images of underlying mitochondria."
[3] Takagi (1932) studied the distribution of chondriosomes in dividing blood cells. He used the yolk sac of chick embryos and made his observations on material sectioned in paraffin. At the metaphase, the chondriosomes were grouped around the poles of the dividing cell; none were located either in or on the spindle. During anaphase and telophase, they moved toward the region of the constricting cell walls.

115

body that has considerable rigidity will push up through the substance of the nucleus when the cell is flattened, even though it is formed in the cytosome. With the nuclear substance displaced, the vacuole appears to be within the nucleus. An additional basis for suggesting that these granules are artifacts is the fact that they tend to occur most abundantly in cells that are most distorted (A, 13, 15, and B, 23).

The second type of vacuole is a highly refractory one. In the drawings each such vacuole is indicated by a blue ring (figs. 224 and 225). The number within a cell varies widely from none to as many as are seen in figure 225, 23, but three seems to be an average number. Only a few are present in the cells of figure 224 A, and by 69 hours incubation (fig. 225) they have practically disappeared; but these vacuoles are typical for the cells of figure 224 B. The nature of the substance they contain, their function, and their specificity are unknown. Microchemical studies, or the tracing of their course of appearance and disappearance with the phase microscope in living cells, might be revealing.

The third type of vacuole is small and round, is not refractile, has a tinge of color, and tends to form clusters. At the stage represented by figure 224 A they are best shown in cell 1, but in B numerous cells show these bodies (4, 5, 8, and 12–14). When they first appear, they are scattered but as they increase in number they form a group of spheres. By 65 hours incubation the individual bodies of these clusters have coalesced and are responsible for the light area in the cytoplasm adjacent to the nucleus. Dantschakoff (1908b and 1909a) observed in her sectioned material the presence of an orange-stained area beside the nucleus of the early erythrocyte found in the yolk sac. Similar orange-staining spheres were illustrated and described by Maximow (1909) in his study of early formation of blood cells in the mammalian embryo. The whole process of differentiation of primary erythroblasts from mesenchyme has been described by Murray (1932). He used tissue culture preparations of the primitive streak of the chick embryo. It was observed that the immature primitive erythrocytes were rather small cells with pseudopodia and with nuclei which contained one or two nucleoli. The cytoplasm was strongly basophilic and contained one or more eosinophilic masses adjacent to the nu-

cleus. From such cells as these arose the later stages in the differentiation process. The orange-stained area may well have consisted of vacuoles of this type. If additional study should prove that the vacuoles seen beside the nucleus both in sectioned material and in dried smears are the same, this would offer an excellent cell organelle that could be used as a common basis for identifying the same cell under two different technics. Dantschakoff (1908b) observed that the light-staining spheres contained centrosomes.

None of the three types of vacuoles or spheres observed in the cytosome of the primary generation of erythroblasts were observed in the cytosome of later generations. This difference between the first and subsequent generations is in agreement with observations by Dantschakoff (1908b) on sectioned material.

Since none of these types of spheres have been observed in later generations of erythroblasts in smears, it might be possible to establish whether later generations are similar to the cells (megaloblasts) [4] of the primary generation and to the megaloblasts of anemia—a question that has been ably discussed by Jones (1943). This author has pointed out that there are differences in nuclear cytology among primary and normal definitive megaloblasts and megaloblasts of anemia.

Studies by the smear method show that such differences certainly do exist in the primary and normal definitive erythroblasts of the chicken. As an example of this difference, the nucleus of the primary erythroblast generally contains two nucleoli. No other blood cell included in this study has been observed to have this number of nucleoli. The chromatin reticular pattern is somewhat coarser in primary erythroblasts than in the cells of a corresponding degree of differentiation in later embryonic generations. The nucleoli seem to be more prominent in the first generation than in later ones but this is probably due entirely to physical causes associated with the coarseness of the screen which permits a better view of the interior of the nucleus than can be obtained when looking through the fine screen that is characteristic of later generations of erythroblasts.

Differences in size among primary erythroblasts have not been specifically mentioned thus far. The differences may be seen by glancing

---

[4] "Erythroblasts" and "megaloblasts" are used as synonymous terms.

at figures 224, 233, and 234, which were selected to show range in size and in nucleocytoplasmic ratio. Mitotic figures are abundant at this age, as shown by cell *16* in figure 224 *A* and cells *21* and *22* of *B*. For persons seeking a large tough cell suitable for the study of the avian chromosomes, the writers know of no better material, although they have not examined the neuroblast that has been used so frequently. In smears fixed in Petrunkevitch No. 2 and stained with May-Grünwald Giemsa it has been possible to count about 60 chromosomes and it is likely that some of the problems in this field could be solved with technics selected specifically for cytogenetic studies.

There is perhaps one word of caution to be given. Cytologic evidence indicates that the prime function of this generation of erythrocytes is to form hemoglobin. This is accomplished independently of the differentiation stages that usually accompany this process. As a result, mitosis is often abnormal, and frequently chromosomes lag behind in the anaphase stage. The abnormalities observed at mitosis in the primary generation of erythrocytes are similar to those reported on mitosis in neoplastic cells. Abnormally large size often occurs in neoplastic cells and an occasional giant cell may be found among primary erythroblasts (fig. 251).[5] Such mitotic abnormalities and giant cells probably mean little or nothing toward the production of later blood neoplasias in the bird but since some embryonic cells have certain points in common with neoplastic cells, the possibility always exists that a residual, dormant cell of this type, if not destroyed, could later be stimulated to reproduce itself. Most primary erythrocytes degenerate along conventional lines, as seen in figures 249, 250, 252, and 253.

Hemoglobin development proceeds very rapidly and by 65 hours incubation (fig. 225) has reached the early and mid-polychromatic stages. This terminology is based on the tinctorial quality of the cytosome and not on nuclear or cytoplasmic differentiation. On the basis of criteria

usually applied to the human species, these cells would still be called erythroblasts, since the term "polychromatic" is applied to cells after the normoblast stage has passed, but for the bird, the usage followed here seems to give maximum uniformity of nomenclature for comparative purposes with other species having nucleated red cells. These terms—early, mid-, and late—refer to the blue, gray, and orange phases of color. As previously indicated, the blue represents a predominant stroma of basophilic material. The gray stage appears gray because there is a mixture of two opposite colors—blue and orange—and as more of the original basophilic stroma is lost, there is no longer a balance and the orange color predominates. In later generations of cells this transition is a period of cytosomal weakness, and artifacts readily appear in polychromatic erythrocytes. In the first generation, however, the transition is so rapid that the cytosome does not develop a weakened condition; hence artifacts are not commonly seen (fig. 225). Artifacts appear in some cells after they have reached the late polychromatic stage (fig. 226). Erythrocytes at 65 hours incubation have taken on spherical shapes but they may be pressed into angular shapes when the smear is made, and there may be overlapping of cells that produces clear bands and crescents in the cytosome (fig. 225, *15* with *17*).

The cytosome is closely packed with mitochondrial spaces that have undergone a change from the rods of the earlier stage to innumerable small granules that give to the cytosome a textural quality, and would be inaccurate if a homogeneous wash of color were applied to the drawings of these cells.

A peculiarity of these cells is the presence of a seemingly ectoplasmic mantle around the periphery of some cells (figs. 225, *4*, and 235), the significance of which is unknown. Illustrations of immature human red cells from various sources have not shown anything similar to it. This leads one to suspect that it may possibly be an artifact associated with the large size of the avian cell. A tendency toward the same type of reaction is shown in some of the cells of figure 226 but this reaction does not reappear in any of the later generations, nor do smaller cells of the same age (fig. 236) show the marginal rim.

At this age (about 65 hours) the nucleoli, usually two in number, are even more distinct than

[5] Dawson (1933a) observed that giant atypical erythrocytes were produced in *Necturus* in the regeneration process that followed a destruction of normal erythrocytes by lead poisoning. The occurrence of gigantism in mammalian erythropoiesis has been reviewed by Berman (1947). It may express itself as a large uninucleated cell, as shown here for the chicken, or as a giant multinucleated cell. The latter may undergo multipolar mitoses and Berman is of the opinion that some of these may return to normal, uninuclear cells.

in the cells shown in the preceding plate. The greater distinctness is due to the contraction of the chromatin network into larger but more widely spaced clumps. Mitotic figures are still abundant, and in cells *20* and *22* of figure 225 it is evident that division reduces the size of the cell to half of the original volume. Undoubtedly cell growth occurs during the interkinetic period but average size decreases as the cells get older (compare figs. 225 and 227).

A statistical study on the percentage of mitosis present in the early embryo has been prepared by Dawson (1936a), who says (p. 262), "In the blood stream there is little restriction of mitotic capacity in the differentiating primitive line until the mature stage is reached."

Two types of cells are distinctly visible at 65 hours. One is the primary erythrocyte line, and the other is the embryo thrombocyte line. The cytology of the latter will be discussed after the description of the red cell has been completed. After 4 days incubation little change is visible in the primary erythrocyte except additional hemoglobin accumulation, a greater range in size, and a sharper distinction between red-cell and thrombocyte lines. The characteristic intensity of cytosomal hue is shown in figures 238–240 and ranges from early to late polychromatic. A comparison of figures 238 and 239 brings out an interesting point—the latter is a small cell with a small, densely stained nucleus and indications of cytoplasmic differentiation, yet the hemoglobin content is low in comparison with that of figure 238, which is not so well differentiated cytologically.

The primary erythroblasts at 65 to 93 hours of incubation shown in figures 235, 236, and 238 may reveal a faint tinge of eosin coloration but in some preparations made at this age the cytoplasm may take a completely basophilic coloration. The benzidine test (p. 231) reveals that, nevertheless, hemoglobin is present (fig. 237). Thus this test demonstrates that basophilic coloration of the cytoplasm does not preclude the existence of hemoglobin and it is for this reason that the stage of erythrocyte development called basophil erythroblast has been omitted from the series of erythrocyte stages presented in table 2.

Hemoglobin is present in erythroblasts of embryos incubated 48 hours, although the cytoplasm is fully basophilic. No benzidine tests were made at this age, but the blood flowing through the vessels of the embryo and area vasculosa is clearly red.

Additional hours of development produce definite changes, which are seen in figure 226 and in figures 241 and 242, where the cytoplasm has lost nearly all of its mitochondrial spaces and the perinuclear, vacuolar space characteristic of earlier stages, is nearly gone. Most of the cells

---

FIGURES 233–243.—Stages in the differentiation of primary erythrocytes selected to show variations in size and structure. 2,470×.

FIGURES 233, 234: *Primary erythroblast from dorsal aorta of an embryo incubated 1 day 22 hours. Same slide as figure 224.*

233 Early primary erythroblast. Large nucleolus fills upper half of nucleus.
234 Primary erythroblast. Lobulations are few and small.

FIGURES 235–237: *Primary erythrocytes from embryo incubated 2 days 17 hours.*

235 Late primary erythroblast. Same slide as figure 225. Rounded cytosome. The effects of an ectoplasmic mantle is characteristic of cells of this size and degree of differentiation.
236 Small early polychromatic erythrocyte. From same slide as preceding figure.
237 Late primary erythroblast. Ralph's benzidine method and M. G. G. Presence of hemoglobin in cytosome indicated by yellow color. Cell equivalent to figure 235—taken from same embryo.

FIGURES 238, 239: *Cells from an embryo incubated 3 days 21 hours.*

238 Mid-polychromatic primary erythrocyte. Still shows a refractile granule and mitochondrial spaces characteristic of erythroblasts.
239 Early polychromatic primary erythrocyte. Less hemoglobin than preceding cell but further differentiation.
240 Late polychromatic primary erythrocyte in mitosis. Polar view of what is apparently metaphase. Embryo incubated 4 days.

FIGURES 241, 242: *Late polychromatic primary erythrocytes from an embryo incubated 5 days 3 hours.*

241 Average size.
242 Small size.
243 Late polychromatic primary erythrocyte. Larger than average, almost a mature cell. From same slide as figure 227

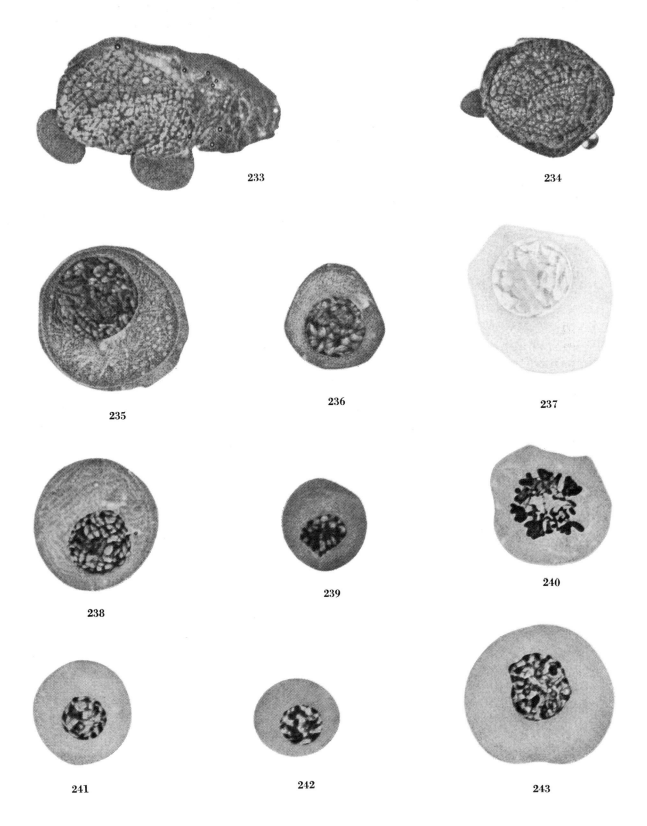

233

234

235

236

237

238

239

240

241

242

243

FIGURES 244–253.—Primary erythrocytes—mature and abnormal.   2,470×.

FIGURES 244–248: *Mature primary erythrocytes.*

244, 245   Same slide. Embryo incubated 6 days 22 hours. The second cell has taken on a slightly oval shape.

246   A rare example of constricted cytosome as well as nucleus, characteristic of amitosis. Embryo incubated 9 days 14 hours.

247   The primary erythrocytes are distinguished from later generations of red cells by the more intense coloration of the cytoplasm. Embryo incubated 8 days 21 hours.

248   A primary erythrocyte in which an oval shape has developed. Embryo incubated 11 days 1 hour.

FIGURES 249–253: *Abnormal primary erythrocytes.*

249   A primary erythroplastid with a body of chromatin material still remaining. Embryo in-cubated 13 days 15 hours. Many examples of degenerating primary erythrocytes are found in older embryos.

250   Poor stainability of the nucleus is characteristic of aging primary erythrocytes. Embryo incubated 15 days 23 hours.

251   A giant late polychromatic erythrocyte—very rare. Nuclear chromatin less dense than normal, thereby revealing clearly the nucleolus. Found in same slide from which figure 240 was taken.

252   Karyorrhexis of nucleus in a primary erythroblast or an early polychromatic erythrocyte, observed rather regularly at young ages. Embryo incubated 2 days 18 hours.

253   Polynuclear primary erythrocyte. Cell shows evidence of aging and decadence. Embryo incubated 9 days 14 hours.

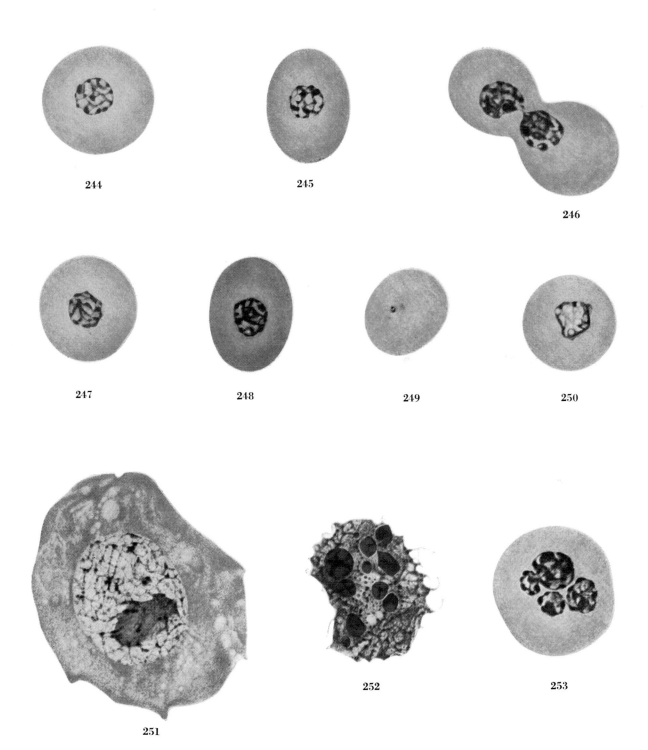

244

245

246

247

248

249

250

251

252

253

FIGURES 254–264.—Developmental stages of embryo erythrocytes following the primary generation, often called secondary or definitive erythrocytes. 2,470×.

FIGURES 254–256: *Erythroblasts. All from the same slide. Embryo incubated 5 days 21 hours.*

254 Early erythroblast.
255 Erythroblast.
256 Late erythroblast.

FIGURES 257, 258: *Late erythroblasts or early polychromatic erythrocytes in mitotic division. Embryos incubated 9 days 18 hours.*

257 Late anaphase.
258 Late telephase.

FIGURES 259–261: *Erythroblasts showing various degrees of failure of nuclear staining. All from the same slide. Embryo incubated 5 days 3 hours.*

259 The nucleus has an empty appearance owing to its incomplete staining.

260 Slight staining toward the right of the nucleus.
261 Overall staining of the nucleus but not sufficiently intense to be fully useful for cell identification.

FIGURES 262–264: *Early polychromatic erythrocytes. Same slide as figures 259–261.*

262 The cytoplasm resembles that of the late erythroblast but the condensation of nuclear chromatin is characteristic of the early polychromatic erythrocyte.
263 A more differentiated cell than figure 262.
264 A more differentiated cell than figure 263.

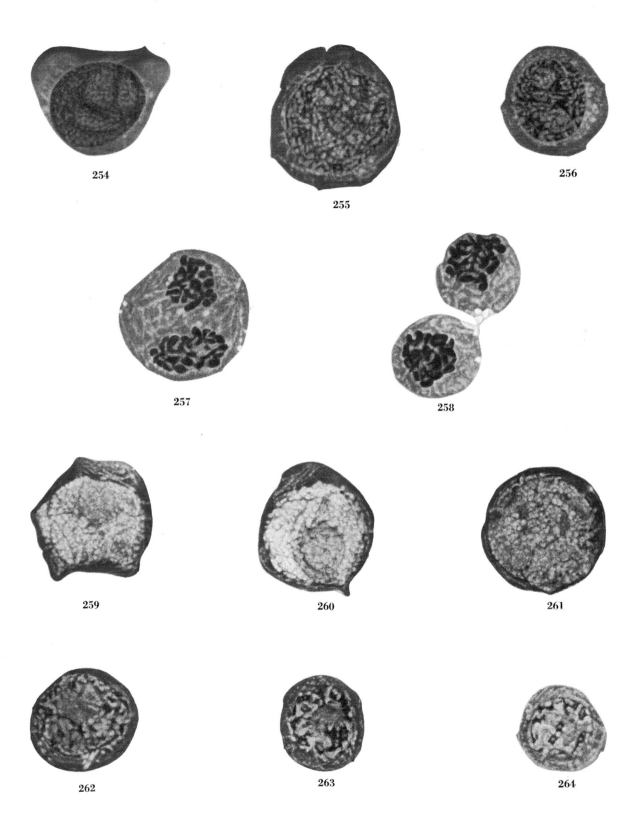

254

255

256

257

258

259

260

261

262

263

264

FIGURES 265–275.—Late developmental stages of embryo erythrocytes; also three cells that show technic artifacts.   2,470×.

265   Early polychromatic erythrocyte, typical of this stage as seen in the late embryo and after hatching. Embryo incubated 5 days 22 hours.
266   Mid-polychromatic erythrocyte.   Cytoplasm fractured.   Embryo incubated 6 days 22 hours.

FIGURES 267, 268: *Late polychromatic erythrocytes.   Same slide as figure 266.*

267   Nearly round cell.
268   Slightly ovoid cell.

FIGURES 269–272: *Mature embryo erythrocytes.*

269   Mature erythrocyte.   Embryo incubated 8 days 21 hours.
270   Mature erythrocyte.   The large cell size, the condensed nucleus, the small nuclear size relative to the cytosome, and the color of the cytoplasm, all suggest that this cell may belong to the primary erythrocyte series.   Embryo incubated 11 days 1 hour.
271   Mature erythrocyte typical of the older embryo. Embryo incubated 13 days 5 hours.
272   Mature erythrocyte identical with the red cell after hatching.   Embryo incubated 16 days.

FIGURES 273–275: *Cells showing the defect of cytoplasmic fracturing.   This generally occurs in the polychromatic stages.*

273   Mid-polychromatic erythrocyte.   Embryo incubated 5 days 18 hours.
274   Late polychromatic erythrocyte.   Disturbed stroma but no unstained spaces.   Same slide as preceding figure.
275   Late polychromatic erythrocyte.   Partial margination of the hemoglobin-bearing stroma.   Embryo incubated 6 days 22 hours.

124

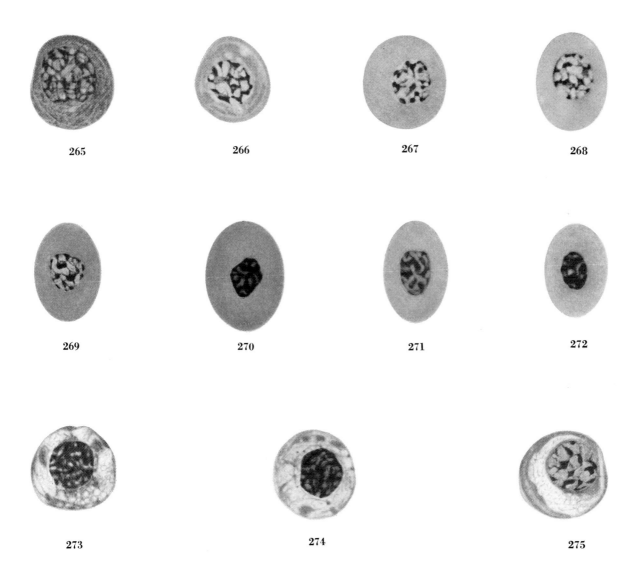

265

266

267

268

269

270

271

272

273

274

275

have reached the late polychromatic stage but a few show the color typical of the mid-stage (fig. 226, *1* and *2*). A different type of cytosome rarefaction appears at this age—the fracture breaks (cells *10* to *12* and others) that in the primary erythrocytes are not as severe as in later generations. Some cells, *3*, for example, show change toward the oval form; the final nucleo-cytoplasmic ratio is not yet established but the nucleus has undergone considerable contraction, and the chromatin now forms coarse blocks. The nucleoli have practically disappeared but mitotic figures are still large and conspicuous. The capability of a cell for mitosis is considered by Osgood and Ashworth (1937) to have considerable value for the proper placement of a cell in its developmental series.

Maturity of primary erythroblasts is attained during the fifth day of incubation and reaches the peak percentage by about the sixth day (fig. 232). Dantschakoff (1908b) states that primitive erythroblasts attain their complete maturity on the fifth day. Figure 227 shows a typical low-power field in which there is a mixture of mature first-generation red cells and early stages of succeeding generations.

The primary erythrocytes still show a wide range in size (fig. 227, *5* and *9*) although they are now all equally mature. Such variation, were it to occur after hatching, would indicate a pathological condition and would probably be classed as anisocytosis. Among these mature cells there are shades of color difference. Although all have a deep orange base color, some of them (cell *5* and the one just below *12*) have some gray mixed with them. The cytosome has lost the coarse textural quality of the erythrocytes at earlier embryonic ages (figs. 235, 236, 238, and 239) and taken on a uniform, finely granular quality (fig. 243). This cytoplasmic texture, characteristic of a cell that is mature or nearly mature, may be observed at 5 days of incubation (figs. 241 and 242).

Since the study of reticulocytes in the blood of the hatched chick came rather late in the program of work, there was no opportunity to reexamine the primary erythrocytes to determine whether they passed through a reticulocyte stage; but Dawson (1936a) showed a series of figures of primary erythroblasts and erythrocytes stained with brilliant cresyl blue, and these closely resemble

what we have pictured for the reticulocytes in the definitive cells after hatching.

The particles near the margin of cell *5* of figure 227 are merely foreign bodies that have fallen on the surface. The nucleus now holds a central position in the cell. There is considerable variation in the ratio of nucleus to cytoplasm and in some of the cells—for example, *2* and *11* of figure 227—the nucleus is smaller relative to the size of the cell than in the definitive erythrocytes. This is a characteristic of the mature primary red cell (figs. 244 and 245). In general the cells and their nuclei are still round, only a few showing a slight elongation.

Chromatin of the nucleus is not so intensely stained in the primary erythrocytes as in the later generations of red cells in the same blood. This type of faint coloration of the nucleus is found as a general characteristic of the primary cells (figs. 244 and 250); where extreme, it has been classified as indicative of deterioration and degeneration, but as seen in figure 227, it hardly seems likely that this is the case at this age. Later generations of erythrocytes first appeared at about 120 hours (5 days) and it is hardly to be expected that the primary generation would be disappearing 21 hours later at a time when the succeeding generations of erythrocytes are just making their appearance. It is true that definite examples of degeneration can be seen at all ages, such as karyorrhexis (fig. 252) and erythroplastid production (fig. 249) in early generations of erythrocytes, and multiple nuclei (fig. 253) in later generations.

Figure 228 shows that new generations have been poured out into the blood and that they have become the dominant cells; only a few mature primary erythrocytes remain—6 to 17 percent of the total number of cells. The nucleus and cytoplasm have the same appearance that they had earlier. It is a question whether these cells ever become oval in large numbers. Cells typical of this age are shown in figures 247 and 248; the latter is slightly ovoid. Degeneration appears in erythroplastid formation, as weak affinity of chromatin for stain, and as pyknotic nuclei (lower left-hand cell of fig. 228). Mature primary erythrocytes become increasingly scarce as the embryo grows older; one is shown in figure 229 (cell *1*) from an embryo 13 days 16 hours old. They may be seen the first day after hatching but not from every chick. None are shown in figure 230.

Figure 246 was included because amitosis is said to occur in human, amphibian, and bird blood cells after reproduction by mitosis has ended. Constricted cells, cells with indented nuclei, and cells with two nuclei can often be found, but according to E. B. Wilson (1925) (quotation on p. 31), amitosis involves constriction of both cytoplasm and nucleus. Of the hundreds of slides examined, this is the only cell which entirely fulfilled the criteria of amitosis and, when a cell having this appearance occurs so rarely, additional evidence is needed before we can consider that amitosis is a normal means of increasing cell number.

Later embryonic erythrocyte generations

The term "later embryonic erythrocyte generations" is used in the legends because it fully differentiates between the cells to which it refers and the cells of the primary generation; but it is a cumbersome term, and in this section the cells will be referred to simply as erythrocytes.

Cells that produce the later generations of embryonic erythrocytes undergo a spurt of multiplication within the lumina of the venous reticulum. According to Dantschakoff (1908b), this occurs on the fourth day of incubation, and the venous reticulum appears at the time the yolk sac membranes grow into the yolk substance.

Cells of this series appear first about the fifth day, as observed by Fennel (1947) and by others who have followed the changing blood picture in the embryo. Dawson (1936a) reports that stem cells of this series appear on the fourth day. It has been our observation that up to 96 hours incubation the only cells present are the primary erythrocytes and the embryonic thrombocytes, and that the blast cells seen on the fourth day belong to the latter series. These quickly differentiate into thrombocytes, and the blast cells seen on the fifth and sixth days are the precursors of the later erythrocytes. Cytologically there is no real difference between the thromboblasts of 4 days and the erythroblasts of 6 days (compare figs. 255 and 280). At 4 days incubation the structural series leads to the thrombocytes, but at 5 days and later it leads to the erythrocytes. Further testing might show that the same stem

cell serves both lines. A common intravascular origin has been suggested for these cell lines. (See Sugiyama, 1926, for review of the literature.) The cells shown in figure 226, *17* and in figure 227, *26* cannot be classified with certainty; either cell may belong to either of the lines mentioned. Blast cells of both lines contain nucleoli. The blast cells of the two lines can be separated fairly accurately later—during incubation and, in the adult, when bone marrow produces these cells.

The erythroblast has a more abundant, more lightly stained cytoplasm than the thromboblast, in which the cytoplasm is a darkly stained rim around the nucleus. In the erythroblast the chromatin pattern is reticulate, whereas in the thrombocyte it is more particulate and punctate.

Anything subsequent to the blast stage is easy to identify; for example, in figure 227, cells *13–15* are mid-polychromatic erythrocytes and cells *16–18* are late polychromatic erythrocytes. Many of the latter type (cells *19–24*) reveal cytosomal artifacts. Early polychromatic erythrocytes are scarce; one is shown in mitosis (cell *25*) and even this approaches the color of the mid-erythrocyte. Differentiation proceeds slowly and even by the ninth day there are only relatively few mature cells; at least there are only a few that give a good vigorous color. Most of them are late polychromatic erythrocytes. By the 13th day mature cells are considerably more abundant, but at hatching or within the first 24 hours after hatching, the dominant cell is the mature erythrocyte, with a few scattered immature cells (fig. 230).

The steps involved in the differentiation process of the erythrocyte line as well as some typical artifacts of the mid- and late polychromatic erythrocytes are shown in figures 254–275. The least differentiated cell observed is illustrated in figure 254. It has a slight amoeboid shape and a smooth-textured cytoplasm, which has a few small spaces. The nucleus is a reticulum with fine meshes, and individual chromatin granules are indistinct. A nucleolus is very faintly visible at the upper side of the nucleus.

A type of blast cell much more commonly found is that shown in figure 255, which is round. The cytoplasm with its mitochondrial spaces is a narrow, strongly basophilic rim around the nucleus. The latter is a coarse reticulum, still without sharp distinction between chromatin and linin network. Another cell taken from the same slide (fig. 256) is smaller but is essentially at the same stage of development as the larger cell except for a slightly more condensed pattern of nuclear chromatin.

Mitosis continues. The cells in figures 257 and 258 were found in the circulating blood of two embryos, both incubated for 9 days 18 hours. The clumps of basophilic cytoplasm are uniformly distributed. In the process of division the cell loses all its identifying marks and it can only be suggested that these two cells are either late erythroblasts or early polychromatic erythrocytes.

The next three cells illustrated (figs. 259–261) probably should be included with examples of artifacts. They are presented with the idea of showing how blast cells appear when they are improperly stained. The cytoplasm in each cell stained well and showed the mitochondrial spaces but, because the nucleus was colored only faintly, the boundary between nucleus and cytosome was not definite and the vacuoles of nucleoplasm and cytoplasm merged. It is interesting to note again that when the surface reticulum is lightly colored the internal structures become visible; thus the existence of a nucleolus is revealed in figures 259 and 260, but in 261, where the reticulum takes the stain more energetically, the nucleolus is only vaguely indicated as lying to the left side of the nucleus.

The failure of the stain to penetrate the nucleus in figures 259–261 is limited to the large blast cells. In more differentiated cells such as figures 262–264, taken from the same slide, the surface chromatin of the nucleus is intensely colored. The difference is not due to cell size since the larger and smaller are equally flattened; it seems more reasonable to suppose that there is a difference in the physical character of the nuclear membrane.

The cytoplasm in figures 262 and 263 shows the same intense, dark blue that is shown in the blast-cell stage; it is still a narrow rim extending only slightly beyond the nucleus, and mitochondrial spaces are still present. The nucleus retains a nucleolus that is conspicuous even in figure 264; yet differentiation has occured, as clearly evidenced by the clumping of the chromatin pattern and the taking up of hemoglobin. This sequence of differentiation is reminiscent of the precocious development occurring in the first generation of erythrocytes, where chromatin clumping and hemoglobin acquisition developed ahead of cellular differentiation.

In the generation succeeding the primary one, the precocious development of these two factors does not get as far ahead of general cellular differentiation as before and, with each succeeding generation, there is a gradual approach to the condition found in the adult bone marrow, where cellular differentiation and hemoglobin accumulation keep pace with each other. Thus, all three cells within this group have been designated as early polychromatic erythrocytes, and in figure 264 the tinctorial quality of the cytosome clearly indicates that hemoglobin is present. Figure 265 has been included under the same category. In this case, however, all the features that are used to measure cytologic differentiation have shifted to indicate a more differentiated cell: the nucleus has become slightly eccentric, the cytosomal rim around the nucleus is greater in proportion to nuclear size than in the preceding cells, the mitochondrial spaces have become small and the chromatin clumps have grown in size and density and in their closeness to each other.

The mid-polychromatic erythrocytes present no difficulty in identification and several examples are pointed out in figure 227, cells 13–15. Figure 266 is a cell at this stage, drawn at a higher magnification. There is, of course, a range of color in the cytoplasm of various cells at this stage as there is for the one before and the one following, and so some mid-polychromatic erythrocytes may appear gray and others nearly blue.

The next stage of development is the late polychromatic erythrocyte (figs. 267–269). The cytoplasm is more homogeneous than it was in the previous stage, and at the beginning of this phase it still contains considerable basophilic material. Many of the cells in figure 228 are at this stage of development. As hemoglobin accumulates, the cell elongates and the ratio of cytosome to nucleus increases. The nucleus also becomes slightly elongated and the chromatin pattern takes on the characteristics of the leptochromatic type of nucleus found in mature cells.

The mature embryo erythrocyte often continues its hemoglobin synthesis until it reaches a tinctorial level equal to that of the primary generation of erythrocytes (figs. 269 and 271).

129

This makes it quite difficult to identify with certainty a cell of the type shown in figure 270, where the cytoplasm is slightly grayish, and the nucleus is shrunken and has started toward degeneration. These are all features characteristic of the primary erythrocyte.

By the end of the second week of incubation and from then on until hatching, the mature erythrocytes are indistinguishable from definitive cells (figs. 228, 229, 271, and 272). The three cells showing artifacts (figs. 273–275) have already been mentioned and they illustrate the defects in greater detail than do the low-power drawings (figs. 227–229). Only the cytosome is affected, never the nucleus. In the cytoplasm any odd effect may be produced.

Embryo thrombocytes

The thrombocytes of the embryo appear as a definite cell line soon after the primary erythroblasts are well established and are clearly present by 68 hours incubation (fig. 225), but whether they are present at 48 hours also (fig. 224) is still undetermined. The cells of 224 *A, 2* and 224 *B, 1* and *2* may be primary thromboblasts. When seen in its entirety, cell 224 *B, 2* resembled in some respects a yolk sac macrophage such as shown in figure 308. The erythrocytes contain hemoglobin and the thrombocytes do not; so if the two cell types are mingled they could be sorted rather readily by Ralph's benzidine method.

There is a peculiar behavior of the primary erythrocytes at the 48-hour age that may have a bearing on the problem. If the primary erythrocytes taken up into the cannula are not discharged immediately onto the slide and there spread so that they dry quickly, they will clump and degenerate, as the thrombocytes will at an older age. Many cells will clump together and their appearance when partly degenerated is similar to figure 224 *A, 11* and *12*. If erythrocytes and thrombocytes come from the same primordial cell, perhaps erythrocytes for a short period of early embryonic life assume a function peculiar to thrombocytes.

Sugiyama (1926) concluded that thrombocytes of the early chick embryo first arose by a transformation of megaloblasts into thromboblasts. The transition involved loss of hemoglobin and reduction in cell size. Our studies have not supported the idea that the thrombocyte series arises from hemoglobin-bearing cells, although it is recognized that a close parallelism in development exists between erythrocytes and thrombocytes. Six other theories on the origin of thrombocytes have been reviewed by Sugiyama. Some have called these small clumped cells of the embryo "lymphocytes," and Sugiyama (1926) presents convincing evidence that this is an error. Typical lymphocytes in his preparations did not appear in the circulating blood of the embryo until 17 days' incubation. Our observations agree with his and further show that lymphocytes, even in the late embryo, are inconstant, and that they do not become a constant, calculable component of the blood until after hatching.

It is obvious from the papers of Dantschakoff (1908b) and Sugiyama (1926) that both authors were studying the same cell, the embryonic thrombocyte. Dantschakoff claimed that primordial cells (large lymphocytes) of the early embryo, produced microblasts and then microcytes (dwarf lymphocytes). She suggested that the dwarf lymphocytes might be related to the spindle cells (thrombocytes) and that the dwarf lymphocytes were different from the small lymphocytes that appeared rather late in embryonic life. According to Dantschakoff (1916a) the latter appeared between the fifteenth and seventeenth day of incubation.

By 65 hours of incubation, the thrombocyte line is easily distinguishable from the erythrocyte line; the cells of the former tend to clump readily but the latter no longer exhibit this property, and since the erythrocyte line is a group of cells fairly well synchronized in development, a structural series does not logically lead back to the blast cell such as shown in figure 225, *25*; yet a complete gradation of cells does lead from this to the small embryonic thrombocytes (fig. 225, *27*), which supports the conclusion that the blast cell shown in figure 225 belongs to the thrombocyte series. The same is true of the cell shown in figure 276 from the same slide. Cell *25* in figure 225 appears to be discharging cytoplasmic blebs; whereas, in figure 276 only large protrusions are present. Both show cytoplasmic spaces but probably the feature that most strongly suggests their thrombocytic affinity is the punctate character of the nuclear chromatin. This cytologic detail of the immature thrombocyte nucleus was not observed by Sugiyama (1926), probably because Wright's stain was used.

Beyond the blast stage, thrombocytes can be identified easily; thus even in one field (fig. 225) two older stages are visible. Cells *24* and *26* are probably at about the same level of differentiation, and cells of this size do not tend to clump together as readily as do the smaller cells (*27*). In the clumping process, cytoplasmic blebs are thrown off. A duplicate slide, made from the same embryo that was used for figure 225, was stained with Ralph's modification of the benzidine test. Two cells (figs. 277 and 278) demonstrate that hemoglobin is absent from the thrombocyte even at an early stage of differentiation. Figure 277 is probably equivalent to cell *26* in figure 225; figure 278 is smaller and the nucleus is not visible. Dividing thrombocytes are sometimes found. Unlike the erythrocytes which maintain a compact cytoplasm, the thrombocytes even during mitosis (fig. 279) can be stimulated to give off protoplasmic fragments.

Spreading and drying the cells is not always rapid enough to prevent degeneration of the thrombocytes. Many of the cells illustrated in figures 276–295 are not typical of what one so often finds on the slide, since the ones selected were those least degenerated. A degenerated thrombocyte looks like a lymphocyte. Not every slide made from a series of embryos is equally productive of early stages, but the embryo that contributed figures 280 and 286 had an abundance of them.

A typical thromboblast at 4 days of incubation is shown in figure 280. It has a narrow rim of cytoplasm that stains an intense dark blue or deep violet. Within are large mitochondrial spaces. The reticulum at the surface of the nucleus in figure 280 appears more clearly defined than that in the nucleus of the amoeboid thromboblast in figure 276. Associated with this more open network is a vague suggestion of a nucleolus.

Failure of the nuclear surface to stain is a common feature of young cells with large nuclei, and three degrees of incomplete staining are shown in figures 281–283. These duplicate the reaction that occurred in young erythrocytes (figs. 259–261) in that the nucleolus is more readily visible than in the well-stained cell. In these three examples, deficiency in nuclear affinities does not influence the quality of cytoplasmic

staining: full differentiation of abundant mitochondrial spaces is attained, especially in figures 283 and 284.

Shifting of the nucleus to an eccentric position may occur in thromboblasts (figs. 283–285) but, as in the erythrocytes, the nucleus tends to remain in the center of the cell, as in figures 280 and 286, and in the four small thrombocytes in figure 225, i.e. *27*. By 4 days of incubation a wide range in stages of development has appeared; the cells form a series of decreasing size and increasing cytoplasmic differentiation (figs. 286–292); yet the impression is gained that this differentiation process does not exactly parallel that which takes place at older embryonic ages and after hatching. Like the primary generation of erythroblasts, this primary generation of thrombocytes seldom produces an oval cell. Later, however, cells of this shape can be found frequently if the preparation is made quickly enough. A few cells with oval shape have been seen at 4 days (fig. 287) and again once or twice at 5 days, but these cases are too rare to be called typical. Sugiyama (1926) pictured a thrombocyte of oval shape, taken from an embryo incubated only 2 days. We have never seen a thrombocyte having this shape in an embryo this young.

The first step in the differentiation process following the blast stage is the loss of staining affinity by the cytoplasm (figs. 286 and 288) and the next is extensive vacuolization (figs. 290 and 291). In figure 290 a single magenta granule appears to be present outside the nuclear margin, and in figure 291 such bodies are numerous. They are not the specific granules of the definitive thrombocyte but resemble extruded chromatin particles more than anything else. The delicate, fine pink granules that are characteristic of definitive thrombocytes never appear in the first generation of thrombocytes; the two bodies shown in figure 293 from an embryo incubated 5 days 21 hours are about the size of definitive granules but belong to the chromidial type.

Thromboblasts soon disappear from the circulating blood of the embryo, after which only large, medium, and small embryo thrombocytes are seen. By the ninth day the occurrence of specific granules is fairly common. The granules may appear as early as the eighth day (fig. 294) but many of the cells still do not show them until later in development. They are present in those cells selected for illustration chiefly because such cells were chosen in order to make more convincing the evidence that these are thrombocytes and not lymphocytes. Lymphocytes, monocytes, and granulocytes are not normally present in circulating blood of the embryo, although cells belonging to these types may be seen occasionally, and they will be considered more fully when the cells found within the hematopoietic organs are described.

It has been indicated already that mature stages from later generations of thrombocytes, like later generations of erythrocytes, approach a higher level of terminal differentiation than did earlier generations and thus during the second week of embryonic development, all cytologic features that characterize the definitive cell can be seen but not exactly as they will appear in the circulating blood of the adult bird. Specific granules of the type shown in figure 296 are atypical in that they are larger than normal and in that each lies within a vacuole. This vacuolar effect may possibly be due to technic since it is found also in mature thrombocytes from the circulating blood of the adult fowl, when the blood smear has been fixed in Petrunkevitch No. 2 and stained with May-Grünwald Giemsa (fig. 202). The general appearance of the cell (fig. 296), the lightly stained vacuolated cytoplasm, the condensation of the nucleus, and the acidophilic affinity of the cell margin, all establish this particular cell as an embryo thrombocyte. Typically the specific granules are distributed among the strands of the cytoplasmic reticulum (figs. 297–299, 302, 303, and 305).

The last-mentioned point, the affinity of the cell perimeter for eosin, is especially significant. This reaction by the cell margin is often seen in embryo thrombocytes of this age. The same reaction occurs in thrombocytes of adult birds (fig. 85), but after hatching, the disintegration process is less frequently stopped at the exact moment when this initial stage in cytoplasmic breakdown would be revealed.

Other examples of crumpling and acidophilic staining of the cell margin, an initial reaction in the disintegration process, are shown in figures 297 to 299. There is merely a single indentation of the cell wall in the first two of these figures, but in the third the entire margin is scalloped. There is a question of whether the shift from a basophilic to an acidophilic affinity (1) was a result of cell disintegration, (2) preceded

it, or (3) was under the control of a different set of factors with little or no causal relationship to cellular breakdown. For the present, only examples can be mentioned, and these do not always support the same hypothesis. Figures 302 and 303 show a definite acidophilic margin and slight diffusion of the reaction into cell protoplasm; yet there is no indication of cell rupture. On the other hand, figure 306 shows cytoplasmic disintegration well started, yet basophilic affinities have been retained, and figure 295 shows both rupture and acidophilic staining. These examples come from different slides. The cytoplasm of thrombocytes under the best conditions stains so delicately that only with optimum illumination correctly aligned can these differences in color and structure be detected.

The cell represented by figure 302 was selected to show that an intact, almost definitive, thrombocyte can be found as early as 9 days 15 hours. This cell was not seen until after a number of slides had been made. This degree of differentiation is not typical for this age. Usually small thrombocytes of mid-embryonic life look like figures 300, 301, and 306, or those of figures 228 and 229. Cells (figs. 300 and 306) were selected for drawing in which specific granules were still visible; when these granules are not visible, disintegrating thrombocytes so closely resemble small lymphocytes that have discharged part of their cytosome, that the identification might be questioned. Some rounded cells (fig. 304) in which specific granules are absent but in which disintegration has not begun can definitely be identified by the lightly stained vacuolated cytosome. If the technic methods could be improved, probably most of the embryo thrombocytes after 10 days of incubation would look like figure 302.

When a cell reaches a stage of degeneration such as shown in figure 301 and a specific granule is not visible, one can only guess at its identity; if it is part of a cluster (fig. 229, *19*) it is probably a thrombocyte, but if it is an isolated cell, it may be a lymphocyte. Generally, however, the nucleus of even the small lymphocyte is larger than that of the thrombocyte.

Even at the end of the second week of incubation, thrombocytes in general have not taken on the definitive form and many, even with specific granules, still have an appearance of immaturity (fig. 305). This may be true until nearly hatching time (fig. 307), but by the 21st day (fig. 230, cells 7 and 8) cells having this appearance can be considered to be truly definitive and mature.

Cells occasionally found in circulating blood of the embyro

Granulocytes may be found in the circulating blood during the last week of embryonic life and occasionally during the second week. Their occurrence, however, is sporadic, and in many smears none were present; yet a study of hematopoietic organs during this same period—and even of organs like the pancreas, which is not a hematopoietic organ in adult life—shows that tremendous numbers of granulocytes are being produced, but apparently they are being held in storage and normally are not liberated until after hatching, so that the typical blood smear even for a few hours after hatching shows only erythrocytes and thrombocytes (fig. 230).

When granulocytes do appear in the circulating blood of the embryo, this question comes to mind: Is it rough handling, or is it infection of the egg, that caused these granulocytes to appear in some embryos and not in others? When the egg is opened, the embryo with its membranes is slid into a bowl of warm saline and then is lifted to a filter paper in a flat Petri dish. Here the amnion is opened, and often in the moving process the other membranes are ruptured or torn away. If the ventral body wall has closed over, the tissues in this region are laid apart in order to expose the heart and then the cannula is inserted. No matter how dexterously these steps are executed, there is still enough roughness to dislodge some granulocytes from embryonic depots.

On the other hand, approximately 8 percent of hens' eggs have been found to carry a bacterial contaminant after all precautions have been taken to prevent entrance of organisms from outside the shell. From indirect evidence viruses also can be transmitted from the hen to the egg (Cottral, 1950 and 1952). Probably our best evidence comes from work done at this Laboratory—evidence that lymphomatosis, a virus disease, is transmitted through the egg (Cottral, Burmester, and Waters, 1954, and Burmester, Gentry, and Waters, 1955). If some eggs carry bacterial or virus infections, and if phagocytic cells are already on hand, it seems entirely pos-

sible that the chick could be stimulated to give a defensive response just as well before hatching as after hatching.

Chick embryos have been inoculated with so many different viruses and bacteria that it is probably safe to say that growth or serial passage of every well-known disease has been attempted on this medium. In nearly every case, the embryo was used merely as a test tube because a better, synthetic one has not yet been devised. Embryos have been used as a culture medium without much regard for possible contamination of the egg. The studies of embryo reactions are often based on grossly visible lesions, which do not tell the full story. Studies of egg-borne diseases must be carried back to the cells of the embryo. These cells must be searched for inconspicuous deviations from the normal, some of which may represent defense reactions to pathogens. The meaning of the presence or absence of heterophils in the circulating blood is a case in point; there is certainly no *a priori* reason why the chick embryo could not be studied in health and in disease just as scientifically as the adult fowl. Zuckerman (1946) has provided us with an example of blood response to infection in the embryo. Introduction of *Plasmodium gallinaceum* stimulated the heterophils to become almost as numerous as thrombocytes. In the differential count on one embryo, there were 44.5 percent thrombocytes; 19.0 percent mature heterophils, and 24.0 percent heterophil myelocytes, a total of 43.0 percent. In addition there were 1.0 percent macrophages, 8.0 percent monocytes, and 3.5 percent lymphocytes.

Roberts, Severens, and Card (1939) found the white cells of the embryo composed of neutrophils and lymphocytes. During the last week of hatching there was a fairly constant number of each of these cell types. Their values were averages and the variability among individual birds was not indicated. No mention was made of the thrombocytes, which in the embryo often look like lympocytes. Whether some, or all, of the white cell types are constant components of embryo circulating blood can be decided definitely only by additional investigations.

The macrophage is another cell sporadically found in smears of blood taken from the embryo heart. The large cell shown in figure 308 came from blood drawn from the dorsal aorta and differs in appearance from all the other cells shown in figures 309–318. The nucleus is immense and has a uniformly delicate granulation. The cytosome carries clear vacuoles ranging from small to very large. There is much to suggest that this cell is a yolk sac or endodermal macrophage. How so large a cell can flow through capillary channels is not understood. Cells of similar size but of different structure were found in blood taken from the heart, but as already mentioned these were present in only a few embryos and absent from most of them, and were found most commonly at about 10 days of incubation. This age (10 days) agrees with the span from 7 to 12 days of incubation when Sugiyama (1926) found macrophages in the embryo blood.

The cell shown in figure 310 is definitely a macrophage although the cytosome contains but a few inclusions, which are represented by several magenta granules and numerous vacuoles. The nucleus was pressed down on some of the vacuoles when the cell dried; these vacuoles made the nucleus appear to be vacuolated also, but actually it was not. An earlier less differentiated stage is represented by the three cells clumped together in figure 309. The nuclear structure is identical with that shown in figure 310, but differentiation of the cytoplasm toward the phagocytic condition of the macrophage has not progressed as far as in the latter cell. The nuclear structure of both of these cells is similar to that observed in macrophages seen so abundantly in blood spots (Lucas, 1946). In blood spots they appeared to be derived from fibroblasts and the same type of cell with long unipolar or bipolar processes was found also in the embryo (figs. 314–316). Whether these precursor cells are reticular cells or fibroblasts needs to be determined, but at least it can be stated that in the embryo and in blood spots of eggs the precursor cell is not a lymphocyte. In the circulating blood of the adult, lymphocytes differentiate into a reactive type cell, and it has been suggested that this may be leading toward a macrophage, but never has a series of stages been observed spanning the gap from the reactive lymphocyte to the type of macrophage shown in figures 310, 313, or 318.

In the same slides that contained the cells of figure 309 were numerous protoplasmic spheres (fig. 311 A to D). Although differing in size they all stained in the same way and resembled closely in structure the cytoplasm seen in figure 309. These cytoplasmic spheres were vacuolated like the cytoplasm of macrophages and probably were pinched off from cells of this type—at least no other cell visible in the blood at this time seemed large enough to have produced them. The cytoplasm of the macrophages has a structure identical with that found in the pinched-off fragments.

Later in the study, cells grouped in a mass were discovered (fig. 312). In nuclear and cytoplasmic structure they were identical with the small group of three discovered earlier (fig. 309). Many large macrophages had been observed up to this time but the bulkiness of this group precluded the assumption that it could get through the smaller circulatory channels. It is entirely

---

FIGURES 276–287.—Early developmental stages of the embryo thrombocytes. 2,470×.

276 Early thromboblast, lobulated stage. Embryo incubated 2 days 17 hours.

277 Either a late thromboblast or a large early thrombocyte. Duplicate slide from same embryo as preceding figure. Treated with Ralph's benzidine and stained with M. G. G. No trace of hemoglobin in cytosome.

278 Medium embryo thrombocyte. Same slide as preceding figure.

279 Thromboblast in the telephase of mitotic division. Embryo incubated 2 days 18 hours.

FIGURES 280–286: *Drawn from the same slide. Embryo incubated 4 days.*

280 Large embryonic thromboblast.

FIGURES 281–283: *Embryo thromboblasts showing incomplete staining of the nucleus.*

281 This type of empty nucleus often seen in blast cells following Wright's stain, less often with M. G. G.

282 A partial staining of the nucleus.

283 Nuclear content well stained but nuclear boundary not well delineated.

284 Embryo thromboblast that shows the punctate character of the chromatin granules.

285 Large embryo thrombocyte. Cytoplasm still shows the structure of the thromboblast. Nucleolus present.

286 Large embryo thrombocyte. Rarely fixed in this round form.

287 Large embryo thrombocyte that shows precocious development to the oval form. Same age as preceding one.

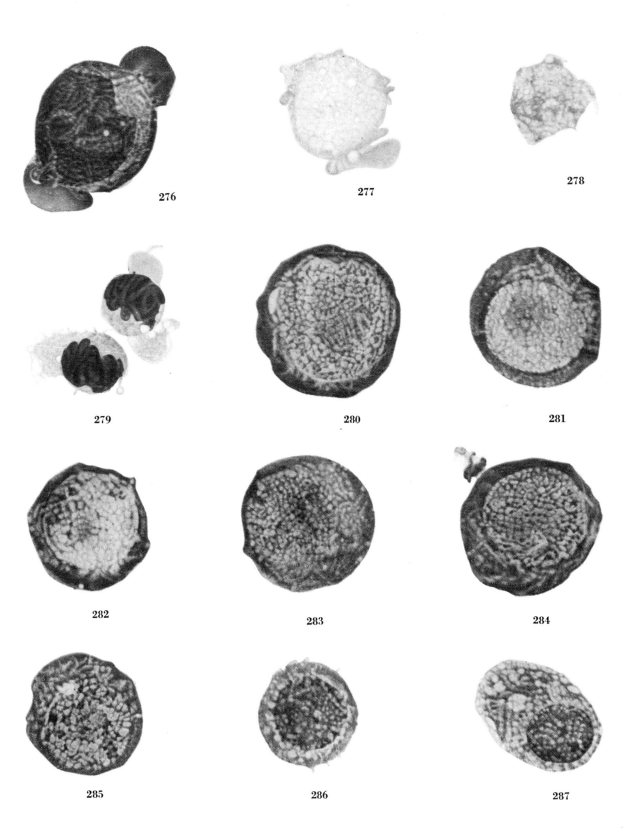

276

277

278

279

280

281

282

283

284

285

286

287

135

FIGURES 288–307.—Late developmental stages of the embryo thrombocyte. 2,470×.

FIGURES 288–291: *Large functional embryo thrombocytes. Drawn from same slide as figures 280–286.*

288 Large embryo thrombocyte showing blebs of early disintegration.
289 Large embryo thrombocyte showing partial loss of basophilic cytoplasm.
290 Vacuolization of cytoplasm with loss of staining affinity. A stage in the differentiation process.
291 Discharge of chromatin granules into the cytoplasm. Found only in well-preserved early embryo material.

FIGURES 292–295: *Medium and small embryo thrombocytes.*

292 Medium embryo thrombocyte. Vacuolization and some discharge of nuclear chromatin.
293 Medium embryo thrombocyte. Several chromatin bodies in cytoplasm. Pink color due to early disintegration of the cell. Embryo incubated 5 days 21 hours.
294 Small embryo thrombocyte. Same type shown in figure 229, *19*. Embryo incubated 7 days 23 hours.
295 Medium embryo thrombocyte. Cytosome partly disintegrated. Embryo incubated 8 days 21 hours.

FIGURES 296–303: *Stages in development and breakdown of late embryo thrombocytes. Embryo incubated 9 days 15 hours.*

296 Medium embryo thrombocyte. Slight autolysis at the cell margin. Cytosome contains more than the usual number of specific granules.

297 Medium embryo thrombocyte. Acidophilia and folding of cell margin are first steps in cell disintegration. Three specific granules present.
298 Medium embryo thrombocyte. Less differentiated than preceding cell. One specific granule.
299 Medium embryo thrombocyte. Folding of cell margin well started. Two specific granules.
300 Small embryo thrombocyte. Much of the cytoplasm lost. One specific granule.
301 Small embryo thrombocyte. Much of the cytoplasm lost. No specific granule visible.
302 Mature embryo thrombocyte. A specific granule at each pole.
303 A binuclear mature embryo thrombocyte. Numerous specific granules.

FIGURES 304–307: *Developmental stages of thrombocyte generations coming late in embryonic life.*

304 Medium embryo thrombocyte. Early stage of development. No specific granules. Embryo incubated 13 days 15 hours.
305 Medium embryo thrombocyte. Later stage in differentiation than preceding cell. Same slide as figure 304.
306 Small embryo thrombocyte. Nucleus and cytoplasm undergoing degeneration. One specific granule.
307 Definitive thrombocyte, nearly mature. One specific granule. Embryo incubated 17 days 14 hours.

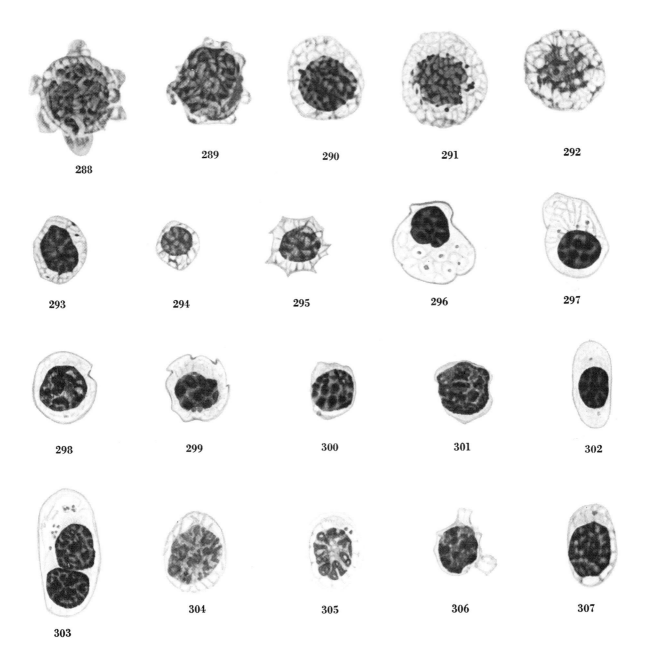

288

289

290

291

292

293

294

295

296

297

298

299

300

301

302

303

304

305

306

307

137

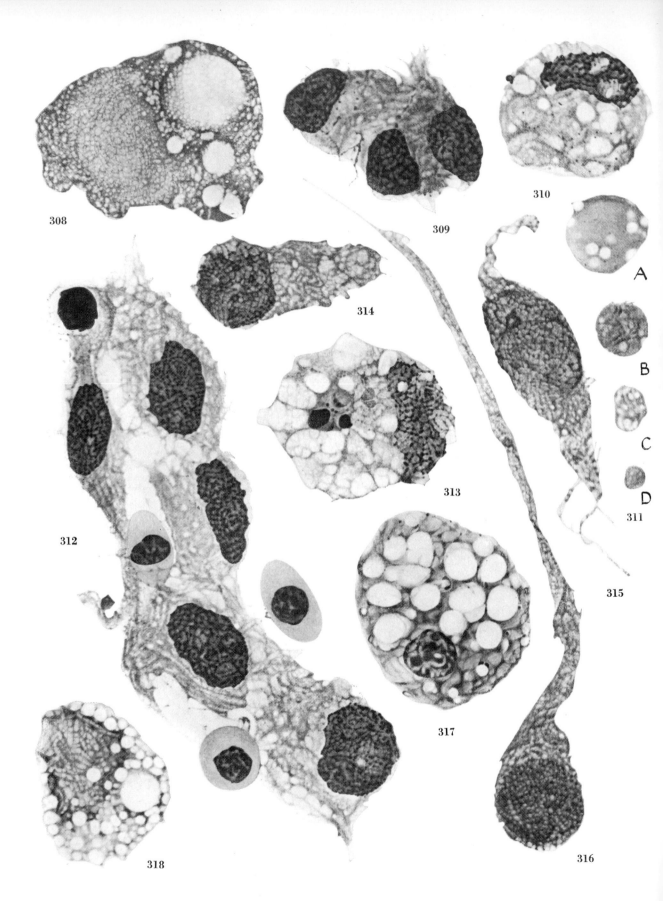

308

309

310

314

A

B

C

D

311

315

312

313

317

316

318

138

possible that an embryo carrying a pathogenic organism could produce masses of reactive cells that, after leaving their point of origin, become thrombi of the circulating channels, but a simpler explanation seems more reasonable at present. When the glass cannula penetrated the ventricle, it was quite likely, if the tip were dull or jagged, that some heart tissue, particularly the lining cells, would be separated from the wall and would then be sucked up with the blood. Hearts from embryos of the same age—10 days of incubation—were used in a test of this hypothesis. They were removed from the body and opened, and the blood was washed out. A slide was pressed against the endothelial surface and from it came the type of cells shown in figures 314–316. Figure 316 was the longest cell obtained by this method. Most of the cells were of the size and shape shown in figure 314 and some were like 315. There is a measure of similarity of nuclear and cytoplasmic pattern between these cells and those of figures 309 and 312, but there is still room for doubt that they are all of the same type.

The endothelial cells of the liver and spleen are phagocytic in pigeons (Kyes, 1915). The cells are capable of ingesting erythrocytes under normal conditions and after the contained erythrocyte has been digested, the hemophage reverts to a flattened endothelial cell. Kyes' observations are mentioned here because it may help toward an understanding of the occurrence of macrophages within the heart of the embryo chick.

It was noted, in the study of blood spots, that macrophages underwent degeneration and only some of the cells retained the punctate pattern of chromatin of the type seen in figures 309, 310, 312, and 313. Often when karyolysis of the nucleus occurred, the underlying nucleolus was brought into view. There is a suggestion that nucleoli are present in figure 312. Nucleoli were conspicuous in some slides of chick embryos that were sent to this Laboratory for cell identification; the embryos had been inoculated with a pathogen from man and the circulating blood showed a series of transitional stages from the reticular cell to the reactive cell.

Some studies have been made on the defense-reaction mechanism in birds but perhaps the greatest need at present is to identify by the smear method the cells that, in the celloidin sectioned material, are called resting amoeboid and wandering cells. As the problem now stands, a study of the actual number of different types of macrophages is confused by differences in technics that make even identical cells look different.

It has been claimed by Dantschakoff (1931) that the endodermal wandering cell was actually the primordial germ cell caught in its migration from the extraembryonic splanchnopleure to the gonadal ridge. Dr. Robert E. Smolker of

---

FIGURES 308–318.—Reticular or phagocytic cells found in blood and vascular organs of the embryo. 2,470×.

308 Early embryo macrophage, yolk sac type. Blood from dorsal aorta. Embryo incubated 1 day 22 hours.

309 Embryo macrophage, beginning differentiation from its stem cell. Circulating blood taken from the heart. Embryo incubated 9 days 16 hours.

FIGURES 310–313: *Mature embryo macrophages and cell fragments. Blood taken from the heart. Embryo incubated 9 days 16 hours.*

310 Mature embryo macrophage. Only a few granular inclusions.

311 Cytoplasmic spheres ranging in size from large to small, A to D. Believed to be pinched-off pieces of macrophage cytosome.

312 A group of macrophage stem cells, essentially mesenchyme. Probably pushed into the cardiac blood stream by the entrance of the cannula. Two nucleoli in each nucleus. Three embryo erythrocytes shown in the field.

313 Mature embryo macrophage containing acidophilic and basophilic inclusions. Vacuolization typical of functional macrophages.

FIGURES 314–316: *Cells from a touch preparation of inner surface of embryo heart. They resemble, but may not be identical with, those of figures 309 and 312. Embryo incubated 9 days 22 hours.*

314 A nearly rounded cell.
315 Cell with bipolar processes.
316 Cell with a long unipolar process.
317 Postmortem degeneration of a macrophage, embryo (21st day of incubation) killed and held in the cold 2 hours. Embryo still had a large external yolk sac. Cell from spleen impression smear.
318 Macrophage from blood of basilic (cubital) vein. Chick just hatched.

the Department of Natural Science, Michigan State University, has demonstrated (personal communication) sections of early embryos that clearly revealed the primordial germ cells. Even in sections they were considerably larger than any of the blood cells seen in the embryo, including the primary generation of erythrocytes. Very probably we have never seen primordial germ cells in our smears.

A final bit of data is the macrophage shown in figure 318. It was not obtained by cardiac puncture but in a drop of blood from the basilic vein of a chick hatched only a few hours before the sample was taken. In some ways the high degree of vacuolization and the rather delicate nuclear pattern resemble the yolk macrophage of a 2-day-old embryo more than they do the macrophages of a 10-day-old embryo.

An impression smear from the spleen of a late embryo that, after killing, was left at room temperature for about 2 hours produced still another type of phagocytic cell (fig. 317). The strong acidophilic reaction of the cytoplasm is characteristic of post mortem degeneration and this type of vacuole formation can be seen in tissue-culture cells when the culture is held under unfavorable conditions. The nuclear structure is entirely different from that found in the 10-day-old embryo; in fact, the entire cell is morphologically different from any macrophage described thus far.

ADDENDUM

Throughout this book and in a recent publication (Lucas, 1959), it has been repeatedly mentioned that in smears or touch preparations the nuclei of erythroblasts and thromboblasts usually reveal their nucleoli, whereas the nuclei of granuloblasts and lymphoblasts rarely do. During the period following the completion of the manuscript, an effort has been directed (1) toward the identification of the tissue components in different hematopoietic organs from which the various blood cell lines take their origin, and (2) toward the identification of equivalent cells in sectioned material with the named stages of development found in touch preparations.

From our studies thus far it appears that the presence or absence of a nucleolus is a variable that is dependent more upon the size of the cell and its level of metabolic activity than upon its being a fixed morphologic structure. We are not including here the pseudo-nucleoli that are chromocenters in some animal cells. From sections showing stages in development of the granulocyte series the nucleolus appears first in the metagranuloblast, reaches its maximum size in the promyelocyte and then disappears during the subsequent stages. The areas on the right of the nuclei in figures 382 and 383 that stain a faint bluish color are probably nucleoli of the basophil promyelocytes.

Ackerman and Knouff (1959) picture the lymphoblast in the bursa of Fabricius with a nucleolus. Our own studies indicate that this is probably true also in the thymus, but it is still uncertain that this is the case in spleen and bone marrow.

Regardless of how universally a nucleolus may prove to be present, based on sections of avian tissues, the usefulness of its variable visibility as a tool in the study of smear preparations is not nullified; by this tool, erythroblasts and thromboblasts can be distinguished from granuloblasts and lymphoblasts.

CHAPTER 4

Blood Cells From Hematopoietic Organs
of the Embryo

There is general agreement that during the life of the chicken, erythrocytes have an intravascular origin and myelocytes an extravascular origin. From the present study, and the work of others, it appears probable that the broader generalization can be made that viable erythrocytes and thrombocytes have an intravascular origin and all leukocytes have an extravascular origin. Basically, this agrees with Dantschakoff's (1908a and 1909a) concept, except that she calls a primitive blood cell a lymphocyte; whereas, in this study a lymphocyte is considered to be the mature stage of a distinct leukocyte line and not a stem cell or primitive blood cell.

The erythrocytes and the thrombocytes are the only two cell types normally present in the circulating blood of the chick embryo. All others that develop within hematopoietic organs are held there until after hatching. Granulocytes appear in great abundance in bone marrow, spleen, kidney, pancreas, and sometimes in the liver and other parenchymal organs. According to Dantschakoff (1908a and b) and Danschakoff (1916b and c), granulocytes also develop in the yolk sac and in the thymus, and Nonidez (1920) found developmental stages in the ovary after hatching. The bird in its hematology is reminiscent of some of its reptilian and amphibian ancestry where blood-cell development is widely scattered over the b o d y (Dawson, 1932). Danschakoff (1916c) observed that in embryo chicks there was a similar wide potency of the mesenchyme to form blood cells. She found that during normal development this potency was restricted to certain tissues but if transplants of pieces of adult organs were made on the allantois of the early embryo, the mesenchyme cells among the striated muscle fibers, and among the cells of liver, kidney, and ovary, and in the walls of major vessels, took on hematopoietic functions. Often the circulating blood simulated that of leukemia.

Were we to judge from information on mammals, we might expect the liver to be an active embryonic hematopoietic organ; but in the chicken it remains practically free of developing blood cells (Bizzozero, 1889, and Dantschakoff, 1908a and b). The difference between birds and mammals may be due to the existence of a large yolk sac in birds and a reduction to a rudimentary condition in mammals. Dantschakoff observed that the liver of the normal chick embryo was not a hematopoietic organ, but according to Haff (1914) it does have such a function for both erythrocytes and granulocytes. The endothelial cells of the liver sinusoids proved to be the point of origin by way of a "large lymphocyte" for the different cell types. Wislocki (1943) observed that in a species of monkey that had adapted the placenta to the function of a hematopoietic organ, the liver had been relieved of this function and showed no blood-cell development. The pancreas of the chick at 19 days of incubation is packed with heterophils. Whether this organ serves as a hematopoietic center or as a storage depot for the granulocytes produced by spleen and bone marrow has not been determined. It was noted by Mrs. Effie M. Denington, a member of the staff of this Laboratory who made these observations, that, among different embryos, there is wide variability in the number of heterophils present.

EMBRYO BONE MARROW

Certain differences between bone-marrow formation in birds and in mammals has been pointed out by Hamilton (1952), who says (p. 508):
"There is never any independent epiphysial center of ossification in long bones of birds, as there is in mammals. The ends of the bones remain cartilaginous for awhile and provide for

141

FIGURE 319.—Embryo bone marrow. Composite from two slides. Embryos incubated 11 days 21 hours. 1,370×.

1   Primordial osteogenic cell in mitosis, late anaphase.
2   This cell resembles a metagranuloblast except for the *Hof*. Contains a few small magenta bodies.
3, 4   Small mature osteoblasts.
5   Large young osteoblast.
6   Two small young osteoblasts clumped closely together.
7   Early mononuclear osteoclast.
8   Large mononuclear osteoclast.
9   Binuclear osteoclast.
10   Multinuclear osteoclast indented by three cells of the granulocyte series.
11   Multinuclear osteoclast.

12   Part of a multinuclear osteoclast showing a magenta sphere near the upper edge.
13   Granuloblast indenting an osteoclast.
14   Heterophil promyelocyte.
15   Heterophil metamyelocyte.
16–18   Mature granulocytes. Some show degradation of the rods.
19   Early polychromatic embryo erythrocyte.
20   Late polychromatic embryo erythrocyte.
21, 22   Mature embryo erythrocyte of the primary erythrocyte type.
23   Mature embryo erythrocyte of the later generations type.
24   A pinched-off protoplasmic mass.

142

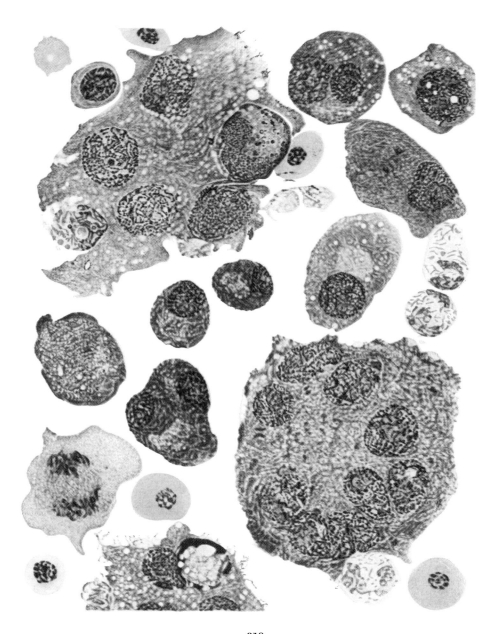

319

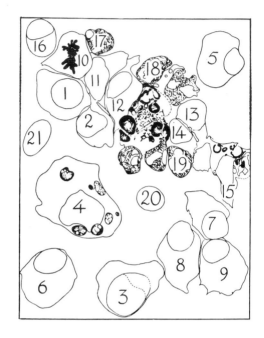

FIGURE 320.—Embryo bone marrow. Composite made from 3 places on the same slide—the long cluster of cells from 1 area, 6 cells from a nearby area, and 3 from another area.   Embryo incubated 12 days.   Nearly the same age as embryo used for preceding plate, yet definitely more advanced in development.   1,370×.

1–3   Primordial osteogenic cells.   Cell 2 is more differentiated than 1 and 3.

4   Primordial osteogenic cell with 2 magenta granules and 5 magenta spheres.

5–9   Large young osteoblasts.

10   A primordial osteogenic cell or granuloblast in mitosis, early anaphase.

11, 12   Metagranuloblasts.   The identification could have been made more certain had they been fixed in their spherical shape.

13, 14   Probably belong to the granulocyte series.

15   A cell with magenta spheres in the cytosome.

16   Heterophil mesomyelocyte.

17–19   All these cells are mature heterophil granulocytes.

20   Late polychromatic erythrocyte with fractured cytosome, a technic artifact.

21   Mature embryo erythrocyte of a later generation.

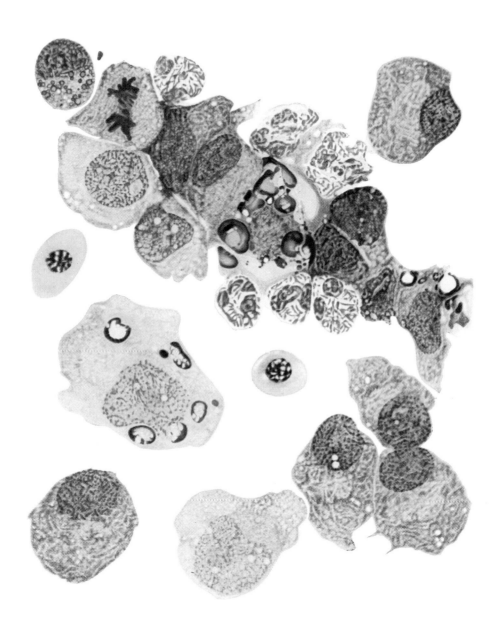

320

FIGURE 321.—Embryo bone marrow.　Embryo incubated 20 days.　1,370×.

1–6	Granuloblasts, all at about the same stage of development.
7, 8	Heterophil mesomyelocytes.
9–11	Heterophil granulocytes with one nuclear lobe.
12–14	Mature heterophil granulocytes with more than one lobe.
15, 16	Eosinophil granulocytes with one nuclear lobe.
17	Mature or nearly mature basophil granulocyte.
18–20	Early polychromatic erythrocytes.
21	Mid-polychromatic erythrocyte.
22, 23	Mature definitive erythrocytes.
24, 25	Erythrocytes showing magenta rings and a rod of heterophils that fell on top of the red cell when the smear was made.
26	Thromboblast.
27	Degenerated thrombocyte.
28	Lymphocyte.
29	Naked nucleus.
30	Smudged nucleus.
31	Partially smudged primordial osteogenic cell.

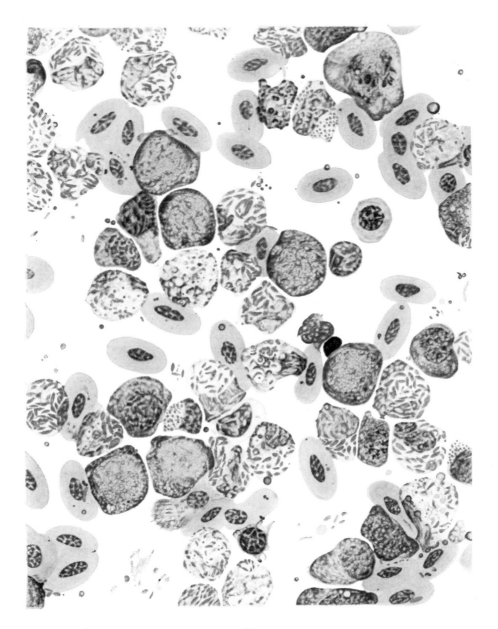

321

FIGURES 322–328.—Embryo bone-marrow cells and serum. 2,470×.

322 Stained serum fluid and granules that almost always cover the cells in embryo bone-marrow smears. Embryo incubated 19 days 18 hours. Figures 319, 320, and 321 drawn with these granules and stained serum omitted.

323 A large young osteoblast, not as typical as those shown in figure 320. Embryo incubated 14 days 11 hours.

324 Primordial osteogenic cell. Some vacuoles with magenta crescents. Embryo incubated 11 days 21 hours.

325 Slightly smudged primordial osteogenic cell. Same slide as in preceding figure.

FIGURES 326, 327: *Mononuclear osteoclasts. Same slide as in figure* 324.

326 Faint acidophilic material filling the cytoplasmic spaces on the upper left side of the nucleus is characteristic of osteoclasts from adult bone marrow. Compare with figure 398.

327 Two magenta spheres at the tip of the cell.

328 Mononuclear osteoclast with numerous magenta spheres. At the left are acidophilic bodies characteristic of the osteoclast. Embryo incubated 16 days 19 hours.

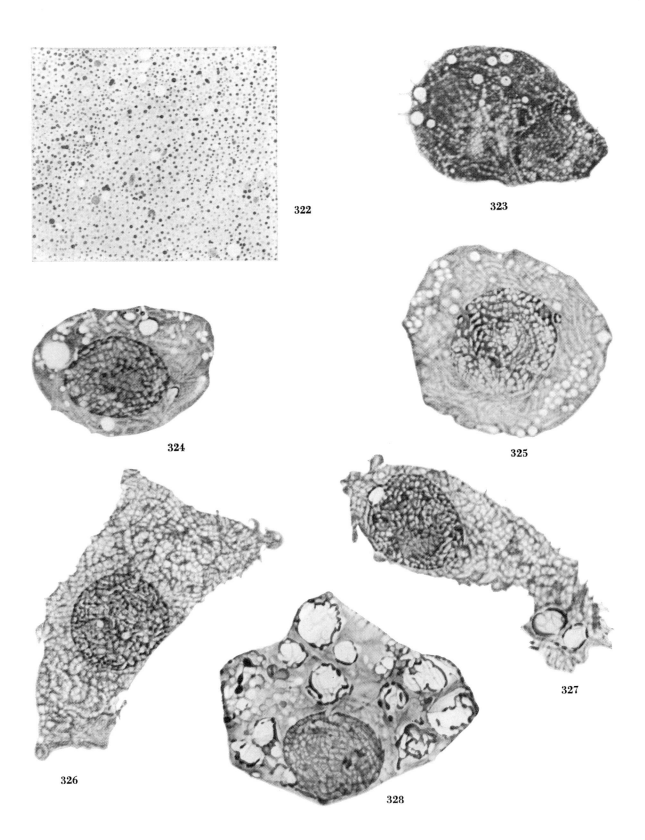

322

323

324

325

326

327

328

149

growth in length, but they are eventually ossified and united with the shaft as the marrow cavity of the latter extends out into them. . . .

". . . The marrow cavity is enlarged by the chondrolytic action of all the vascular elements, but chiefly by the walls of the budding blood vessels. As the chondrocytes are liberated from their enclosing matrix, they rapidly degenerate and are apparently not converted into marrow cells as previously believed; the cells of the marrow are presumably brought in from the mesenchyme and periosteum by the intrusive blood vessels.

"In birds, calcification does not precede absorption of the cartilage, as it does in mammals, until the greater part of the marrow cavity is formed. The cones of cartilage, referred to above, that are continuous with the articular cartilages, are absorbed about ten days after hatching."

The histologic details of cartilage and bone formation in the appendages of the embryo chick have been described by Dantschakoff (1909b). The marrow cavity appears in the humerus, tibia and femur on the eighth to ninth day of incubation. She finds that the initial perforation into the region of the marrow cavity comes from the action of osteoclasts breaking through the thin wall of newly formed bone. The opening permits the entrance of surrounding mesenchyme cells.

She divides marrow cavity production into two phases (p. 876):

"In der Entwicklung des Knochenmarks bei den Vögeln gibt es eine gewisse, ziemlich lange, vom 9, bis 12. Tage dauernde Periode, während welcher seine Struktur und seine Differenzierungsprozesse sich so sehr von dem endgültigen Zustand am Ende des fetalen Lebens unterscheiden, dass es wohl berechtigt ist, wenn ich diese Periode von den übrigen trenne, und das Mark während derselben als primitives Knochenmark bezeichne. Das hauptsachlichste Unterscheidungsmerkmal dieser Periode ist das vollständige Fehlen einer Blutbildung in den Gefässen, diese letzteren dienen zu dieser Zeit bloss zur Ernährung des Gewebes und enthalten zirkulierendes Blut, welches aus mehr oder weniger reifen Elementen besteht. . . ."[1]

The description of these first vessels is as follows (p. 877):

"Die Blutgefässe haben im primären Knochenmark eine sehr charakteristische Lage. In der Mitte, parallel der Längsachse der Markhöhle, verläuft eine Arterie, die sich in den äussersten Teilen der Höhle stark erweitert und dann in zwei noch breitere dünnwandige Venen übergeht. Ein Unterschied im Inhalt der beiden Gefässe existiert vorläufig nicht. Die Kapillaren sind spärlich."[2]

The histogenesis of bone has been a secondary consideration in this study, but osteoblasts and osteoclasts were encountered during the search for early stages of blood-cell development.

When the femur of a chicken, incubated about 12 days, is split open so that a plug of marrow projects beyond the spicules of bone and this is touched to a slide, cells of the types shown in figures 319 and 320 are found. The embryo that produced the cells shown in figure 319 was a few hours younger than the embryo that produced figure 320. In all bone-marrow smears made at this age an abundance of serum granules as in figure 322, is always present. Numerous smears were made to get one sufficiently clear for detailed study. For this reason, the low-power drawings in figures 319 and 320 are composites. Serum granules were present in the fields from which these two plates were made but were omitted in the drawing.

The least differentiated cell in bone-marrow smears from embryos of 11 to 12 days of incubation is the type shown in cell *1* of figure 319. Figure 320 shows three additional cells belonging to this category. Cells *1* and *3* of figure 320 are typical of the early osteogenic cell and cell *2* is somewhat more differentiated. The lightly stained cytoplasm is the most characteristic feature, along with a pattern of scattered, basichromatin granules that are delicately stained.

---

[1] Translation: In the development of the bone marrow in birds there is a certain rather long period, lasting from the 9th to the 12th day, during which its structure and its process of differentiation are so distinct from the final circumstances at the end of the fetal life that there is good reason for me to separate this period from the rest, and to designate the marrow during this time as primitive bone marrow. The most important mark of distinction of this period is the complete lack of a hematopoietic process in the vessels; at this time these serve only to nourish the tissue and contain circulating blood, which consists of more or less mature elements. . . .

[2] Translation: The blood vessels have a very characteristic location in the primary bone marrow. In the middle, parallel to the longitudinal axis of the marrow cavity, there runs an artery that widens greatly in the outermost portion of the hollow and then merges into two still wider thin-walled veins. At the time there is not any distinction in the contents of the two vessels. The capillaries are scanty.

The nucleolus is visible in 2 of the 3 cells shown in figure 320.   Since primordial osteogenic cells are relatively rare, it has not been possible to study them in as wide a variety of circumstances as would be desirable.   At one time it was thought that they stained lightly because they were partially squashed, and the nuclear staining in figure 325 and in cell *31* of figure 321 may be evidence for this; but the idea has been given up because, if squashed, the chromatin should show some liquefaction.   It is agreed that they are probably delicate and easily broken, but they have been seen intact in sufficient numbers to warrant the belief that they make up a distinct cell type.

Cell *2* of figure 319 shows cytoplasmic differentiation leading toward the osteoblast or the granulocyte.   Had a nucleolus been visible, the possibility of development toward the granulocyte would have been excluded.   Cell *2* of figure 320 shows differentiation toward the osteoclast.   It is believed that both osteoblasts and osteoclasts of these cell lines arise from a common stem cell, called the primordial osteogenic cell, which, as shown in these figures, is a large cell with abundant pale-staining cytoplasm and a definite nucleolus.   At the same time osteogenic activity is taking place, myelocytes also are making their first appearance.   This cell has many features in common with the primordial osteogenic cell.   The nuclear structure of cell *2* of figure 319 resembles that of a myelocyte, but the strong mitochondrial spaces, the intense blue staining, and especially the clear area beside the nucleus indicate that it is an early osteoblast. The magenta granules are not so large as they typically are for myelocytes and there may be some question of whether they are on or in the cell; if they were in it, the fact would add weight to the idea that this was a metagranuloblast or an early promyelocyte.   In figure 320 somewhat similar cells (*11* and *12*) have been identified as metagranuloblasts and probably cells *13* and *14* are the same.

Dantschakoff (1908b) states that the bone marrow begins its blood-forming function on the 14th day of incubation.

Large young osteoblasts (cell *5* of fig. 319 and cells *5–9* of fig. 320) show their immaturity by their large size, lightly stained cytoplasm, open reticulate chromatin pattern, and clearly visible nucleoli.   Vacuoles are present in the cytosome and some of these are pushed up into the nuclear substance but they are not so abundant as in the osteoclasts.

Small mature osteoblasts (cells *3*, *4*, and *6* of fig. 319) are more differentiated than their precursors, the large young osteoblasts.   The cytoplasm stains more intensely than any other cell of the marrow.   Mitochondrial spaces are not so distinct as they were previously and the clear area adjacent to the nucleus is often masked. The nucleus retains the eccentric position it previously had but now it is smaller, and the chromatin pattern is condensed, which causes it to stain more intensely.   All these features are shown in the high-power drawing of a cell from an embryo incubated 14 days 11 hours (fig. 323).   Osteoblasts may clump as in cell *6* of figure 319 but this apparently binucleated condition does not make this an osteoclast like cell *9*.

These small cells are called mature because they are morphologically identical with cells observed adjacent to bone in sections.   They have a darkly stained cytoplasm and a distinct paranuclear area.   The texts on general histology call these blast cells, but, functionally, they are mature.[3]   They form a row along the bone spicule and produce a bone matrix.   Eventually they will be surrounded by this matrix and will rest within a lacuna; they will then be called osteocytes.

Cells *7* and *8* of figure 319 are mononuclear osteoclasts.   The appearance of the cytoplasm of one of these cells is quite different from the cytoplasm of the other; cell *8* has many orange-colored granules to the left of the nucleus and no vacuoles; cell *7* has only a few orange-colored bodies but has many vacuoles.   The binucleate cell, *9*, also has numerous vacuoles but no orange

---

[3] This Atlas may not be a suitable work in which to propose changing the name of the functional bone-producing cell from osteoblast to something more appropriate, but it does seem somewhat confusing to retain the suffix "blast" through all the developmental stages of this cell.   It is recognized that "large young osteoblast" is not an adequate substitute term for the immature stage.   Any attempt to standardize hematologic nomenclature should include all the connective-tissue derivatives, the phagocytic cells, and the cells of the circulating blood and their developmental stages, and this must come from the united efforts of many scientists.   The same confusion exists in assigning terms to the developmental stages of the osteoclast.   They could be called osteoclastblasts and osteoclastcytes, but these terms are awkward.   For the present the stages are separated on the basis of the number of nuclei, on the assumption that the number is a fair measure of the stage of differentiation.

bodies; the multinucleate cell, *10*, has both; cell *11*, which is similar to *10*, has neither. The cell in figure 326 is shown under high magnification to reveal the orange bodies in greater detail. These characters are present in some cells, and are absent from others. This is true not only in the embryo but also in the adult bone marrow (figs. 398 and 399). Regardless of these variations the bone marrow of the bird contains but a single type of giant cell, the osteoclast, whereas in mammalian bone marrow there are two types—the one just mentioned and the megakaryocyte, which produces platelets. Nucleoli found in the binucleate and mononucleate stages of development are still retained in the nuclei of the fully differentiated osteoclasts of bone marrow from adult birds.

A conspicuous nucleolus, characteristic of the osteoclast, may be found also in tissue culture of this cell (Hancox, 1946). This author expressed the opinion that the multinucleated condition of this type of giant cell arose by a fusion of cells, rather than by multiple division of a nucleus within a single cell.

The cytoplasm of some multinucleate osteoclasts contains magenta-colored bodies. Some of these bodies have irregular shapes; some, like the example in cell *4*, of figure 320, are spherical; and some—see those between cells *12* and *14* of figure 320—are masses of stainable substance without definite form.

A series of mononuclear osteoclasts have been drawn under high power in order to give a closer view of this substance. Figure 326 is a young osteoclast showing the characteristic vacuolization of the cytoplasm, but without magenta-colored strands. In figure 324 a slight amount of this material exists in the form of curved bars concentric to the vacuole walls. Two spheres are shown in the lower tip of figure 327; the magenta bodies contained within them are not as definitely an integral part of the cell as are the curved bars in figure 324. A rather extreme condition is shown in figure 328, where many vacuoles contain many, twisted threads of this substance, but more important is the fact that at the left side of the cell this substance appears to be undergoing a transition to the typical orange masses characteristic of osteoclasts generally.

The magenta substance seemed to have a predilection for osteoclasts even in the early stages (cell *15*, fig. 320). This was not always the case, however, and other cell types might show vacuoles with colored strands of this type. These magenta masses did not appear in sectioned material, which suggested that they are artifacts but did not prove it.

Sometimes magenta masses occur in the serum outside the osteoclasts. Since they appear to merge with the serum, it is possible that serum condensations on the cells at the time the slide is made could account for all these irregular magenta-stained bodies but certainly this is not a convincing conclusion at present.

Another possibility considered was that this substance represented a dissolved cartilaginous matrix taken up by the osteoclasts, or that cells containing this substance represented hypertrophied and degenerating cartilage cells liberated into the expanding marrow cavity. Cartilage at the end of the femur was pressed hard against the slide in making the smears but no cells were found with a morphology that would support the idea that magenta-colored masses and strands arose from cartilage cells. In fact no evidence was obtained by the smear method that cartilage cells were liberated into the marrow cavity after the cartilage was dissolved. By the section method, Dantschakoff (1909b) observed that viable cartilage cells survived after the lacunae broke down. She stated (p. 874):

"Die Knorpelzellen, die dabei aus ihren Kapseln befreit werden, bieten besonders bei dem ersten Auftreten der Markhöhle keinerlei Anzeichen von Degeneration. Sie bleiben als runde helle Zellen zwischen den Elementen des von aussen eindringenden Mesenchymgewebes liegen. Einige von ihnen, die dem Rande der Höhle unmittelbar anliegen, zeigen sogar im Gegenteil mitotische Teilungsfiguren. . . ." [4]

Concerning their later history, she says (p. 882):

". . . Die aus den Kapseln befreiten Knorpelzellen vermischen sich in der engsten Weise mit den Elementen des in dasselbe Gebiet eindringenden jungen Mesenchyms. Bei ihrer allmählichen Entfernung von der Knorpelgrenze scheinen sie sich zu strecken und Ausläufer zu bilden.

---

[4] Translation: The cartilage cells which thus become free of their capsule do not give any sign of degeneration especially at the first emergence of the marrow cavity. They persist as round clear cells among the elements of the mesenchyme tissue that is penetrating from the outside. On the contrary, some of them, lying right against the edge of the hollow, exhibit mitotic division forms.

Ähnliche Bilder lassen mich annehmen, dass die sich befreienden Knorpelzellen an der Ausbildung des Knochenmarkstromas aktiv teilnehmen können. Mit Sicherheit kann man bloss ihre unmittelbare Teilnahme an der Blutbildung verneinen. Es ist aber sehr schwer, etwas bestimmtes über ihr weiteres Schicksal auszusagen, weil sie ja wenigstens zum Teil, wie gesagt, allmählich alle histologischen Merkmale der umbebenden Mesenchymzellen annehmen und infolgedessen nicht mehr erkannt werden können." [5]

Granulocytes in all stages of development from granuloblast to mature heterophil are found in figures 319 and 320. The developmental stages will not be described here since they are to be discussed fully under adult bone marrow, but one characteristic noted at this time is the tendency of heterophils, whether they be immature or mature, to clump with other cells. Three heterophils lie within marginal depressions of the osteoclast, cell *10* of figure 319, and in figure 320 cells of various types, including heterophils, have clumped together. Developmental stages of erythrocytes do not clump. Fennel (1947) reports (p. 237) that "Giant . . . cells frequently give rise to one or more granulocytes by the production of cellular blebs. Such blebs ultimately pulled away from the surface and became free. Giant cells under other conditions fragmented to form thrombocytelike cells." The cellular details shown in his drawings of this process taken from vital-stained preparations are not sufficient to permit determination of whether his giant cell was an osteoclast, a macrophage, or a clump of cells. Nothing has been observed in this study to indicate that any type of giant cell ever produces thrombocytes or granulocytes.

The marrow, during embryonic life, is involved primarily in the production of granulocytes and erythrocytes, and although probably more erythrocytes than granulocytes are actually produced, it appears to be the other way around because the erythrocytes are discharged into the circulating blood and the granulocytes are held in depots until after hatching. A study of the whole matter of relative production rates in various hematopoietic organs should be carried out. It should include a study of the yolk sac. Hematopoiesis in the yolk sac has been omitted from this study for two reasons—first, it does not lend itself to the smear method and, second, it has been covered by the extensive writings of Dantschakoff (1908b) on sectioned material and of Sabin (1920) on living preparations. The importance of using the smear method for a study of erythropoiesis and granulopoiesis in the case of the pigeon has been emphasized by McDonald (1939), who says (p. 293), ". . . The chief advantage of the imprint method is that it brings out the finer structural features, especially those of the nucleus, which are so important in critical studies of immature cells. . . ."

Granuloblasts are much more abundant in the bone marrow before hatching (cells *1–6*, fig. 321) than after. Six of them are shown in one field and they occur in the spleen at this age (fig. 330) in the same high concentration as in bone marrow. Actually cells *2* and *4* are the least differentiated; the nucleus lies in the center of the cell and the rim of cytoplasm is narrow and stains intensely blue. The remaining cells show definite changes leading toward the metagranuloblast—the nuclei have a slightly eccentric position, some of them show points of chromatin condensation, and the cytoplasm is partially broken up by mitochondrial rods. At the metagranuloblast stage, which is not represented on this plate, the cytosome shows vacuoles and inclusions by which a reasonably accurate guess can be made as to the type of granulocyte the cell will be when it is mature. This is not the case in the blast forms shown in cells *1* to *6*.

Cell *7* of figure 321 is classified as a heterophil mesomyelocyte but actually it has barely passed the promyelocyte stage. The magenta rings, the indefinite boundary of the nucleus, and the pale-orange precursor bodies are all present in cell *7*, but in addition there are a few darkly stained orange bodies. When they have elongated, the orange bodies will be the definitive rods. Their presence is the basis for calling the cell a mesomyelocyte. Cell *8* is also a mesomyelocyte but it is somewhat older than cell *7*. All the characteristics of the promyelocyte are still present but

[5] Translation: The cartilage cells released from the capsule mingle in the most intimate way with the elements of the young mesenchyme that are penetrating into the same territory. As they gradually get farther from the cartilaginous boundary they seem to stretch out and to form outrunners. Similar pictures lead me to assume that the cartilage cells that are freeing themselves can take an active part in the formation of the bone marrow stroma. One can with surety only deny their direct participation in hematopoiesis. But it is very hard to state anything certain about their future destiny, since, as has been said, they gradually take on, at least to some extent, all the histological earmarks of the surrounding mesenchyme cells, and hence cannot be recognized any longer.

more of the definitive bodies are visible. Some of the bodies appear in the round form and some in the rod form. The total number is less than half of the number found in the mature heterophil. A metamyelocyte is shown in the heterophil above cell *28* of figure 321. This cell does not yet have a full complement of rods but the nucleus has condensed until its boundary is distinct.

Other cells (*9–11*) are mature, or nearly so, but since they contain but a single nuclear lobe they would be classed as juveniles or as band cells in mammalian blood terminology. Mature heterophils are abundant throughout the smear and some of those having more than one lobe are designated by the numbers *12–14*.

Eosinophils also are held in depots until after hatching. Two cells each with a single nuclear lobe are indicated by numbers *15* and *16* (fig. 321) and, in the same field, part of one other cell is shown at the border. With the exception of cell *15,* all these cells are of the small type that, in the bone marrow, is considered to be the source of the small eosinophils sometimes found in the circulating blood (figs. 181–183).

The basophil (fig. 321, *17*) is an adult cell in which the distortion due to action of water on the granules is as great as in the circulating blood, and the poor stainability of the nucleus is as evident here in the bone marrow of the embryo as it was found to be in the circulating blood of the adult (fig. 190).

In this field of bone marrow, no erythroblasts are present but there are three early polychromatic erythrocytes (fig. 321, *18–20*). These examples show considerable range in size, yet all are already older than erythroblasts. Cell *21* is a good example of a mid-polychromatic erythrocyte. There are no late polychromatic erythrocytes in this field, and the remaining erythrocytes are mature. It is assumed, not that these mature erythrocytes represent cells held in storage, ready to be discharged later, but that they came into the bone marrow by way of nutrient vessels from outside.

Cell *26* (fig. 321) has been identified as a thromboblast. It has the characteristics of the early stage of this cell line in its densely stained nucleus and cytoplasm. Had the cell not been pressed out of shape during the making of the smear, its identification would have been more certain, but it does not have the characteristics

typical of the erythrocyte or the granulocyte line. Previously it was stated that the erythrocytes and the thrombocytes of an early embryo were difficult to separate; but with increasing age of the embryo, separation becomes easier, and in the adult marrow there was relatively little confusion.

Naked nuclei and smudged cells (fig. 321, *29* and *30*) need no additional explanation, and the primordial osteogenic cell (*31*) has already been discussed. The most important cell remaining for consideration is *28,* which has been called a lymphocyte. It appears to be a small cell undergoing bleb formation. The nucleus is too large for the definitive thrombocyte; moreover, if it were a thrombocyte the structure of the nucleus would not have been so clear cut and definite at this stage of cytoplasmic disintegration.

EMBRYO SPLEEN

The spleen is an organ that develops quite early in embryonic life; according to Hamilton (1952), it appears on the last half of the fourth day. Efforts to procure satisfactory impression smears before the beginning of the eighth day were unsuccessful because the cells were so fragile that all broke, and the naked nuclei were covered by a layer of blue-stained tissue fluid. The smears resembled that portion of figure 329 where there are naked and ruptured nuclei and strands of dissolved chromatin; therefore no intact, recognizable cells could be seen. By the eighth day some cells remained unbroken in carefully made smears. Why cells should be delicate in early embryonic life and much tougher at older ages is not known; cytologically they appear identical at both ages, and the size does not change much with age. All the serum granules and disturbing elements in the smear were included when the drawing (fig. 329) from the spleen of the 8-day-old embryo was prepared.

Danschakoff (1916a) reviewed the early development of the avian spleen and reaffirmed her observations on the function of lymphocytes as the progenitors of other cell types. Antibodies against adult spleen tissue were produced by transplanting pieces of the spleen to the allantois of the embryo.

A review of the differences in the histology of the avian and mammalian spleens has been given by Lucas et al. (1954).

Whereas the embryo bone marrow produced both granulocytes and erythrocytes in about equal numbers, in the embryo spleen it is the granulocyte that is the dominant cell. After hatching, the spleen becomes predominately a lymphocytogenic and monocytogenic organ. The shift in the cell picture is shown graphically by a comparison of figure 329 (8 days of incubation), figure 330 (12½ days of incubation), and figure 331 (35 days after hatching). In the first of this series of three plates are two typical metagranuloblasts (cells 1 and 2) and in the same field are numerous others (cells 3–6) that are covered too heavily with stained serum to show the details of their structures.

The next stage in development of the granulocyte is the promyelocyte, in which vacuoles and magenta granules and rings are present in the cytoplasm adjacent to an eccentric nucleus. Most of these characteristics are to be found in cell 7, and lightly stained orange spheres are present also. This cell has been classified as a promyelocyte. Had some of the spheres taken on the dense coloration that occurs antecedent to the transformation into definitive rods, the cell would have been classed as a mesomyelocyte.

Cell 8 clearly fulfills the characteristic of the mesomyelocyte. This particular cell has no definitive rods but now there are present numerous darkly stained orange spheres that represent the precursor substance. In this cell the nucleus has become smaller and the chromatin more condensed. Other developmental stages are not shown in the field; cell 9 and the cell below 8 have already differentiated into the mature form.

Cell 11 of figure 329 is an erythroblast; the chromatin pattern of the nucleus and the faint nucleolus are the features which most readily identify it. The unnumbered blast cell at the bottom of the plate is probably of the same type but the details of its structure are masked in part by the serum. There are at least five small embryo thrombocytes in the field; two of them are indicated at 12. One cell (10), in the prophase of mitosis, cannot be identified because the cytoplasmic structure is not sufficiently distinctive and the nuclear pattern has been lost in the process of cell division.

The interval between 193 and 299 hours of incubation has wrought developmental changes that advance the architecture of the spleen to a level that will be maintained up through the hatching process. Since a low-power drawing had been made of the bone marrow both at 12 days and at 20 days of incubation, it was originally planned that a low power drawing of the spleen would also be made at these ages, but a study of spleen impression smears made after 12 days of incubation showed that no significant changes had taken place in cell types; therefore a drawing at 20 days of incubation has been omitted. The spleen at 8 days of incubation is at about the same level of development as bone marrow 4 days later, as far as the general appearance of the cells in the smears is concerned.

When the spleen has reached its 12-day level of development, blast forms of granulocytes become relatively rare. Only two examples (cells 1 and 2) are shown in figure 330. One is shown only in part, but the narrow, dense blue-stained ring of cytoplasm in cell 2 is typical of the structure of such cells in the hatched chick. Most of the cells of this line in figure 330 have reached the metagranuloblast and promyelocyte stages of development. However, figure 330 cannot be taken as representing an exact replica of what every slide examined at 299 hours of incubation will show because among smears from a dozen embryos there will be definite shifts in the dominant cell type of a particular series. This might be accounted for on the basis of slight differences in developmental rates that always exist among embryos or on the basis of cycles in cell production. The latter would agree with the suggestions given in the literature for blood-cell development in the yolk sac and bone marrow.

Cells 3–6 (fig. 330) are identified as metagranuloblasts of the heterophil line but they are not so clearly typical of this stage as is the eosinophil metagranuloblast (cell 11). A question might be raised regarding cells 3–6, in which the nuclear structure, instead of retaining the delicate, lightly stained pattern of the granuloblast, shows an increased density of staining and clumping of chromatin, which is characteristic of the early erythrocyte line; had nucleoli been visible in these cells as in cell 12, these 4 cells would have been called erythroblasts. One expects to find in the metagranuloblast stage an eccentric, faintly stained nucleus that has an indefinite boundary between it and the adjacent highly vacuolated cytosome.

Cells 7 to 10 show the precursor spheres from which develop the densely stained orange bodies. In cell 7 they are barely visible as light orange bodies from the vacuoles produced in the metagranuloblast stage. In cell 9 the spheres are slightly more intensely colored. In cells 8 and 10 a few orange spheres are almost as darkly stained as in the mesomyelocyte stage, but in none of the four cells (7–10) have the orange spheres taken on the deep eosin coloration that precedes the elongation of a sphere into a definite rod. Description would probably be facilitated if names were given to the lightly and the darkly stained orange spheres; when a thorough cytological and cytochemical study of rod production has been made, logical names will suggest themselves.

Cell 12 of figure 330 is an erythroblast and is clearly identified by its typical structure as belonging to the blast stage of development. Such cells are relatively rare at this age. Numerous early polychromatic erythrocytes are present. Cells 13 and 14 are examples; so is the cell located between 3 and 4. Cells 15 to 17 are examples of mid-polychromatic erythrocytes, and cells 18 to 21 of late polychromatic erythrocytes. There are cells in the field other than those designated by number; they also belong to these various groups. Mitosis, at least in the embryo, can take place in late polychromatic erythrocytes (cells 23–27) and, of course, at earlier stages of development also (cell 22). It would be interesting to follow the plasmosome nucleolus during mitosis and note how it is reconstituted during the interkinetic period, but the technics used here are not suitable for such a study.

Thrombocytes are less common in smears from hematopoietic organs than from circulating blood and it may be that this is due to the delay in opening the embryo and dissecting out the organ before the smear is made. It is quite possible that in fixed and sectioned material some thrombocytes undergo degeneration and become cells that resemble small lymphocytes or naked nuclei. A reinvestigation of thrombocyte development from stained sections might help to clarify the stages in thrombocyte differentiation. Cell 29 (fig. 330) is a thrombocyte of medium size and looks somewhat like figure 289, except that the chromatin is less clumped. Typical small thrombocytes are shown in the cells numbered 30 in figure 330.

Smudged cells are present in every smear and usually are more numerous than the one example shown in figure 330, 31.

BLOOD CHANGES AT HATCHING

During the 24 hours after the hatching of the chicks dramatic alterations occur in the circulating blood, spleen, and bone marrow. The most complete change appears in the spleen, where a general outpouring of heterophils is followed by a massive development of lymphocytes and monocytes. Within several days following hatching the bone marrow becomes an organ that produces, predominately, erythrocytes, thrombocytes, and granulocytes. No extensive series of illustrations covering these events has been prepared, chiefly because in any period of rapid transition what may be seen at one moment in one chick may be entirely different in another.

Notes were taken on smears from a group of chicks ranging from a few hours to several days after hatching. The actual protocol taken at the time probably tells the story as well as a more studied rewrite of the same thing. We recommend a similar study to anyone who has attained some proficiency in cell identification and is grasping for a feeling of the dynamics of development and balance as it occurs hidden from our usual vision.

Throughout this transition period there was considerable variability between birds and it would be necessary to use a larger number of chicks at each age to determine the exact typical sequence of events. At each period usually four chicks were used.

1 TO 3 HOURS POSTHATCHING

Circulating blood.—Only in an occasional chick was the number of white blood cells anywhere near a normal ratio; in most cases, the number was definitely below normal. This was especially true in regard to the lymphocytes, monocytes, and basophils. The predominant cell in the early chick blood, just after hatching, is the heterophil. The other cells come into the picture at a later age. Even the heterophil, immediately after hatching, may be absent from the blood (fig. 230). Immature stages of erythrocytes are usually present.

FIGURE 329.—Embryo spleen. Embryo incubated 8 days 1 hour. At this age it is difficult to obtain a good smear because of the great fragility of the cells and the masking by the stained serum fluid and granules. 1,370×.

1, 2	Metagranuloblasts.	10	Immature cell in mitosis, prophase.
3–6	Metagranuloblasts in which the cytoplasm is masked by the overlying stained serum.	11	Embryonic erythroblast.
		12	Embryonic thrombocytes.
7	A heterophil promyelocyte.	13, 14	Broken cells with liberated naked nuclei.
8	Heterophil mesomyelocyte with many eosinophilic spheres, some light and some dark.	15	Strands of chromatin from the nuclei of cells broken when the slide was made.
9	Mature heterophil.		

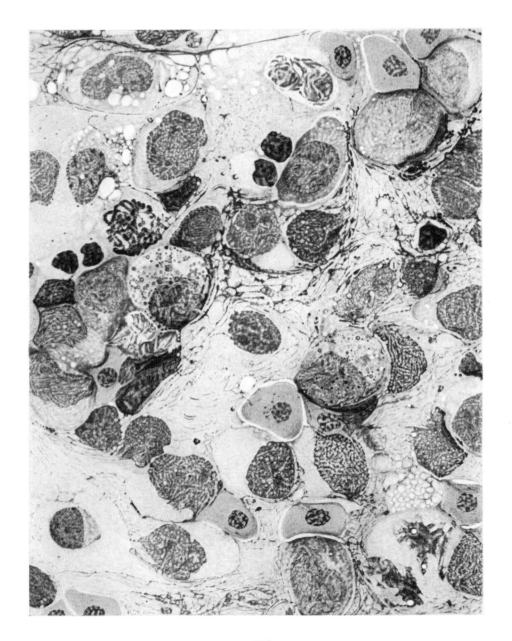

329

FIGURE 330.—Embryo spleen.   Embryo incubated 12 days 11 hours.   1,370×

1, 2 Granuloblasts.
3–6 Metagranuloblasts.
7–10 Heterophil promyelocytes.
11 Eosinophil metagranuloblast.
12 Erythroblast.
13, 14 Early polychromatic erythrocytes.
15–17 Mid-polychromatic erythrocytes.
18–21 Late polychromatic erythrocytes.
22 Mid–polychromatic erythrocyte in mitosis, probably early anaphase.

FIGURES 23–27: *Late polychromatic erythrocytes in mitosis.*

23 Early prophase.
24 Late prophase, nuclear membrane broken down.
25, 26 Late prophase, uncoiling of spireme thread.
27 Late anaphase.
28 Late embryo thromboblast or early embryo thrombocyte.
29 Medium embryo thrombocyte.
30 Small embryo thrombocytes.
31 Smudged cell.

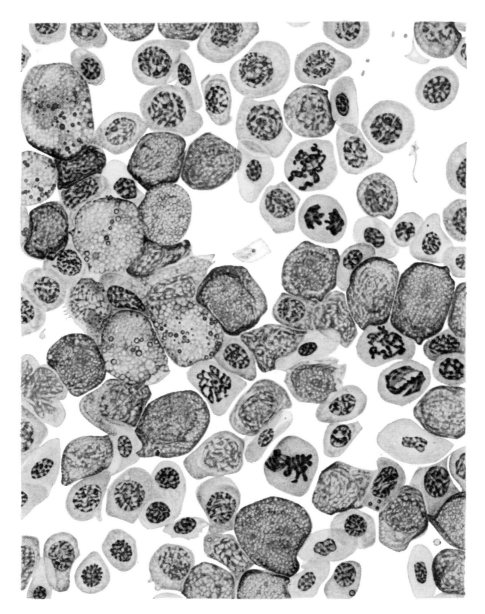

330

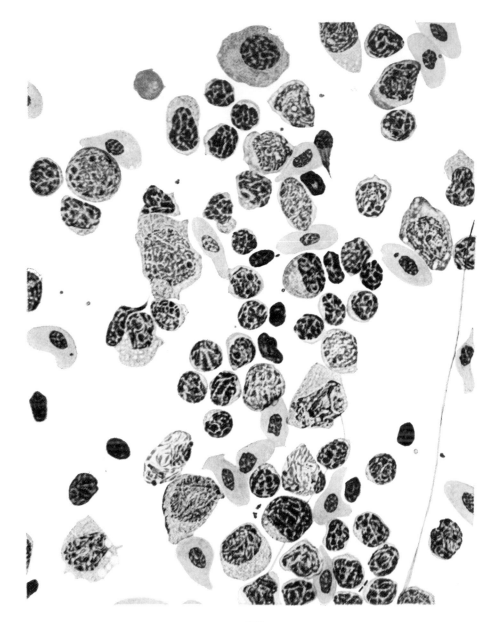

331

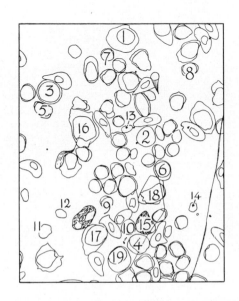

FIGURE 331.—Spleen of chick 35 days after hatching.   1,370×.

1 Early immature plasmacyte.	12–14 Naked thrombocyte nuclei.
2 Late immature plasmacyte.	15 Mature heterophil.
3 Immature lymphocyte.	16 Possibly a monoblast or early immature monocyte
4–6 Mature lymphocytes, medium size.	17, 18 Early immature monocytes.
7–10 Mature lymphocytes, small size.	19 Late immature monocyte.
11 Naked lymphocyte nucleus.	

Spleen.—Apparently at the time of hatching, and very rapidly thereafter, the spleen discharges its heterophils; thus, in this period of 1 to 3 hours, one can find a spleen filled with numerous mature heterophils; in other cases, at the same age, there will be very few heterophils, and in their place will be early eosinophil metagranuloblasts, and even the early lymphoid series is making its appearance. At this period of transition it is quite common to see numerous macrophages in the spleen. At this age and even up to 24 hours of age there are many opportunities to study the development of the eosinophil and the lymphocyte.

Bone marrow.—Of the 4 chicks used at this age, 2 showed numerous late heterophils, and 2 did not. There appears to be a transitional change in the bone marrow. It probably begins somewhat earlier than 1 to 3 hours after hatching, because the bone marrow is already taking over the hematopoietic function in regard to granulocytes that the spleen is giving up. In addition, in the bone marrow one finds numerous examples of the red cells from early to late stages of development. Mononucleated osteoclasts were always present in these early stages, and were particularly numerous in one case where very few heterophils were present in the bone marrow. Osteoblasts also were visible, but in those smears where heterophils are numerous, osteoblasts are relatively rare. The third cellular element coming up at this time is the thrombocyte series. Just as early erythroblasts may be found, so also may early thromboblasts be identified. These are relatively large cells and have a characteristic punctate, strongly granular nucleus that stains more intensely than the erythroblasts. Most of these cells, however, contain a well-developed nucleolus. This structure aids in the identification of the cell, but in the thromboblast it is often masked and covered over by strongly stained chromatin spheres. The thrombocyte as it gets older has, typically, a very dark blue cytoplasm and frayed edges. In these early bone marrow smears the transitional stages down to the small thrombocyte can be followed. The fully formed thrombocyte, however, does not have the form present in the circulating blood because of degeneration of the cytoplasm that takes place during fixation. Cells of the thrombocyte series are never numerous in the bone marrow but some are always present.

8 TO 12 HOURS POSTHATCHING

Circulating blood.—At this stage there may be some holdover of what was found at 1 to 3 hours, because the dominant type of cell among the white blood cells is the heterophil. Sometimes the white blood cells are few in relation to the red cells and sometimes they are at about the normal ratio. At this age the number of heterophils is generally out of proportion to the other white blood cells and the lymphocytes and monocytes are definitely fewer than they will be later. It is characteristic of the circulating blood of the recently hatched chick that the red blood cells show a wide range of immature stages of development, but predominantly

the stages most commonly seen begin at about the mid-polychromatic erythrocytt and continue on to maturity (fig. 230). One gathers the impression by comparing the development of red blood cells as seen in the bone marrow with that seen in the circulating blood that there is a tendency for the bone marrow to throw out the cells at about the mid-polychromatic erythrocyte stage or a little earlier. Later stages are present in the bone marrow but cells of older ages do not dominate the picture.

Spleen.—In the 4 chicks used at this age (8 to 12 hours) there was a wide range in the number of heterophils but in general they had almost completely disappeared and in their place were numerous eosinophils in about the mid-stage of development. Many macrophages were present and there was an increase in number of small lymphocytes. In another chick at this same age there was a moderate number of mature heterophils with developing eosinophils and developing basophils; in the third chick there were numerous early heterophils, practically no eosinophils, and some early basophils; and in the fourth there was a mixture of mid-heterophils and early eosinophils. In spite of this variability, there still exists an extensive discharge of the heterophils into the circulating blood. This is followed by a wave of development of eosinophils and perhaps in some cases an additional group of heterophils and basophils. At this time, also, there is some indication that the lymphocytes are taking the dominant place that they will hold later in the spleen.

Bone marrow.—In the bone marrow of all these chicks (8 to 12 hours) there were a great many mature heterophils. This seems to be characteristic of the bone marrow at this stage and later. Almost equally conspicuous are the developing red blood cells and the scattered thrombocytes. Some small thrombocytes are present also, and one can find the developmental stages in the production of granulocytes, but these are mingled with the adult stages and are not so conspicuous as they are in the spleen.

24 HOURS POSTHATCHING

Circulating blood.—At 24 hours the white blood cells in the circulating blood are predominantly heterophils. Other cell types are present, of course, but they have not reached their usual ratio and, in many cases, lymphocytes or monocytes, or both, may be lacking or at least be so scarce that a great deal of searching is required to find them. At this stage there are abundant examples of late-developing red cells.

Spleen.—Only in 1 of the 4 chicks at this age was there even a moderate number of mature heterophils in this organ. At this stage the lymphocyte development is coming into view. This is an excellent stage at which to study lymphopoiesis: some of the cells can be traced back to lymphoblasts and to the reticular cells from which they appear to have come. Among these early lymphoid cells are some eosinophil myelocytes, usually quite early in their development. Numerous macrophages are still present.

Bone marrow.—At this stage in the bone marrow there is a variation from a very high percentage of mature heterophils to relatively few, and red blood cells are dominant. These two are always present simultaneously but the ratio varies at this age.

1 DAY 18 HOURS POSTHATCHING

Circulating blood.—At this age there is still a dominance of heterophils and a general absence of the agranulocytes in the circulating blood.

Spleen.—At this period the dominant picture is lymphoid with a variable number of heterophils, both early and late stages. Early stages of eosinophil development are present also.

Bone marrow.—In one of the specimens there were still a few primordial osteogenic cells but otherwise there was a fairly constant picture of mature granulocytes and red-cell developmental stages.

4 DAYS 18 HOURS POSTHATCHING

Circlating blood.—In one chick there was a normal blood picture and in the other there was still a predominance of granulocytes and a lag in lymphocyte development.

Bone marrow.—In both cases the bone marrow contained a great many fully developed heterophils as well as developmental stages of red cells.

5 DAYS 18 HOURS AND 6 DAYS POSTHATCHING

Circulating blood.—The chick at 5 days 18 hours showed an abnormal number of monocytes; lymphocytes were relatively few; the heterophils were not predominant; and there were some basophils. The 4 slides taken at 6 days show a fairly normal picture and a fairly normal proportion of the different types of white cells.

Spleen.—In every case the dominant picture is lymphocytogenesis with only a few granulocytes developing. In some slides, stages in lymphocytogenesis are well shown.

Bone marrow.—All the bone-marrow slides show about the same cell types as do those for the preceding age. This is a good age for study of developmental stages along the various lines. In one slide a thromboblast was clearly seen.

8 DAYS POSTHATCHING

Circulating blood.—In most of these smears there was the usual ratio of white cells to red cells and the different types of white cells were present in their usual proportions. In one chick there was a monocytosis and many cells were smudged. This seems to be the stage at which monocytes make their appearance; some of these monocytes show the typical reticular appearance of the cytoplasm.

Spleen.—Occasionally there are some late heterophils in the spleen but it is now predominantly a lymphoid picture.

The circulating blood, 7 days posthatching, is illustrated in figure 231. The structural character of a lymphocyte, a monocyte, a heterophil, and a basophil, as well as of some thrombocytes and erythrocytes at this age, is shown. This proportion of leukocytes to erythrocytes is greater in the field selected for illustration than is usually found.

The spleen after its reorganization produces blood smears of the type seen in figure 331, which was from a chick 35 days posthatching.

The statement has been made several times that granulocytes held in hematopoietic organs of the embryo are discharged into the circulation soon after hatching. A contrary point of view has been given by Nonidez (1920) from his study on eosin-staining cells in the gonads of bantams. They were abundant in the embryo and began to disappear after hatching but he concluded that the cells did not pass into the blood stream, but underwent disintegration and were taken up by special cell elements and endothelial lining cells of blood vessels. In the protocol numerous macrophages were noted in the spleen at 1 to 3 hours, 8 hours, and 24 hours after hatching (which agrees with the observations made by Nonidez on the tissues of the gonads), and 1 phagocytic cell was pictured in figure 317. From the data thus far accumulated it would appear that both gonad and spleen tissues are acting similarly, but additional study is needed to determine whether the granulocytes of the embryo organs after hatching are the definitive cells of the circulating blood or whether all the masses of embryo cells are destroyed and only those developed in the bone marrow after hatching reach the circulating blood. Danschakoff (1916a) observed in sectioned material what has been reported here that, after hatching, earlier leukopoietic functions are reduced and the spleen becomes chiefly a lymphocyte-producing and an erythrocyte-destroying organ.

Plasma cells are rare in the normal chicken

but may be seen in spleen and bone marrow occasionally. According to T. Makinodan (personal communication), plasma cells are abundant in the spleen under experimental conditions. These cells are only rarely observed in our stock of untreated adult chickens. The pure light-blue color of the cytoplasm and the few mitochondrial spaces of the early immature plasmocyte separate it from other cells. Other identifying features are the clear area adjacent to the nucleus and the presence of vacuoles of uniform, small size in the cytoplasm. An early immature plasmocyte with one vacuole is shown in cell *1* of figure 331. Early in the differentiation process, the nucleus shows a contraction of chromatin into large, dense clumps and the cell shows an amount of cytoplasm relative to nuclear size that exceeds the proportion found in other cells, especially at the corresponding stage of differentiation. Other cells at the same stage of development would show a reticulum of chromatin in the nucleus.

From this early stage to the late immature plasmocyte there is a diminution in size of both nucleus and cytosome (cell *2*). Usually the *Hof* is definite but often the dense blue of the cytosome masks it. A plasmocyte at this stage resembles a mature osteoblast and it has been suggested that they may have a common cell of origin. Plasmocytes and osteoblasts look so much alike that they could be confused readily in the bone marrow, but in the spleen it is assumed that osteoblasts are not present. In the bone marrow it is the clear blue color of the plasmocyte that aids in distinguishing it from the osteoblast, which takes a violet hue. The observations on the cytology of plasma cells, made by Dantschakoff (1909b) from sectioned material, agrees closely with the description given here, based on impression smears. From sections of bone marrow, she observed that plasma cells are always located inside vessels and that they became especially numerous when the bird suffered from generalized exhaustion. Irradiation by X-rays caused the formation of plasma cells in the thymus (Danschakoff, 1916b).

Lymphocytes are the dominant cells of the spleen beginning with the second day posthatching. Mjassojedoff (1926) found the spleen of the adult fowl to be predominately a lymphocyte-producing organ. This is true to a greater degree in birds than in mammals. At 35 days of age (fig. 331) developmental stages can be seen in abundance. Previous to this study of the spleen, the thymus had been examined by the smear method and drawings had been made of the changes in cell morphology from lymphoblast to small, mature lymphocyte (figs. 334–338). These cells will be described in more detail when the plates illustrating the thymus are described, but several lymphocytes in figure 331 are worthy of mention here.

Cell *3* is an immature lymphocyte; the narrow rim of cytoplasm in a cell of this size with this peculiar nuclear pattern (partly reticular and partly clumped) is typical for the young lymphocyte. Somewhat similar examples of this were found in the circulating blood (figs. 96–98) and under these conditions they were called mature lymphocytes of medium size, but as found in the young spleen they are called immature lymphocytes. This certainly appears to be an inconsistency in cell identification but it is more a reflection of the fact that in spite of a great deal having been written about the lymphocyte, we actually know less concerning its developmental stages than we do of any other leukocyte. Perhaps this is in part due to the fact that those who have written most about the lymphocyte have regarded all sizes from the largest to the smallest, including all stages of cytoplasmic and nuclear differentiation, as insignificant in comparison with the fact that the cell is totipotent in its capacity to produce other cells, and that every lymphocyte is a hemocytoblast, or common stem cell, to all other cells.

In the circulating blood of one chicken the lymphocytes may be small and in another they may be predominantly of medium size. The graph (fig. 152), based on numerous slides, shows a typical distribution curve for size. More on the size of lymphocytes will be given in chapter 6. Careful statistical studies on the relation of size to the health of the individual are needed. From studies on the thymus at least three stages of development can be recognized—lymphoblast, immature, and mature. This represents fewer subdivisions than for any other cell type. It is suggested that lymphocytes of the type shown in figures 96–98 are immature and to regard them as such makes the developmental series consistent, but we do not yet have experimental data for the circulating blood that enable us to say that, when a differential count is made, the lymphocytes of medium size with reticular nuclei should be classed as immature and only small lymphocytes with dense chromatin should be called mature.

The medium-sized lymphocytes of figure 331 (cells *4–6* as examples) show a degree of chromatin clumping intermediate between the immature lymphocyte (cell *3*) and the small lymphocyte (cells *7–10*) but the character of the cytoplasm does not change significantly from one stage to the other as seen in the spleen; however, in the lymphocytes of the thymus some differences in cytoplasmic structure did occur.

It is generally agreed in mammalian hematology that monocytes arise in the same organs where lymphocytes have their origin, and this appears to be true in birds also, but in avian species there are no lymph nodes, which are the organs chiefly responsible for lymphocytes and monocytes in mammals. The spleen of birds after hatching is a lymphogenic organ and it is not surprising that developmental stages of monocytes should also be present in this organ. In the protocol above, developmental stages of the monocytes were mentioned as occurring in the circulating blood of the young chick. Jordan's (1938) statement (p. 731) concerning the development of blood cells in the lung fish (*Protopterus ethiopicus*) is interesting: "While monocytes are probably formed in the general circulation, they may also arise in the spleen." The idea of the maturation of monocytes in the circulating blood was expressed also by Dawson (1933a). His studies of hematopoiesis were based on the amphibian, *Necturus*. In this species, some monocytes arose in the spleen but most of them differentiated in the lymphogranulopoietic aggregations scattered through the tissues.

A superficial examination of the cells in figure 331 might lead to the suggestion that large cells of the type shown at *16* are metagranuloblasts, but a closer examination shows that this is a different cell. The nucleus is a typical monocyte nucleus even at this early stage and there is no tendency toward vacuolization of the cytoplasm as in metagranuloblasts. In the early immature monocyte (cells *17–18*) there is some further condensation of the nucleus to a condition seen in many monocytes but no bodies characteristic of granulocytes appear in the cytoplasm. The late

immature stage (cell *19*) is readily recognizable as a monocyte and cells like this are commonly seen in the circulating blood. The *Hof,* azurophilic staining of the cytoplasm, and nuclear indentation have not yet appeared.

The implication was given under the discussion of thrombocytes in bone marrow that it was difficult to see how such labile cells as thrombocytes could retain their normal morphology during the procedure leading up to the fixation of tissue. Impression smears fix the cells more quickly than the average fixative, which penetrates a block of tissue relatively slowly (Underhill, 1932, and Medawar, 1941); yet even in the smear practically every thrombocyte appears as a naked nucleus (*12–14* are examples). Even *11*, which has been labeled as a naked lymphocyte nucleus because of its larger size, may actually be the nucleus of an immature thrombocyte.

A few mature heterophils may be seen in spleen smears at this age but whether they represent cells brought in by way of the splenic arteries or are cells that developed in this locus during embryonic life, and have not yet been discharged into the circulation, cannot be determined.

LYMPHOCYTOGENESIS IN THE THYMUS

Cells of the thymus have been called thymocytes but they are identical with lymphocytes, and the latter term has been used here. Wiseman (1931b and 1932) differentiated 5 stages in the cytomorphosis of lymphocytes: lymphoblast, young cell, mature cell, old cell, and degenerate cell. The classification presented for the lymphocyte series in table 2 (p. 10) includes the first 3 of these 5 stages.

Many smears were made before a satisfactory one was obtained; most of them failed to show as many intact cells as have been illustrated in figure 332 *A*, which came from an embryo incubated 9 days 4 hours. The fragility of the cells continued well past the age of figure 332 *B* (11 days 10 hours); yet in the older ages large lymphoblasts were relatively rare.

The high-power drawings (figs. 334–338) were made after searching the slide to find suitable stages in an embryo that had been incubated 14 days 11 hours. At the earlier ages, because there was so much distortion of the cells and because the serum precipitate was so dense, it was difficult to distinguish between mesenchymal cells and young lymphocytes. In 332 A no attempt has been made to place a label of lymphocyte on any of the cells, although some of them appear to be undergoing a transition from primordial (mesenchyme) tissue to lymphoblasts.

Cell 1, which is fairly well preserved, shows a faint nucleolus in the lower part of the nucleus, and other cells in the same field show nucleoli vaguely. It is this type of cell in the older chicken that would be called the reticular cell. Somewhere in the transition to the lymphoblast the nucleolus is lost, or at least it becomes hidden beneath the delicate reticular pattern of the chromatin at the surface of the nucleus. In figure 334 this is true even when the chromatin is lightly stained. As stated before, whether a nucleolus is actually present must be determined from sections but, if present, it definitely disappears before the stage of the small lymphocyte has been reached. This has been confirmed in sections by Dantschakoff (1908b and 1909a).

In Sundberg's study of lymphocytogenesis (1947) in man and other mammals, observations were made that were almost identical to those reported here for birds. She found that a reticular cell was the precursor for the lymphocyte line. The nucleus of the reticular cell showed a nucleolus, whereas this organelle if present in the lymphoblast was not visible. The reticular cell described by Sundberg closely resembles in appearance the primordial osteogenic cell of the embryo chick bone marrow (fig. 320, cells 1–4).

Broken nuclei produce long strands of stained basichromatin across the slide and sometimes it looks as if a particular strand could be traced back to the granule in the nucleus out of which it had formed a streamer (fig. 332 A, 8). Some cells (like the two to the right of cell 1) stain intensely and the chromatin is clumped, but the cells are crowded and thus fail to show clearly the type to which they belong. They resemble in a general way the amoeboid wandering cell described by Dantschakoff.

Cells from an embryo that has been incubated 11 days (fig. 332 B) were somewhat better preserved in smears than were cells taken from embryos of younger ages; hence the cells that are going to produce granulocytes can be identi-

fied. The thymus has a lesser granulopoietic function than the spleen. Cell 11 has many structural characters of the promyelocyte but the magenta masses are not the sharply defined rings and granules usually found, which might be due to the unfavorable environment in which it was fixed. Cell 12 is definitely atypical. Some might identify it as a macrophage, and cell 11 as its early stage. It also is reminiscent of the peculiar defect noted in bone marrow where large spheres and masses of magenta material were deposited in the cytosome of primordial osteogenic cells (figs. 320 and 328). Cell 12 may well be a naked nucleus surrounded by cytoplasmic residue and serum artifacts.

Cell 1 in figure 332 B closely simulates the primordial cells of 332 A but, also, it is identical in appearance with the type of cell called the lymphoblast (fig. 334). The lymphoblast decreases in size during differentiation and, although the chromatin is not clumped, it does become coarser (cells 2 and 3) and forms what is called an early phase of the immature lymphocyte; soon the forming of blocklike clumps of chromatin begins, usually at one side of the nucleus, which indicates that the differentiation process has reached the late phase of the immature stage (cells 4 and 5). Cell 5 in the circulating blood would probably be called a mature lymphocyte of medium size. Small mature lymphocytes are present at this age but none are shown in the field that has been illustrated.

The thymus at this age is not a suitable source of material for making smears and evidence for this is shown by the distortion exhibited by dividing cells 6 and 7; these may be compared with dividing cells in the spleen at 12½ days, where the mitotic figures are well preserved.

The cells shown in figures 334–338 represent a developmental series taken from the thymus when the embryo had been incubated 14 days 11 hours. Search was made for well-preserved cells. All cells as large as figure 334 had nuclei that took the stain poorly. This poor reaction has happened before with May-Grünwald Giemsa but usually there were similar cells on the same slide or equivalent slides that showed the nuclear surface well stained. With Wright's stain, cells this large and immature rarely show the nucleus properly stained.

By the methods used here a nucleolus is not visible at any stage of lymphocytogenesis although, as pointed out earlier, it is present in the primordial embryonic cell from which the lymphoblast is derived. Even if it can be demonstrated by sections that a nucleolus is present, this would not invalidate the usefulness of the smear method as a means of differentiating between the early stages of various cell lines, and for practical purposes it can be stated that, in smears, erythroblasts and thromboblasts have nucleoli and that lymphoblasts and granuloblasts do not. (For discussion of monoblasts, see Lucas, 1959.)

The cells in figures 335 and 336 are still sufficiently large to be designated as immature lymphocytes, and the immature cell (fig. 122) found in circulating blood closely resembles figure 336. Other cells somewhat more advanced in development in which the chromatin shows early stages of clumping have already been discussed in connection with figures 331 and 332, and the medium and small mature lymphocytes (figs. 337 and 338) will be mentioned again in connection with figure 333.

The general appearance of a smear from the thymus 35 days after hatching is practically indistinguishable from a smear of the spleen at the same age. The medium to small lymphocyte is the dominant cell of both organs, but the developmental stages of the monocytes have not been identified in the thymus. Cell 3 (fig. 333) is a rather small lymphoblast similar to figure 335; cells that are not much smaller reached a stage of nuclear clumping equal to the immature lymphocyte (cells 4 and 5 and the cell below 17). There are many medium and small mature lymphocytes, some of which are indicated by cells 6–12. In these the chromatin is clumped into heavily stained blocks. As mentioned earlier, at low magnification there are no visible significant changes in cytoplasmic structure during the differentiation of the lymphocyte, but under high magnification (figs. 334–338) mitochondrial spaces may be seen in some of the young cells. The spaces disappear as the cell grows older.

The framework of the thymus is composed of reticular cells and their fibers. These cells are often called epithelial or epithelioid cells. In section they are readily recognized by the acidophilic cytoplasm, which is large compared with the small nucleus. Cells in section show very little structural detail in the cytosome but in smears considerable structure is visible, the most conspicuous being the mitochondrial spaces. A well-defined plasmosome nucleolus lies near the center of the nucleus in cell 1 of figure 333. The color taken by the cytoplasm is similar to that of the plasmacyte of the spleen (fig. 331). Cell 2 is a slightly crushed reticular cell.

Not as many reticular cells are found in smears as might be expected from the large number seen in sections because in making them the loose cells in the meshes of the reticulum are given up more readily than the framework itself. The reticular cells seen here are very similar to the primordial osteogenic cells of the embryo bone marrow, and if the cells of figure 332 A could be laid out, separate from each other, it is probable that both the reticular cells and the primordial osteogenic cells would have an appearance quite similar to the mesenchyme of the embryo. The reticular tissue of the adult organism is said to be more like the embryonic mesenchyme especially in potentiality for producing other cell types than any other connective-tissue cell of the body.

Danchakoff (1916b) in her study of thymus development in the chick embryo concluded that the cells of the thymus cortex are derived from small lymphocytes that originally came from mesenchyme cells. The small lymphocytes are said to produce fibroblasts, macrophages, plasma cells, and myelocytes.

Granulocytes are common in the thymus, and in sectioned material the heterophils often lie in a mass of reticular cells and debris that form a Hassall's corpuscle. Other cells found in the avian thymus but not in the mammalian gland are the isolated striated muscle cells. The eosin-staining affinities of these cells cause them to stand out conspicuously from the blue nuclei of the lymphocytes (Wassjutotschkin, 1913 and 1914). It was expected that these cells would be seen in smears but none were found.

FEATHER SHEATH CELL

This is not a blood cell and is not directly related to one. It is a contaminant that was found on many slides made from late embryos. Before its significance was known, it caused a great deal of confusion and concern. It was called an x-cell when discovered, and that name

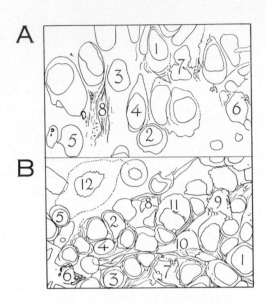

FIGURE 332.—Embryo thymus.

A   Embryo incubated 9 days 4 hours.   Mesenchymal cells of the embryo thymus early in its development. 1,370×.

   1   Primordial cell with a nucleolus.

   2   A rounded primordial cell.

3, 4   Cells in which the cytoplasm is merged with the stained serum.

   5   Naked nucleus.

   6   Broken, naked nucleus.

   7   Shrunken, broken cells.

   8   Strands of basichromatin from broken nuclei.

B   Embryo incubated 11 days 10 hours.   1,370×.

   1   Lymphoblast.

2, 3   Early immature lymphocytes.

4, 5   Late immature lymphocytes.

6, 7   Mitosis, prophase.   Cells probably are developing lymphocytes.

8–10   Smudged, naked nuclei.

11, 12:   *Identification uncertain; either macrophages or heterophil promyelocytes.*

   11   Closely resembles a promyelocyte.

   12   A highly atypical cell. It contains magenta spheres like the primordial osteogenic cell.

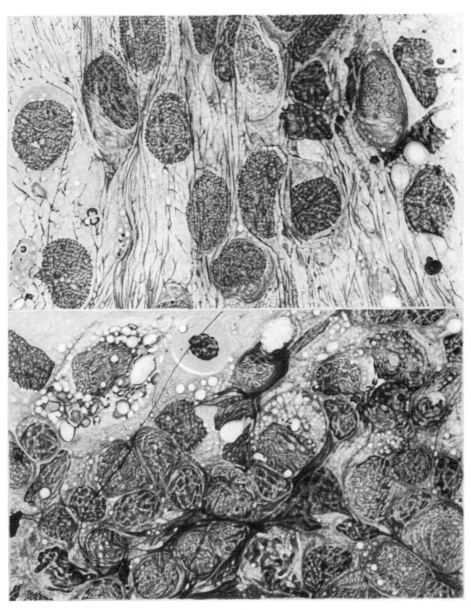

332

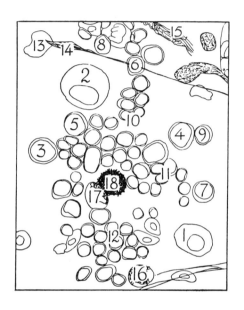

FIGURE 333.—Thymus.   Chick, 35 days after hatching.   Composite drawing from 4 places on same slide.   1,370×.

1   Rounded thymus reticular cell.   A primordial cell.
2   Slightly squashed reticular cell.
3   Lymphoblast.
4   Immature lymphocyte at transition to mature lymphocyte.
5   Immature lymphocyte, slightly more differentiated than 4.

6–9   Medium mature lymphocytes.
10–12   Small mature lymphocytes.
13–15   Smudged nuclei.
16   Mature heterophil.
17   Smudged heterophil.
18   Mature basophil.

333

FIGURES 334–338.—Stages in the development of lymphocytes in the thymus. All figures from the same slide. Embryo incubated 14 days 11 hours. 2,470×.

334 Large lymphoblast. Nucleus incompletely stained.
335 Lymphoblast at transition to immature lymphocyte.
336 Immature lymphocyte.

337 Mature lymphocyte of medium size.
338 Mature lymphocyte of small size.

174

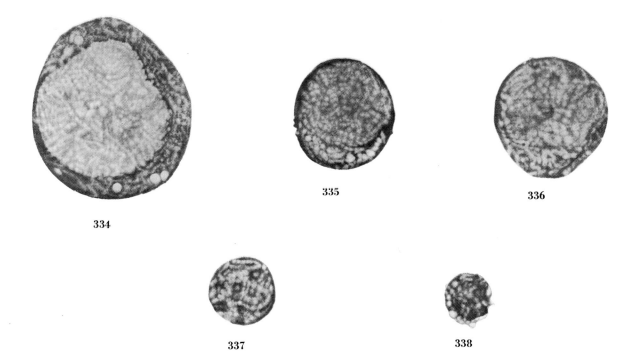

334

335

336

337

338

FIGURES 339–342.—Squamous epithelial sheath cells covering down feathers. These cells separate readily and as a contaminant frequently fall on impression smears made from embryonic and young chick organs. 2,470✕.

339 A relatively small cornified down-sheath cell found in bone-marrow smear. Oval area of dead nucleus slightly to the left of center. No keratin granules. Chick just hatched.

340 An elongated down-sheath cell found in bone-marrow smear. Dead nucleus in the center. Numerous keratin bodies formed in the cytoplasm. Chick just hatched.

341 A large and slightly smudged down-sheath cell found in a spleen smear. Coalescence of keratin bodies. No nucleus visible. Orange body with a dense nucleus is a broken erythrocyte on the surface of the sheath cell. Embryo incubated 20 days 4 hours.

342 A final stage in the keratinization of a down-sheath cell found in bone-marrow smear. Remains of the dead nucleus visible in the center. Embryo incubated 19 days 19 hours.

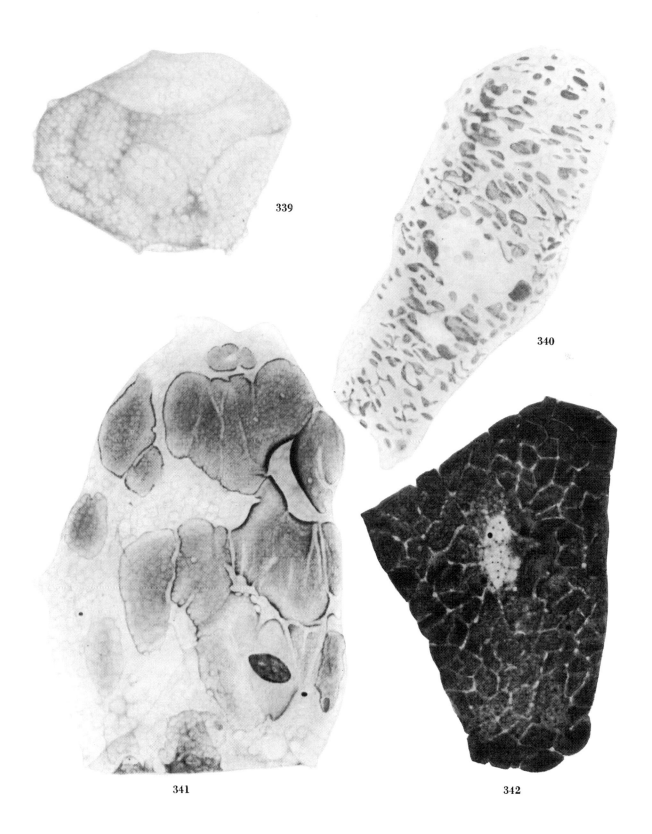

339

340

341

342

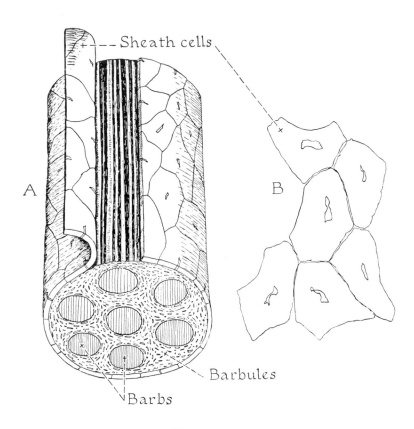

FIGURE 343.

A   Part of an emerged down feather in which is diagramed the down-sheath cells that enclose
the barbs and barbules of the down feather.
B   The sheath forms a simple squamous layer of keratinized dead cells.

indicated the state of knowledge about this cell for a considerable length of time.

Cells like figure 342 were most commonly seen. They occurred in most bone-marrow smears and later in some spleen smears. Since all the cells in figures 339–342 were drawn at the magnification used for other high-power drawings, it is apparent that they were many times larger than erythrocytes. When cells like figure 340 were found, a protozoan parasite was suspected, but none were known that closely approached this morphology and retained a large central nucleus. As different tissues were used for smears, the more widely did these cells seem to be distributed. Finally, after they had been seen in smears from connective tissue of the groin region and from air sacs as well as from bone marrow, thymus, spleen, and bursa, it became evident that this was a contaminant.

A search for the source led to an examination of the surface of the late embryo and of the young chick, the scalps of the people who were making the slides, and the towels used to wipe the hands and instruments.

The x-cells were obtained only from the surface of the chick. If a slide was covered with albumen and the down was brushed with a pencil while the newly hatched chick was held several inches above the slide, many cells of the type shown in figures 339–342 were seen. It was then but a short step to locate the sheath of cells that encloses the emerging down. When they were seen in sheets, as in 343 *B*, it was evident whence they had come. The remarkable thing about them was their ability to separate themselves so easily and completely from other cells of the same epithelium that nearly always they were found as isolated cells. Although their source was now known, there was still the question of how they came to be a contaminant on impression smears, since the down of many embryos was wet and it was unlikely that the cells could be spread by air. The crevices of the mouse-tooth forceps used to pull the tissues apart carried these cells. Although the forceps were not touched to the slide when the smear was made, they must have been the chief source because, subsequent to this period of investigation, no down-sheath cells appeared in smears if the teeth of the forceps were carefully cleaned after each step in the dissection process.

After it had been learned that these cells were specifically associated with the down of the young chick or the late embryo and that they were readily separated and disseminated, it was decided to conduct an experiment with two of the men who take off the chick hatch each week. This Laboratory maintains a quarantine, and a man coming onto the premises changes his clothes, washes his hands, and puts on boots and coveralls furnished by the Laboratory. When men enter the incubator rooms, a second change of clothing is made. After the two men had taken off the hatch they went through the quarantine in reverse, so that they entered the Laboratory in their street clothing. Previously 6 albuminized slides had been prepared. Now each man was asked to brush his hair about 6 inches from 3 of the slides.

All 3 slides of 1 group showed sheath cells when stained, and 1 of the other 3 slides showed them. Therefore, any truly effective quarantine should eliminate the possible transfer of these cells from one group of chicks to another, or else it should be shown that these desquamated cells cannot serve as carriers of pathogenic organisms.

The cells selected for illustration are intended to show three steps in the process of keratinization (figs. 339, 340, and 342) and one atypical cell (fig. 341). In figure 339 a nuclear ghost is indicated by its slight orange color and oval shape. In this cell the cytosome is uniformly vacuolated and the ground substance takes a light-blue stain. Often the thin edges of these cells are folded and in this case there are 2 folds, 1 above and 1 below the level of the nucleus.

Usually the cells have greater length than width. The nucleus is orientated with its long axis transversely placed across the middle of the cell (fig. 340). It, of course, is dead and no chromatin particles are visible, only a faint orange coloration without structure. Keratin particles develop in the cytosome from many separate centers. Some grow larger and flow together with adjoining masses. The typical appearance of the last stage when no more keratinized material can be packed into the cell is shown in figure 342. The nuclear ghost is visible in the center of the cell. The cytosome is divided into multisided angular compartments with a small residue of blue-staining cytoplasm between them to mark their boundaries. The intense affinity of the keratin for the stain makes cells at this stage of development appear nearly black under low magnification.

The cell shown in figure 341 is atypical in that the keratin has flowed together into large, irregular masses. The nucleus does not show and the orange body with its blue nucleus is an erythrocyte on the surface of the cell. The general appearance of the down-sheath cell is suggestive of a partially squashed cell but there is little evidence beyond its atypical appearance to indicate that this was the case.

The barbs and barbules of the chick down are held by a thin layer of these epidermal cells (fig. 343 A). Upon drying, the sheath breaks readily, allowing these structures to spread and assume the fluffy appearance characteristic of down.

CHAPTER 5

Blood Cells From Bone Marrow of the Hatched Chicken

Bone marrow of the adult chicken differs in its general appearance from the bone marrow of the embryo or the recently hatched chick by its abundance of mature erythrocytes. Blast and developmental stages are present but are not so numerous as in the younger ages. These shifts in the incidence of different cell types with age will be described more fully when table 10 is discussed.

Jordan (1936 and 1937) has described the bone marrow of several species of birds. In the marrow of all young birds he found lymphoid nodules. These he regarded as centers of hematopoietic activity, especially of erythrocytes. He also observed small vessels plugged with lymphocytes. Jordan and Robeson (1942) observed after splenectomy in pigeons that the lymphoid foci and plugged vessels in the bone marrow were increased. Their interpretations need to be reviewed rather critically in the light of observations made since then that lymphoid foci are abnormal in endocrine glands (Payne and Breneman, 1952), in vessels of nerves and among nerve fibers (Oakberg, 1950), and in the pancreas (Lucas, 1949; Lucas and Oakberg, 1950; Lucas, Craig and Oakberg, 1949; Lucas and Breitmayer, 1949; Lucas, 1950 and 1951; Oakberg, 1949 and 1951) and in the liver (Denington and Lucas, 1960; Lucas et al., 1954). The spleen like the bone marrow is a hematopoietic organ, and in addition to the white pulp, contains lymphoid foci. Statistically, these are related to the infection by the agent of avian lymphomatosis (Lucas et al., 1954). Before similar lymphoid foci and plugged vessels in the bone marrow can be accepted as normal for birds, it should be demonstrated that these are not equivalent to the abnormal lymphoid foci and plugged vessels found in other organs of the body.

A study by Erdmann (1917) of chicken bone marrow in tissue culture failed to produce a variety of differentiated cell types from the small lymphocyte. Cultures in a plasma medium showed, first, a degeneration of mature and late polychromatic erythrocytes and some maturation of granulocytes, but this was followed by degeneration. There was no evidence of cell division in myelocytes or in microlymphocytes. Hetherington and Pierce (1931) gave a confirmatory observation when they noted that in explants of the buffy coat of chicken blood, all of the lymphocytes degenerated after 48 hours.

Mention has been made of practically all the developmental stages that are to be found in the bone marrow of the hatched chicken but a special effort has been made to bring them all together in a series of drawings under high magnification (figs. 345–399) in order that studies of bone marrow in the chicken can be made as useful for diagnosis and for following the course of diseases as bone marrow studies have been in human medicine.

ERYTHROCYTES AND THROMBOCYTES

The erythroblast shown by cell *1* of figure 344 is almost an early polychromatic erythrocyte. Younger blast cells may be seen in figures 345–347. The last of the three closely duplicates cell *1* of figure 344. Cell *2* is an early polychromatic erythrocyte but shows slightly less condensation of chromatin than either of the cells represented by figures 347 and 348. In the low-power field (fig. 344) there are no good examples of mid-polychromatic erythrocytes, although cell *4* has not passed far beyond this stage. Beside the two cells at *3*, there are several additional late polychromatic erythrocytes in the field. Cell 5 is one of these in division, which again demon-

FIGURE 344.—Bone marrow from a chicken, 145 days old.   1,370×.

1	Late erythroblast.
2	Early polychromatic erythrocyte.
3, 4	Late polychromatic erythrocytes.
5	Dividing late polychromatic erythrocyte.
6–8	Mature erythrocytes.
9	Thromboblast.
10	Early immature thrombocyte. Typical cell at this stage for adult bone marrow. Added to the drawing from another bone-marrow smear.
11	Disintegrating mature thrombocyte.
12	Metagranuloblast.
13–15	Mature heterophils.
16	Basophil mesomyelocyte.
17	Mature or nearly mature basophil.
18–21	Lymphocytes, medium and small.
22–25	Cells slightly smudged.
26, 27	Smudged naked nuclei.

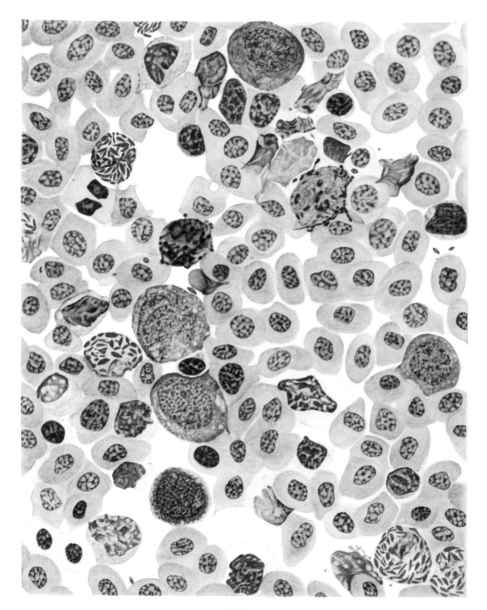

344

FIGURES 345–356 —Cells of the erythrocyte series found in the bone marrow of adult or nearly adult chickens. 2,470×

345 Large early erythroblast. A cell this large and immature is relatively rare in adult bone marrow. Nucleolus occupies the right third of the nucleus.

346 Erythroblast.

347 Late erythroblast. This cell and the preceding one are typical of the erythrocyte stem cells in bone marrow.

348–349 Early polychromatic erythrocytes. Both show faint indications of their nucleoli at the lower left of each nucleus.

350, 351 Mid-polychromatic erythrocytes.

352–354 Late polychromatic erythrocytes. Each cell in the series is slightly more differentiated than the preceding one.

355 Cell with full complement of hemoglobin as judged by the color and a fully differentiated nucleus but with a round shape.

356 Normal mature erythrocyte.

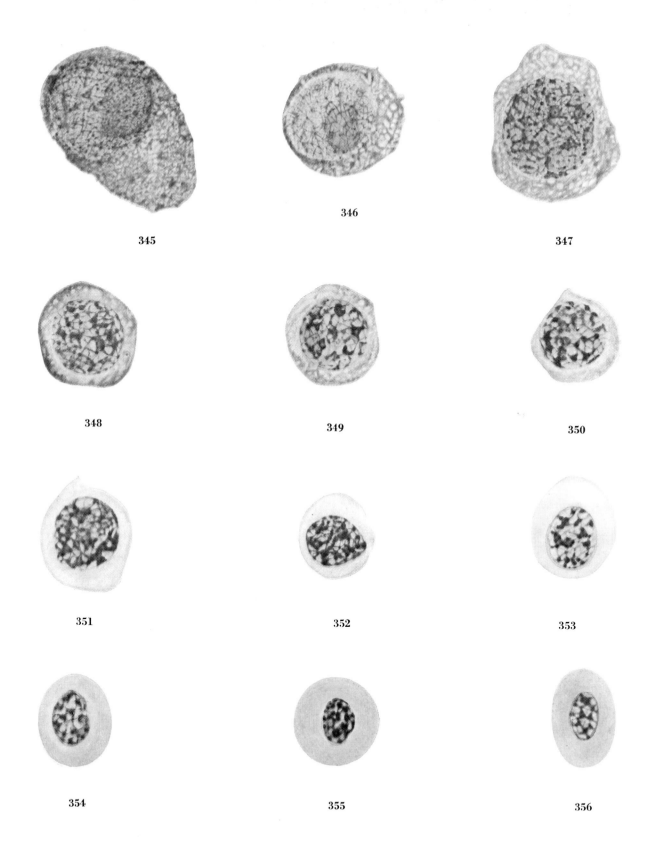

345

346

347

348

349

350

351

352

353

354

355

356

FIGURES 357–365.—Cells of the thrombocyte series found in bone marrow.   Figures 357, 363, 364, and 365 from the adult bird and 358–362 from 6-day-old chick.   2,470×.

357, 358   Thromboblasts.   A nucleolus is present in each but is faint because masked by chromatin granules, which are dense.

359–362   Early immature thrombocytes.   The lighter peripheral cytosomal margin as in figure 362 is characteristic of thrombocytes at this age but may represent an early disintegration reaction.

363   Mid-immature thrombocyte.

364   Late immature thrombocyte.

365   Mature thrombocyte.

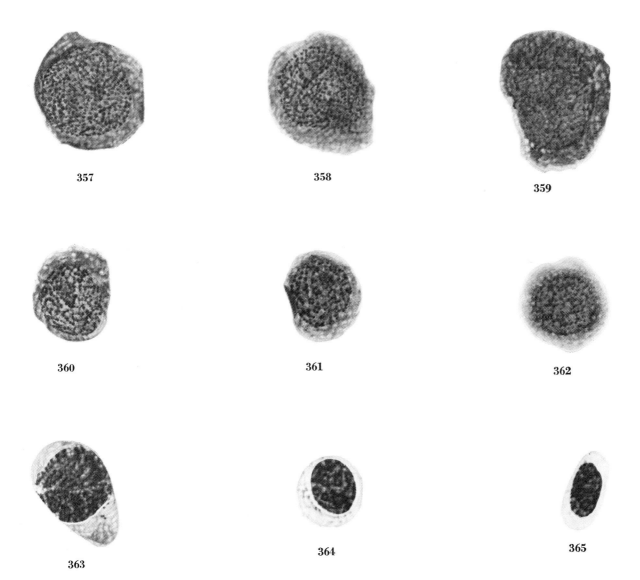

357   358   359

360   361   362

363   364   365

FIGURES 366–377.—Cells of the heterophil granulocyte series found in bone marrow of adult chicken, except figure 376, which was from a day-old chick.   2,470×.

366 Large early granuloblast. This size is found but rarely.

367 Typical early granuloblast. It is not possible in the granuloblast stage to determine which type of granulocyte will be produced from it.

368, 369 Heterophil metagranuloblasts.

370–372 Heterophil promyelocytes. Magenta rings are present and also cytosomal vacuoles containing rod precursor spheres.

373, 374 Heterophil mesomyelocytes. The beginning rods are indicated by the darkly stained bodies coming from the precursor spheres.

375 Heterophil metamyelocyte. More than half of the full complement of rods have appeared.

376 Heterophil metamyelocyte in mitotic division. Early telephase.

377 Mature heterophil.

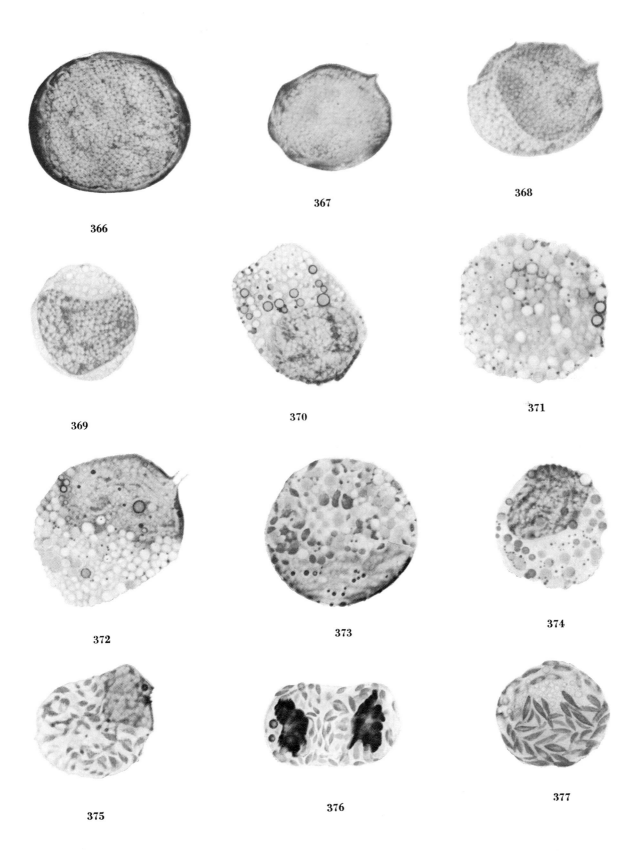

366

367

368

369

370

371

372

373

374

375

376

377

189

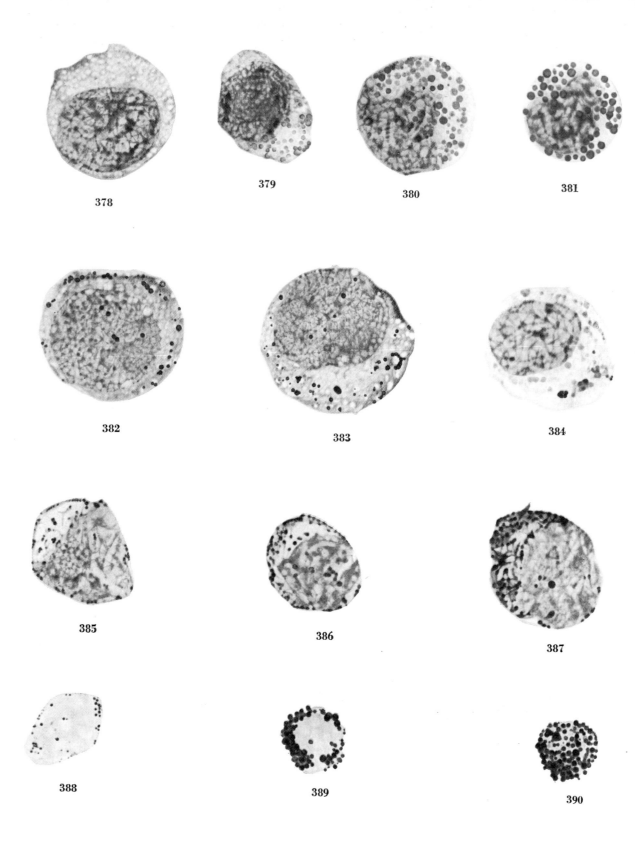

378

379

380

381

382

383

384

385

386

387

388

389

390

strates that mitosis can occur in birds relatively late in the differentiation process, and in the erythrocyte development of the human being this would be equivalent to about the normoblast stage.

All of the field of figure 344 was drawn as it appeared under the microscope except for one cell (10) and that was added from another slide. Cells 9 and 10 form two stages in the thrombocyte series. The former is the blast stage and is relatively rare but is recognizable by its punctate pattern of nuclear chromatin. Cell 10 is the most commonly seen early thrombocyte and was added to the drawing so that its size and coloration could be compared with those of young erythrocytes and myelocytes in the same field. Its rim of dark-violet cytoplasm with a tendency to stain more lightly at the periphery is a characteristic of the early thrombocyte (fig. 362), at least as seen in bone marrow.

Mature thrombocytes that have not disintegrated are rarely seen in smears from bone marrow for reasons already discussed. One ruptured thrombocyte (cell 11) can be identified by the remnant of acidophilic cytoplasm that is still attached to it. A close study of the several naked nuclei in the field reveals that some could have come from thrombocytes but some undoubtedly came from broken erythrocytes.

When numerous fields of bone marrow are examined it is not hard to find all stages in granulocytic development in the embryo, but the bone marrow of the adult, unlike that of the embryo, seldom shows more than 1 or 2 early stages in a single field. Only 2 stages of development of the heterophil series are shown in figure 344—the metagranuloblast (cell 12) and mature cells (13–15). A badly distorted basophil (cell 16) has been labeled as a meso-myelocyte because it appeared to have less than half the normal number of basophilic granules, but in view of the disintegrating effect of aqueous solutions it may be older. Cell 17 is either a mature or nearly mature basophil.

In all bone-marrow smears there are smudged cells, some that are slightly crushed (cells 22–25 of fig. 344) and others (cells 26 and 27) that are destroyed beyond recognition.

Lymphocytes (cells 18–21) show a range from medium to small but they are all mature and in this particular field there is no evidence that the bone marrow is a lymphocytogenic organ. A better measure of this function comes from a study of table 10. These mature lymphocytes shown in figure 344 could have come into the bone marrow by way of the circulating blood, as most of the mature erythrocytes presumably did.

In figures 345–390 and 391–397 an attempt has been made to show each cell line as completely as possible. Obviously, many cells are similar to those pictured in the circulating blood and in other hematopoietic organs, but even considering all the cells pictured, relatively few examples are shown of each cell type, and no matter how extensive the illustrations may be they cannot substitute for the actual examination of slides where, in a short time, far more cells than those represented in this volume can be seen.

Three erythroblasts from bone marrow, differing considerably in appearance, have been illustrated (figs. 345–347). Two show nucleoli and one does not; one has a narrow band of cytoplasm and two have extensive cytoplasm. The type represented by figure 345 is rare. Most of the erythroblasts seen in adult bone marrow look like figure 346 or 347. The latter with its

---

FIGURES 378–390.—Cells of the eosinophil and basophil granulocyte series from bone marrow of adult chicken, except figure 379, which was from a day-old chick.   2,470×.

378   Eosinophil metagranuloblast.
379   Eosinophil mesomyelocyte.
380   An eosinophil mesomyelocyte more differentiated than the preceding cell.
381   A late eosinophil metamyelocyte.
382, 383   Basophil promyelocytes.   Figure 383 is slightly more differentiated than figure 382.

FIGURES 384–386: *Basophil mesomyelocytes.*

384   Early phase of the mesomyelocyte.

385   Mesomyelocyte with a moderate number of basophilic granules.
386   Late phase of the mesomyelocyte.
387   Basophil metamyelocyte.

FIGURES 388–390: *Basophil granulocytes from bone marrow fixed in methyl alcohol and stained in thionin.*

388   Mesomyelocyte.
389   Metamyelocyte.
390   Mature basophil.

denser chromatin pattern is somewhat more differentiated than the cell in figure 346.

Erythroblasts have been seen in the circulating blood of the adult (figs. 9 and 121), in the circulating blood of the early embryo (figs. 224 and 233–235), in the later embryo (figs. 254–256), and in embryo spleen (figs. 329 and 330). To all of these Sabin (1920) applied the term "megaloblast," but it has been claimed that the stem cells of all erythrocytes at all ages are not alike and also that those of normal blood are not identical with those of anemia (Jones, 1943). Anemias have not been studied in the chicken but from the other observations it is evident that all erythroblasts do not look alike cytologically. The differences are due in part to the fact that the erythroblast is not a static cell covering one point of time in development, but is a cell that during the differentiation process can often be divided into early and late phases, both of which are capable of mitosis and the production of progeny.

Another factor that modifies the cytology of the erythroblast is the degree of urgency for hemoglobin. In the first generation of erythrocytes it is evident that a high rate of hemoglobin acquisition has been given priority over cytologic differentiation. With each generation of erythroblasts there is a gradual change to the definitive condition where the taking on of hemoglobin becomes an integral part of cell differentiation.

As this study shows, the erythroblasts under these various conditions have a different appearance cytologically. Thus the names primary erythroblast, embryo erythroblast, and definitive erythroblast have been used. It is conceivable that under the stress of a severe drain on the erythrocytes in the adult these cells might be pushed back to the same demand for new hemoglobin that occurred in the first embryonic generation. Under these circumstances it might be expected that they would look alike, but under normal conditions the definitive erythroblast of the bone marrow does not look like the primary erythroblast, and thus there is less confusion if specific terms are used whenever possible.

Beyond the erythroblast there are three polychromatic stages that cover the period of differentiation from a cell with a small amount of hemoglobin up to one with its full capacity. These three stages are, of course, arbitrary ones, and in setting them up an effort has been made to divide the range into equal parts. In spite of full awareness that there were three stages in this range, and after considerable deliberation had been given to the criteria of color and cellular morphology, there were times when immature erythrocytes on a particular slide were not named as they should have been. It was felt that the difficulty might be due to a tendency, inherent in human nature, to divide any continuous variability into smaller units. If such a tendency were to influence an investigator when he had a slide under examination, and if the slide did not have the full range of polychromatic erythrocytes in the fields examined, the investigator might be impelled to divide what range there was into three parts. Repeated surrender to this tendency—one slide to the next, or one day to the next—might result in inconsistent determinations. After the drawings for the Atlas were completed and arranged, a uniform scheme was set up and with the illustrations in hand there has been no recent difficulty in calling cells of the same type by the same name.

Early polychromatic stages of the bone marrow are represented by figures 348 and 349, and both show shadows of nucleoli against the lower nuclear margins. The first of these two cells is not far removed from the blast stage and the second has a cytoplasmic coloration approaching the mid-polychromatic erythrocyte. In these cells mitochondrial spaces are still visible; yet in some examples of early polychromatic erythrocytes the textural quality of the cytosome may be as uniformly homogeneous as in later stages of development.

Mid-polychromatic erythrocytes are represented by two drawings (figs. 350 and 351); the one in the first drawing is the younger. In these particular examples, the nucleus is still large relative to the size of the cell. In some mid-polychromatic erythrocytes the nuclei may show greater chromatin condensation than in figures 350 and 351. They may be more like the one shown in figure 352. This figure shows a cell lying at the borderline between the mid- and late stages of erythrocyte development. The cell has been placed in the late stage group because the basophilic substance has almost disappeared and the acidophilic materials in the stroma are beginning to dominate. The cell represented by figure 353 is clearly more differentiated than the preceding one and not as far along in its development as the cell in figure 354. Accompanying the increase in hemoglobin is a slight elongation of the cell and an increased nuclear condensation. The tawny color, so often observed in late polychromatic erythrocytes just before maturity, may be due to the diffusion of basophilic granular material associated with the reticulocyte stage of development.

Differentiated cells with a full complement of hemoglobin and a small nucleus with a condensed chromatin pattern of the mature cell, yet with a round, rather than an oval shape, may be found in the bone marrow of the adult chicken (fig. 355). When such cells were observed in the embryo, they were interpreted as representing an atypical condition associated perhaps with forced development, and probably the same can be said for such cells when they appear at older ages. A mature, normal, typical erythrocyte is illustrated by figure 356 and is identical with those seen in circulating blood, even to the tone of cytoplasmic color, in spite of the fact that the cells in the bone marrow were stained with May-Grünwald Giemsa and those of circulating blood with Wright's.

Thromboblasts were not recognized in the bone marrow until after the developing stages had been worked out in the circulating blood of the embryo. One reason was that they resembled the erythroblasts. In fact, one cell in this series (fig. 357) was originally placed among the erythroblasts, but its punctate nuclear structure soon indicated that it was in the wrong series. Two stem cells of the adult bone marrow, the granuloblast and the thromboblast, have narrow cytoplasmic rims of cytoplasm around their nuclei. The cytosomes take an intense violet color, but these two cell types are readily distinguishable by their difference in nuclear structure.

The erythrocyte was divided into five levels of development and the same number of subdivisions has been proposed for the thrombocyte, but for the thrombocyte series these are based on structural and size changes without the assistance of significant tinctorial changes as in the erythrocytes; thus it has been somewhat difficult to establish terminal criteria for each stage of development of the thrombocyte. The thromboblasts are large cells (figs. 357 and 358) with a densely stained cytosome that has numerous vacuolar and mitochondrial spaces.

The appearance of definitive thromboblasts of the bone marrow is not much different from that of the embryo thromboblast (figs. 280–284). In both, the nucleolus may or may not be visible, depending upon the extent to which the plasmosome is masked by the overlying chromatin. The frayed appearance of the peripheral margin of the cytoplasm seen in figure 362 may also occur in the blast stage.

The term "early immature thrombocyte" is a rather awkward one; perhaps other investigators, after they have reexamined the problem, will think of a shorter name. In the early immature thrombocyte, there is some clumping of the nuclear chromatin and often the structure of the nucleus will appear similar to that of the partially autolysed cell where the chromatin clumps have vague indefinite boundaries like those shown in figure 363. Figures 358 to 362 were made from cells of the bone marrow of the 6-day-old chick rather than from the adult because there were a large number of early stages available for observation. This made it possible to arrange them in their proper developmental sequence.

The mid-immature thrombocyte has already acquired the characteristics that definitely identify it as a thrombocyte—namely, the shift in nuclear staining from violet to purple, the appearance of definitive granules (fig. 363) and the elongation of shape as in the immature embryo thrombocyte. The cell at this stage of development has a deep basophilic cytosome, which, during differentiation to the late immature stage, fades to a lightly stained cytoplasmic framework (fig. 364). The cell has not yet assumed its mature oval shape. The nucleus is still larger than in the mature stage; it is still round, rather than oval. Cells of this type are often found in the circulating blood, as shown in outline (fig. 88 i). Late immature and mature thrombocytes may be found in bone marrow but they are not common; usually they have undergone at least partial disintegration. The cell shown in figure 365 is identical in appearance with that in figure 73—a thrombocyte from circulating blood.

GRANULOCYTES

The classification of granulocyte stages of development has been outlined in table 2, which gives 6 steps for the heterophil, 5 for the eosinophil, and 5 for the basophil. Each of the 3 granulocytes reveals the characteristics of each of the 6 steps in development; but in the eosinophils and basophils, 2 of the stages have been telescoped and the name chosen for the combination is the last one in the series.[1]

The granuloblast is identified by its large nucleus surrounded by a narrow rim of cytoplasm densely stained. Relatively few cytoplasmic spaces are in the cytoplasm (figs. 366 and 367), and these lie adjacent to the nucleus.

The intensely colored narrow rim of violet-stained cytoplasm, combined with the delicately stained nuclear reticulum and lack of visible nucleolus, makes the granuloblast readily recognizable even under relatively low magnification. Figure 366 is the largest granuloblast observed, and figure 367 represents the size usually seen. These cells resemble very closely the lymphoblast, but are different from the thromboblast and the erythroblast.

The scheme presented in table 2 has been written under the assumption that the granuloblast has equal potentialities to produce a heterophil, eosinophil, or basophil. Early in this study it was thought that the stem cell for each type of granulocyte had a different appearance, but it has since been decided that these were either metagranuloblasts or promyelocyte stages. Hamre

---

[1] Six subdivisions of the granulocyte series are suggested in the First Report of the Committee for Clarification of the Nomenclature of Cells and Diseases of the Blood and Blood-Forming Organs (1948), and Dr. L. W. Diggs states (personal communication), ". . . it is my opinion that terminologies used in human hematology and widely accepted and understood, should be used for lower animals when applicable." This is a commendable point of view; unfortunately it has been necessary to depart in some cases from the terminology proposed by the Committee because the definitions associated with certain terms used in studies on blood of mammals do not adequately cover the observations made on birds. As pointed out by Jones (1949), zoologists, embryologists, and physiologists all have a stake in these problems.

"Myelo" is an inappropriate term for immature stages of granulocyte development because it means "marrow," and in the birds granulocytes develop in many organs other than the bone marrow. To have substituted the term "granulocyte" for "myelocyte" would have been acceptable as far as the developmental stages are concerned but would have conflicted with the term almost universally accepted for the adult cell. It seems confusing to use the term "myeloblast" for the earliest stage and "progranulocyte" for the next stage and then follow with two myelocyte stages. Therefore, for this study on avian hematology these terms have been changed to "granuloblast" (an old term) and "metagranuloblast," respectively; these are followed by the pro-, meso-, and meta- stages of the myelocyte, and these are followed by the mature cell. The prefix "meso" was used so that each of these phases of development could be identified without confusion, and so that the term "myelocyte" without any prefix could be used as a general term signifying the full range of development from the metagranuloblast up to the mature cell. Metagranuloblast is a new term.

has prepared a colored plate showing granulopoiesis; it was based on the use of a different stain but in the sequence of stages (Hamre, 1952) there was nearly complete similarity with the data given here. The privilege of examining his data before publication has been helpful in this complex problem. He did not set apart as a separate stage what has been given here as the metagranuloblast.

The metagranuloblast is derived from the granuloblast by a great expansion in the cytoplasm at one side of the nucleus, and by an increase in the vacuolization of this portion of the cytosome. Often the remainder of the cytosome is unchanged from the condition characteristic of the granuloblast—that is, it stains an intense violet color. This was the case in figure 368 but not in 369. At this stage the nucleus may remain round (fig. 368) or it may be partially collapsed (fig. 369). The reticular pattern of the nucleus may be just as finely patterned and delicately stained as in the granuloblast stage, or it may show clumping. The nucleus collapses or becomes irregular in shape more readily in the heterophil metagranuloblast than in either the eosinophil metagranuloblast or the basophil promyelocyte. Also, the chromatin condensation is greater in the last two cells. The metagranuloblast stage of the heterophil and of the eosinophil can be readily separated. The difference is apparent when a comparison is made between figure 368 and 378. In the heterophil, the boundaries of the vacuoles are rather indefinite and they appear oftentimes as spaces in a reticulum, but in the eosinophil they are round areas with clean-cut boundaries. This difference was the chief factor in calling cell 11 of figure 330 an eosinophil metagranuloblast rather than a heterophil of the same stage.

One group of hematologists (Anonymous, 1949) gives only the term "myelocyte" to cover the entire span of specific granule production. In avian blood for the heterophil at least, there is a definite stage of development between the metagranuloblast and the stage where specific granules first appear. Microscopically, it is one of the most conspicuous of the entire progression and it would be awkward not to have a name for it. Its two outstanding characteristics are the presence of (1) cytoplasmic rings and granules that take the same intense magenta stain as the nucleus and (2) light-staining orange spheres (figs. 370–372). In figure 370 only vacuoles are present in the cytosome but in figure 371 some vacuoles are filled with lightly stained orange spheres, and in figure 372 one or two of these spheres have taken on the dark-orange color that places them at the transition where the specific bodies make their appearance. Because the stages antecedent to specific granule production can be followed so readily in birds, it seems that use of avian blood would be advantageous in further study of the early stages of granulopoiesis. The magenta rings and the granules vary in number; in some cells there are but few and in others they are abundant. The nature of the stainable material inside the magneta ring is not known.

The small granules are of two types; one takes a magenta stain and the other, a deep orange. If figures 370 and 372 are compared, it will be noted that in the latter the *magenta-stained* granules are scattered around the orange-stained spheres and not in them; but in figure 371 many of the *orange* granules lie in the exact center of each sphere and others do not. These orange granules are abundant in figure 374. The question has come to mind repeatedly, Are the orange granules identical with the central bodies of the mature heterophil granulocyte? It might seem that this should be easy to determine by following the development of the rods to see where the granules go, but the presence or absence of a central body in the rods is not constant, as was seen in figures 154–165, and not a single rod in figures 373–377 shows a central body inside it. In figure 372 the small granules lie at the periphery of the orange spheres.

It was the opinion of Dantschakoff (1908b) that there was metachromasia of the specific granules of heterophils during the early stages of differentiation. This reaction would agree with the observations reported in the paragraph above, to the extent that the first granules to appear are of two types, magenta-staining and pale orange-staining. The magenta rings appear to be a different organelle than the magenta granules and were not observed by Dantschakoff in her sectioned material. In a study by Lucas and Denington (1956, unpublished data) magenta rings were observed in sectioned material.

The nucleus of the promyelocyte may be distinct but often it appears as in figures 371 and 372, where nuclear boundaries are vague, and at this stage they appear the same as they do in the embryo spleen.[2]

Several steps are involved in the production of a rod. First a vacuole is formed, it is occupied by a light-orange sphere, which progresses to a darkly stained orange sphere, and this in turn becomes a rod. The development of a sphere and its transformation into a rod mark the beginning of the mesomyelocyte stage (figs. 373 and 374).

The mesomyelocyte stage has a nucleus that may be large and indefinite (fig. 373) or small with definite chromatin clumps (fig. 374). Also, some magenta rings and granules may persist (fig. 373). The process of rod differentiation is more advanced in figure 373 than in 374; in the latter it is not much farther than the "dark-orange sphere" stage. When the rods form

---

[2] One clinical hematologist, after seeing colored reproductions of these avian myelocytes, said:

"The myelocytic series may be drawn exactly as they appeared, but if that is true, they appear to be inadequately stained. If we had a human bone marrow or blood smear that had nuclei which were as pale and the structures as ill defined as painted, we would say that the stain was unsatisfactory, would not attempt a differential or diagnosis and would ask for better stained preparations or a restain of the same preparation. A combination of Giemsa as a counterstain for the Wright's or a change of the buffer water or a longer staining time might give better results."

Various technics, including Wright-Giemsa, have been tried, and although differences in the appearance of the cells may occur—with the same or different technics—the general picture of heterophil granulopoiesis as shown here is representative for the normal chicken. Nothing has been seen that supports the idea that avian myelocytes look the way they do in impression smears because inappropriate technics were chosen or because appropriate technics were faultily applied. It is suggested that the promyelocytes often appear the way they do because the cell undergoes extensive hypertrophy, both of the nucleus and cytosome, as one of the first steps in heterophil myelopoiesis and because the firm vacuoles and the light-orange bodies give a honeycomb appearance to the nucleus and cytosome by puncturing these structures at the time the cell is flattened in the process of making the smear (fig. 371).

A little later in development, nuclear detail becomes visible again (fig. 374). In the interim the nucleus has not changed its appearance to any great extent (compare figs. 369 and 374). Therefore, not much has been lost by using a technic (May-Grünwald Giemsa) that does not reveal all the details of the nucleus at the promyelocyte stage. On the credit side, this stain reveals the subtleties of changing form and color in the rod precursors, which seems important when studying granulocyte development. When Petrunkevitch's No. 2 was used on spleen myelocytes, followed by May-Grünwald Giemsa, the border of the nucleus could be traced readily, and the nucleus appeared as a large body containing a delicate granulation, but the cytoplasmic inclusions suffered severely by this technic.

The author of the paragraph quoted here is not mentioned here by name for the reason that it is not intended to make this volume a springboard for a controversy. He is respected as an outstanding clinical hematologist of human blood and he may be expressing an opinion that would be shared by all hematologists of mammalian blood who look at these illustrations. A common ground of understanding is, of course, necessary for any discussion and this can be reached more quickly when it is recognized that many details of human and avian blood are not the same.

they produce bodies of irregular shape—some pointed, some rounded, and some multiangular.

After the cell has developed about half of its normal complement of rods, it is called a meta-myelocyte up to the stage where, at maturity, it has the full number of rods. This is a purely arbitrary division and admittedly not exact, but it would be still more difficult in avian blood to follow the criterion "Bean or kidney shaped nucleus" (Anonymous, 1949) because, with approaching maturity, the typical artifact of the heterophil nucleus becomes apparent; therefore, in figure 377 it would be impossible to say whether this cell had an indented or bean-shaped nucleus but it is quite evident that it has about as many rods as the cell will hold.

Figures 375 and 376 are examples of meta-myelocytes. In both there are one or two magenta rings still carried over to this late stage; usually, of course, they have disappeared by this time. From figure 376 it is obvious that mitosis does not stop at the granuloblast stage or even when the specific granules first appear.

Developmental stages of eosinophils are as scarce in the bone marrow as are the mature forms in the circulating blood. The finding of developmental stages went slowly but eventually after enough cells had been studied certain definite features were established that helped to separate them from heterophils. The qualities of cytoplasm and nucleus that make the eosinophil metagranuloblast distinguishable from the heterophil of the same age have already been discussed in part. The nucleus of the eosinophil throughout its developmental stages generally is more intensely stained than that of the heterophil. Usually the vacuoles are clear—almost refractile—but as shown in figure 378 a few faintly stained bodies are visible. These differentiate directly into the specific granules, and the meso-myelocyte (fig. 379) shows a full scale of tinctorial range from the faintest to the darkest. It is this direct transition from seeming vacuole to definitive granules that eliminated the promyelocyte stage. There appears to be nothing equivalent to the magenta rings.

In the heterophil the developmental steps of the precursor spheres were moderately well synchronized in their formation; whereas, in the eosinophil, development of the spheres begins at different times, so that all stages are present at any one time. Even in the older age (fig. 380) the full range—vacuole to faint sphere to dark sphere—is clearly shown and the framework cytoplasm has the same pale-blue color that it has in the adult cell.

In the legend for figure 380 this cell is called a mesomyelocyte, and this stage, as defined here, is one that has less than half of its granules. At first glance this cell appears to have half of its granules, or more. But this cell and the heterophil are dealt with in the same way—only those granules are counted that have arrived at maturity and have their full tinctorial density. On that basis the cell definitely has less than half of its granules.

Had the late metamyelocyte (fig. 381) been found in the circulating blood it would probably have been counted as a mature cell—similar cells from circulating blood, shown in figures 177–180, have been so named. The difference is that the cytosome of the cell in figure 381 was not fully packed with granules. When the eosinophil of the circulating blood was discussed, it was pointed out that the specific granule for this cell varied from a large homogeneous body to a group of four small bodies in a cluster. At no time have the small bodies been found in the developing stages of eosinophils in embryo spleen or adult bone marrow. This variation is an important one, and will be discussed again when the blood of ducks is described, but its significance in the cytomorphosis of the cell is still unknown.

Studies of basophil and eosinophil differentiation are handicapped by the fact that so small a proportion of cells belong to these groups. As with the eosinophil it has been assumed that the granuloblast stage of the basophil has the same appearance as described for the heterophil. When cells like those in figures 366 and 367 are found, there are no identifying cytologic landmarks to indicate the direction in which they will develop. It was not difficult to locate cells that resemble those in figures 384–386, but cells like figures 382 and 383 were classed at first as heterophils because they showed magenta bodies. Further study proved, however, that they were not quite identical with those in the heterophils. In the cells under study the magenta bodies were predominantly granules ranging from small to large; the large ring characteristic of the heterophils was absent or relatively rare. There were a few small rings as is shown in figure 382, but these are not like the large thin-walled rings shown in figures 370–372. It was chiefly because of these characteristics that the decision was made to place a cell found in the circulating blood (fig. 193) among the basophils and not among the heterophils.

The question arises, At what stage of development are the cells that are represented by figures 382 and 383? It is best that the magenta bodies be ignored for the time being and that attention be given to the nucleus and cytoplasm. The cytoplasm of cell 382, slightly hypertrophied at one side of the nucleus, is vacuolated and is beginning to lose the strong basophilia of the granuloblast. If it did not have the magenta granules it would be classed as an early metagranuloblast, and figure 383 would be classed as a slightly more differentiated cell at the same stage, but the presence of the magenta bodies has been given as characteristic of the promyelocyte. It is as if two steps in development had been compressed into one; therefore it is identified by reference to its most conspicuous feature and is called a promyelocyte—this is simpler than contriving a new name to cover the two phases of development.

This immediately raises the question, Are these magenta bodies the specific granules characteristic of basophils? If they are, these cells should be called mesomyelocytes. At present the opinion is held that these are not mature specific granules and it is suggested that the definitive basophilic granules of the more mature cell develop out of the faintly stained substance of the vacuoles. Thus, when the granules first appear, they are the pale-magenta bodies shown in figure 384 and from this pale staining condition, by a progressive transformation, they produce the dark-magenta bodies shown in figure 384 and more abundantly in the three succeeding figures. The nucleus of the basophil promyelocyte does not lose its sharp boundary or the details of its internal structure. This is because the cytoplasmic vacuolization in the basophil is not so vigorous as in the heterophil.

On the right side of the nucleus of figure 382 is a bluish shadow that looks very much as if a nucleolus were present below the surface. This may be the case but in the granuloblast nucleus it is not typical. (See addendum, p. 140.)

Figures 384–386 are all mesomyelocytes, yet each of the cells in the series is older than the one preceding. Cell 384 represents the first step in the production of fully differentiated basophil granules, and cells 385 and 386 show an increasing number. By this method of fixation and staining they appear to lie on a reticulum, but in cells 388–390, which are fixed in methyl alcohol and stained with thionin, no network joining the granules is visible. It is probable that the network is an artifact and the idea of differentiation of granules from vacuolar substance was stated only as an opinion because it is obvious that in the bone marrow, as well as in the circulating blood, aqueous solutions tend to dissolve and distort the basophil granules. The nucleus also seems to be adversely affected by the technic treatment (figs. 385–387). Figure 387 is a late metamyelocyte.

There is need for additional search for a technic that will preserve the basophil granules and still reveal the detailed structure of the cell. Methyl alcohol and thionin preserve the granules, but nucleus and cytoplasm stain alike and have such a delicate blue color that no structural details are visible; so when it is stated in the legend that figure 388 is a mesomyelocyte, figure 389 a metamyelocyte, and figure 390 a mature basophil granulocyte, this is based only on the number of granules present.

PLASMA CELLS

Plasma cells may be found in spleen and bone marrow but are not common in normal healthy chickens. A few examples from bone marrow have been seen and are presented here, and some that were observed in the spleen are illustrated in figure 331, but in no case has a cell been found that could qualify structurally as a plasmablast. The possibility that such a cell might be the primordial osteogenic cell in bone marrow or the reticular cell in the spleen is a reasonable assumption since the early immature plasmacyte (fig. 331, 1) resembles these primordial cells. Mjassojedoff (1926) found numerous plasma cells in the loose connective tissue of adult chickens. He considered this abundance to represent a point of difference from mammals where they are said to be scarce.

Figure 391 represents the earliest stage that has been found. The cytoplasm form a much larger area around the nucleus than is characteristic of blast cells but is considerably less than found in the mature plasmacyte, and this particular cell has been called an early immature plasmacyte. The cytosome shows a mixture of mitochondrial spaces and the spherical vacuoles that are typical for the plasmacyte, both immature and mature. The bluish color taken by the cytoplasm has little or no red in it; thus it has an azure quality usually not found in other cell lines. The nucleus, even at this stage of immaturity, stains intensely; the chromatin is uniformly distributed but is composed of blocks larger than commonly found at this early stage of differentiation. This was true also of the immature plasmacyte pictured in the spleen (cell *1*, fig. 331).

The next four cells (figs. 392–395) are classed as late immature plasmacytes . They are almost as large as the early immature plasmacyte but proportional size of the nucleus has decreased. The sequence in this progressive change is indicated by the arrangement of figures. The most differentiated cell of the group is figure 395, in which a small nucleus lies at one side of a large cell having a strongly basophilic cytoplasm. During this process the chromatin aggregates into large clumps, but the clumps do not fill the entire nucleus. In figure 393 the cytosome is filled with small vacuoles; in the others there is a range in size from small to large.

The mature plasmacyte (figs. 396 and 397) is smaller than the immature stages. The nucleus still holds an eccentric position in the cell. The *Hof,* which was present in some of the immature cells, usually persists. Thus, the *Hof* is present in figure 396 and absent from 397. Vacuoles characteristic of plasmacytes are still present in the cytosome. A drawing was made of a cell identified as a mature plasma cell in the circulating blood, but since the cell occurred only once among many slides examined, the drawing has been omitted. It did not have a vacuolated cytoplasm, and this raised some doubt that it was a plasmacyte.

OSTEOCLASTS

Osteoclasts can be found in most bone marrow smears. They are readily recognized by their large size (figs. 398–399). Cells of this size are multinucleated, as shown in figure 399. Search was made for a mononucleated osteoclast and it was thought that such a condition had been found in figure 398, but beneath the pink-stained material in the center of the cells were faint traces of other nuclei. Small mononucleated cells like those found in the bone marrow of the embryo (figs. 319, 326, and 327) probably exist in adult bone marrow, also, but were not seen.

The cytoplasm of osteoclasts in smears seems to merge into the surrounding serum and only rarely can one identify with any accuracy the exact boundary all the way around the cell; often it appears as shown at the left end of figure 399. The cytoplasm forms a network and in it are vacuoles of various sizes and granules of various sorts; most of the latter—for example, the rods and magenta rings from heterophils—fell on the surface of the cell when the smear was made. Sectioned material usually gives an indication that the osteoclast has polarity—one end pressed against the spicule of bone and the other free in the marrow cavity. The appearance of the cell in figure 399 would suggest that the left side of the cell has been adjacent to the bone and the basophilic right end toward the cavity.

DIFFERENTIAL COUNTS ON BONE MARROW

Differential counts have been made on the cells of bone marrow in the chicken at 3 ages before and at 4 ages after hatching. One hundred cells were counted from each of five chicks at each age. The average was based on 500 cells. This number is small for bone-marrow studies but, even in this preliminary survey, certain ratios and trends are indicated. Late polychromatic and mature erythrocytes are abundant at all the ages covered in table 10, but it is questionable whether the fluctuations in the two cell types have significance; for example, where there were 16.8 and 29.2 percent at 285 hours, 49.6 and 18.4 percent at 347 hours, and 6.0 and 29.4 percent at 481 hours. Stages younger than the late polychromatic erythrocyte are always scarce.

Thrombocytes are present at all ages and are distributed fairly uniformly among the various stages of development except for the thromboblast. None of these were found at any of the ages examined, and the same was true for lymphoblasts, monoblasts, and immature and mature plasma cells.

Immature and mature lymphocytes were found at 285 hours, and appeared at all ages after hatching. No monocytes were found in this survey until after hatching.

The heterophil is the dominant granulocyte and is present at all ages and the incidence of granuloblasts just before hatching (481 hours) is higher than after hatching. The data in table 10 indicate that this is true also of the other immature and mature stages of the heterophil. The same tendencies are indicated in the eosinophils, where they were found most abundantly at 347 and 481 hours incubation age; after hatching they remained at a fairly low level. Perhaps the same tendency is indicated also in the basophils but the number of cells counted was too small to definitely establish a picture of a prehatching rise.

Among miscellaneous cells, some primary erythrocytes were observed at 285 hours and none after that. This cell is one that is known to arise in the yolk sac; therefore it was probably brought into the bone marrow through the embryonic circulation.

Osteogenic activity was indicated at 285 hours but none later except perhaps immediately after hatching, and the fact that the elongated reticular cells were found only at these same two ages is probably due to more than chance. Two macrophages were included in the counts at 285 hours and again at 8 days after hatching, but it would be expected that this cell might be seen at any age. Mitosis for all types of cells was 1 percent or less. The number of squashed cells fluctuated irregularly. Cells that could not be identified were most abundant at 285 hours. Following that there was a downward gradient until the percentage reached a level of 0.2 at 4 days 18 hours, and a level of 0.4 at 8 and at 175 days.

In respect to cell counts the data presented here differ greatly from those presented by Burmester, Severens, and Roberts (1941). They found large numbers of lymphocytes, whereas we found only a few. The data by Forkner (1929) for the adult chicken show some differences from that given in table 10. Our data show a higher heterophil than eosinophil count, whereas Forkner's values have the reverse order. He did not include thrombocytes in his tabulation. His lymphocyte count was considerably higher than ours.

Marvin (1954) calculated the total number of bone marrow cells in both femurs and both tibia in a strain of young White Carneau pigeons. His mean normal value on 4 pigeons was $10^6 \times 32 \pm 5$ cells for the total marrow of these four leg bones.

Table 10.—**Differential counts**

Cell type	285 hours of incubation						347 hours of incubation						481 hours of incubation					
	Bird					Average	Bird					Average	Bird					Average
	1	2	3	4	5		1	2	3	4	5		1	2	3	4	5	
	Pct.	Pct.	Pct.	Pct.	Pct.	Pct.	Pct.	Pct.	Pct.	Pct.	Pct.	Pct.	Pct.	Pct.	Pct.	Pct.	Pct.	Pct.
Erythrocyte series:																		
Erythroblast	1	1				0.4	1	3	1		2	1.4		6	1	6	1	2.8
Early polychromatic erythrocyte		1				0.2	1	2	2	1	1	1.4	3	7	3	4	2	3.8
Mid-polychromatic erythrocyte	1	3	2		1	1.4	5	8	5	6	2	5.2	3	9	1	9	4	5.2
Late polychromatic erythrocyte	29	1	13	22	19	16.8	41	56	55	50	46	49.6	5	18	2	4	1	6.0
Mature erythyrocyte	27	2	51	42	24	29.2	10	18	15	24	25	18.4	17	15	38	30	47	29.4
Thrombocyte series:																		
Thromboblast						0						0						0
Early immature thrombocyte		1				0.2	1				1	0.4				1		0.2
Mid-immature thrombocyte		2				0.4	1				1	0.4	2	3		1	1	1.4
Late immature thrombocyte	1	1	1		1	0.8	1			1	1	0.6	2		1			0.6
Mature thrombocyte		3	5	1	3	2.4				1	1	0.4		1		1		0.4
Lymphocyte series:																		
Lymphoblast						0						0						0
Immature lymphocyte	3	3	2			1.6						0						0
Mature lymphocyte		6	6	1		2.6	1					0.2						0
Monocyte series:																		
Monoblast						0						0						0
Early immature monocyte						0						0						0
Late immature monocyte						0						0						0
Mature monocyte						0						0						0
Heterophil series:																		
Granuloblast			1			0.2			5	3	3	2.2	3	3	5	6	2	3.8
Metagranuloblast		1				0.2			2		6	1.6	4	4	1			1.8
Promyelocyte		2				0.4	9	4	8	8	7	7.2	20	7	10	9	16	12.4
Meso- and metamyelocyte		1			1	0.4						0	12	11	12	12	6	10.6
Mature heterophil	5	28	1	1	7	8.4	4	1	2			1.4	13	10	14	4	12	10.6
Eosinophil series:																		
Metagranuloblast						0						0						0
Mesomyelocyte						0	1					0.2	1					0.2
Metamyelocyte						0	2	1		1		0.8	2	2	2	3		1.8
Mature eosinophil		1				0.2	7			1	1	1.8	3	1	1	1	1	1.4
Basophil series:																		
Promyelocyte						0		1			1	0.4						0
Meso- and metamyelocyte						0			1			0.2	1	2			1	0.8
Mature basophil		3				0.6						0	1					0.2
Miscellaneous cells:																		
Primary erythrocytes	1		2	2	6	2.2						0						0
Primordial osteogenic cells	3	4	2	4	3	3.2						0						0
Osteoclasts	1	1				0.4						0						0
Osteoblasts	2	1	4	5	17	5.8					1	0.2						0
Plasmacyte series						0						0						0
Elongated reticular cells	10	9	3	8	3	6.6						0						0
Macrophages		1		1		0.4						0						0
Cells in mitosis		1	1			0.4	2	1		2		1.0				1		0.2
Squashed cells	12	7	1	9	10	7.8	5	2			1	1.6	7		5	4	4	4.0
Unidentified cells	4	16	5	4	5	6.8	8	3	4	2		3.4	1	1	4	4	2	2.4

After hatching																							
1–3 hours of age						4 days 18 hours of age						8 days of age						175 days of age					
Bird					Average	Bird					Average	Bird					Average	Bird					Average
1	2	3	4	5		1	2	3	4	5		1	2	3	4	5		1	2	3	4	5	
Pct.	Pct.	Pct.	Pct.	Pct.	Pct.	Pct.	Pct.	Pct.	Pct.	Pct.	Pct.	Pct.	Pct.	Pct.	Pct.	Pct.	Pct.	Pct.	Pct.	Pct.	Pct.	Pct.	Pct.
2	....	....	....	3	1.0	6	....	2	2	2	2.4	....	2	2	5	1	2.0	....	1	....	....	2	0.6
3	....	3	....	4	2.0	2	4	2	3	4	3.0	3	3	2	....	....	1.6	2	....	2	1	4	1.8
2	3	2	6	10	4.6	5	11	7	8	8	7.8	6	9	6	3	7	6.2	....	2	2	4	7	3.0
5	9	4	2	4	4.8	29	31	27	18	11	23.2	24	28	12	13	28	21.0	6	26	15	30	11	17.6
69	63	56	64	48	60.0	37	18	38	27	27	29.4	44	30	52	49	45	44.0	76	51	60	50	38	55.0
....	....	....	....	....	0	....	....	....	....	....	0	....	....	....	....	....	0	....	....	....	....	....	0
....	....	....	....	....	0	1	1	1	....	2	1.0	....	2	....	1	....	0.6	....	1	....	....	....	0.2
....	1	1	....	....	0.4	1	3	2	3	2	2.2	1	....	....	....	....	0.2	4	1	1	1	....	1.4
....	....	2	....	6	1.6	....	4	....	3	1	1.6	1	....	....	1	....	0.4	1	1	2	....	4	1.8
3	5	1	2	5	3.2	2	2	4	4	8	4.0	2	3	1	3	....	1.8	2	3	1	1	7	2.8
....	....	....	....	....	0	....	....	....	....	....	0	....	....	....	....	....	0	....	....	....	....	....	0
....	....	....	....	....	0	1	....	....	2	1	0.8	1	1	....	1	....	0.6	....	....	1	....	1	0.4
2	2	2	4	2	2.4	1	2	2	1	1	1.4	....	3	1	4	1	1.8	2	2	2	5	9	4.0
....	....	....	....	....	0	....	....	....	....	....	0	....	....	....	....	....	0	....	....	....	....	....	0
....	....	....	....	....	0	....	....	....	3	....	0.6	2	1	1	2	....	1.2	1	3	1	....	3	1.6
....	....	....	....	....	0	....	....	....	2	1	0.6	1	....	....	....	....	0.2	....	1	....	....	....	0.2
....	....	....	....	....	0	....	....	....	1	....	0.2	....	....	....	....	....	0	....	....	....	....	1	0.2
....	....	1	....	1	0.4	1	....	1	1	2	1.0	....	....	2	1	2	1.0	....	....	1	3	1	1.0
....	....	....	....	....	0	....	....	....	....	2	0.4	....	....	....	2	1	0.6	....	....	....	....	1	0.2
....	2	....	....	2	0.8	1	7	....	2	2	2.4	1	....	2	1	....	0.8	....	....	....	1	1	0.4
1	....	2	....	2	1.0	1	7	3	7	7	5.0	2	1	8	4	3	3.6	....	4	....	....	....	0.8
5	3	14	10	5	7.4	1	4	4	6	11	5.2	10	8	7	5	10	8.0	2	....	3	1	3	1.8
....	....	....	....	....	0	....	....	....	....	....	0	....	1	....	....	1	0.4	....	....	....	....	....	0
....	....	....	....	....	0	....	1	....	2	....	0.6	....	2	....	....	1	0.6	....	....	....	....	....	0
....	....	....	....	....	0	1	1	....	....	....	0.4	....	2	....	....	....	0.4	....	....	....	....	1	0.2
....	....	1	1	....	0.4	....	....	....	1	1	0.4	....	1	....	1	....	0.4	1	....	1	....	....	0.4
....	....	....	....	....	0	....	1	....	....	....	0.2	....	....	....	....	....	0	....	....	....	....	1	0.2
....	....	....	....	....	0	....	....	....	....	1	0.2	....	....	....	....	....	0	....	....	....	....	....	0
....	....	1	1	....	0.4	....	....	....	....	....	0	....	....	....	....	....	0	....	....	....	....	....	0
....	1	....	1	....	0.4	....	....	....	....	....	0	....	....	....	....	....	0	....	....	....	....	....	0
....	....	4	....	....	0.8	....	....	....	....	....	0	....	....	....	....	....	0	....	....	....	....	....	0
....	....	....	....	....	0	....	....	1	....	....	0.2	....	....	....	....	....	0	....	....	....	....	....	0
3	1	2	1	....	1.4	....	....	....	....	....	0	....	....	....	....	....	0	....	....	....	....	....	0
....	....	....	....	....	0	....	....	....	....	....	0	....	....	....	2	....	0.4	....	....	....	....	....	0
....	....	1	....	....	0.2	....	....	1	....	1	0.4	....	....	....	....	1	0.2	....	....	....	....	1	0.2
2	2	1	8	8	4.2	9	3	4	5	5	5.2	1	4	2	1	....	1.6	3	8	3	3	2	3.8
4	7	1	1	....	2.6	1	....	....	....	....	0.2	....	....	1	....	1	0.4	....	....	1	....	1	0.4

Blood Cells of Other Avian Species

DESCRIPTION OF CELLS

Although this study has been concerned primarily with the blood of the chicken, the authors have not been unmindful of the requirement, implicit in the title of this volume, that attention be given to the blood of other species of birds.

Specimens have been collected from other domestic birds and from wild birds. But cells from such specimens are illustrated and described only if they differ appreciably from cells found in chicken blood. There seemed to be no reason why a cell from another species should be illustrated and described if its counterpart in chicken blood could be readily located in the Atlas.

Table 11 lists the birds from which specimens were taken. The study included the circulating blood of all these species and the bone marrow of many of them.

After the blood cells of the chicken, with all their variations, have been thoroughly studied, no difficulty should be experienced in identifying the various blood-cell types in other birds, because the same cell type is closely similar in appearance in most avian species. The only possible points of confusion have been illustrated in figures 400–410, and are to be found in the

Table 11.—Birds, other than the chicken, from which blood-cell specimens were taken

Order and family	Species [1]		Number of specimens	Order and family	Species [1]		Number of specimens
	Scientific name	Common name			Scientific name	Common name	
ANSERIFORMES				STRIGIFORMES			
Anatidae.........	Branta canadensis...	Canada goose.........	11	Strigidae.........	Bubo virginianus....	Great horned owl......	4
	Anas platyrhynchos..	Mallard duck (Mallard).	15	PICIFORMES			
	Defila (Anas) acuta..	American pintail duck (Pintail).	2	Picidae..........	Dryobates (Dendrocopos)) villosus.	Hairy woodpecker.....	1
	Nettion carolinense (Anas carolinensis).	Green-winged teal.....	2		Dryobates (Dendrocopos) pubescens.	Downy woodpecker....	3
	Mareca americana...	Baldpate duck (American widgeon).	2	PASSERIFORMES			
	Spatula clypeata.....	Shoveller duck (Shoveler).	2	Paridae..........	Penthestes (Parus) atricapillus.	Black-capped chickadee.	2
	Erismatura (Oxyura) jamaicensis.	Ruddy duck.........	2	Sittidae.........	Sitta carolinensis....	White-breasted nuthatch.	1
FALCONIFORMES				Turdidae........	Turdus migratorius..	Robin..............	1
Accipitridae........	Accipiter cooperi (cooperii).	Cooper's hawk.......	2	Sylviidae........	Regulus satrapa.....	Golden-crowned kinglet.	1
	Buteo borealis (jamaicensis).	Red-tailed hawk.......	5	Sturnidae........	Sturnus vulgaris.....	Starling............	1
GALLIFORMES				Vireonidae.......	Vireo olivaceus......	Red-eyed vireo......	1
Phasianidae........	Phasianus colchicus..	Ring-necked pheasant..	16	Compsothlypidae (Parulidae).	Vermivora peregrina..	Tennessee warbler....	3
Meleagrididae......	Meleagris gallopavo..	Domestic turkey......	41		Dendroica virens.....	Black-throated green warbler.	1
COLUMBIFORMES					Dendroica striata.....	Black-poll warbler....	3
Columbidae.......		Laboratory pigeon.....	25	Fringillidae.......	Richmondena cardinalis.	Cardinal............	1
		Laboratory dove......	11		Passerina cyanea....	Indigo bunting.......	1
CUCULIFORMES					Carpodacus purpureus.	Purple finch........	1
Cuculidae........	Coccyzus americanus.	Yellow-billed cuckoo...	1		Spinus pinus.......	Pine siskin..........	3
	Coccyzus erythropthalmus.	Black-billed cuckoo....	1		Pipilo erythrophthalmus.	Towhee (Rufous-sided towhee).	1
					Junco hyemalis......	Slate-colored junco....	1

[1] Names in parentheses are from the fifth edition (1957) of "Check-List of North American Birds," by a committee of the American Ornithologists' Union; others are from the fourth edition (1931).

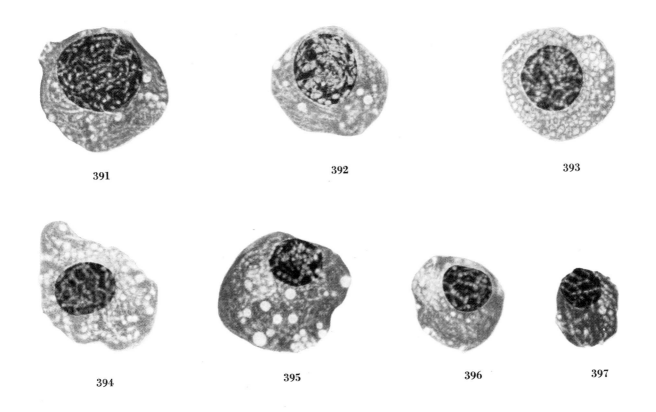

FIGURES 391–397.—Cells of the plasmacyte series found in bone marrow of adult chickens.   2,470×

391   Early immature plasmacyte.
392–395   Late immature plasmacytes.
396, 397   Mature plasmacytes.

FIGURES 398, 399.—Osteoclasts from the bone marrow of adult chickens. 2,470×.

398 Osteoclast that appears to have but one nucleus, but others were present at lower focal levels. Acidophilic material in the central portion characteristic of osteoclasts.
399 Multinucleated osteoclast. Boundary of cell often difficult to determine.

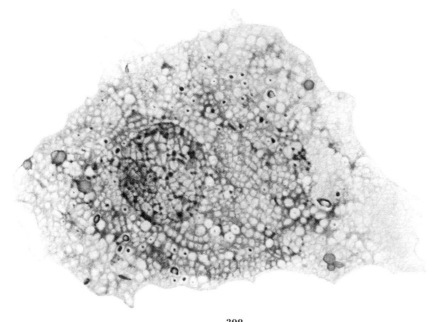

398

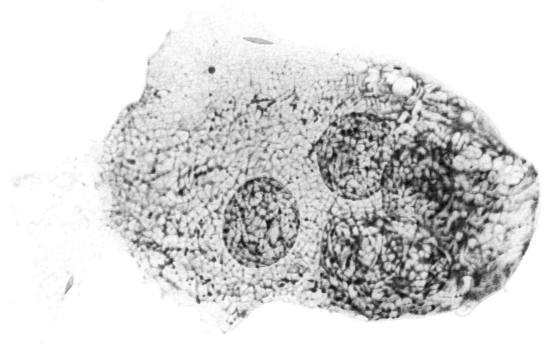

399

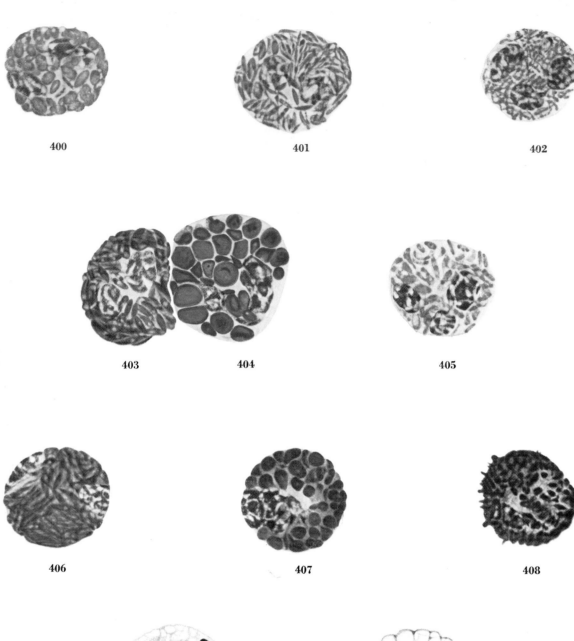

400   401   402

403   404   405

406   407   408

409   410

heterophils and eosinophils of ducks and turkeys. Cullen (1903) noted that in guinea hens and in kingfishers the percentage of heterophils was lower than for eosinophils, a relationship that was the reverse of that found for other species of birds, therefore, close attention was given to these cells in the blood of wild birds and it was readily apparent that the confusion arose from the fact that heterophils and eosinophils are highly variable in their appearance; some heterophils resemble eosinophils and some eosinophils resemble heterophils. Confusion has been created by the fact that in some species—the duck, for example—the eosinophils are often rare, and it may be that, in making differential counts, certain variants of the heterophils were classified as eosinophils and the remainder as heterophils.

Figure 400 is a heterophil from a mallard duck taken in Michigan and figure 401 is from an individual of the same species taken in Utah. It should not be assumed that the cytologic differences are due to geographic habitat; this much variation can be found in a group of slides from a species within a particular locality. One of these cells (fig. 400) has broad, short, rounded rods that look much like large eosinophil spheres (compare with fig. 404). The rods of figure 400 are not uniformly stained. The density of staining is greater toward the edge of the rod than toward the center. The clear area of the center is not sharply defined like the vacuole in the center of the rod in chicken blood (fig. 166).

The rods in another specimen of mallard duck were small, narrow, and tapering with pointed ends (fig. 401). It is this shape that is characteristic of heterophil rods in most birds. In the specimen from which the heterophil (fig. 401)

was taken, the eosinophils, of which figure 402 is an example, looks somewhat like heterophils. This similiarity in appearance is a possible cause of confusion.

The two types of specific inclusions are not actually alike when examined under high magnification. The specific eosinophilic granules are composed of very small bodies that appear to lie on a network. If the granules merge with the network, because they are small or because there is no color difference between the two, the network may then simulate a mass of poorly preserved rods in a heterophil.

Wright's stain, when applied to chicken blood, often incompletely colors the chromatin of the heterophil nucleus. Heterophils of many other species show the same artifact. The difference in staining affinity between the nuclei of heterophils and eosinophils has been utilized to aid in distinguishing the two cell types, and a search for this difference is always made at the beginning of a study on blood from a species not previously examined.

Incomplete nuclear staining of heterophils is shown in figures 400, 401, and 403, and complete nuclear staining of eosinophils in figures 402, 405, and 407.

When a specimen is found where the heterophil nucleus stains as well as the eosinophil nucleus, considerable study may be required before the two cell types can be distinguished readily. Hewitt (1942) faced the same problem in the selection of proper terms for heterophils and eosinophils. Eosinophils with round granules occurred only in bone marrow. Therefore, without attempting to solve the homologies of heterophils and eosinophils in ducks with those

---

Figures 400–410.—Granulocytes from ducks and turkeys. 2,470×.

Figures 400, 401: *Heterophils from adult male mallard ducks. Wright's stain.*

400 From Lowell, Mich.
401 From Utah.
402 Eosinophil from same slide as preceding one.

Figures 403, 404: *Two granulocytes adjacent to each other. From a baldpate drake. Wright's stain.*

403 Heterophil.
404 Eosinophil.
405 Eosinophil. Ruddy duck. Juvenile male. May-Grünwald Giemsa.

Figures 406–408: *Granulocytes from the turkey. Wright's stain.*

406 Heterophil.
407 Eosinophil from same slide as preceding one.
408 Basophil.

Figures 409, 410: *Turkey granulocytes from a smear fixed in Petrunkevitch No. 2 and stained with May-Grünwald Giemsa. Same bird as the one from which figures 406 and 407 were taken.*

409 Heterophil.
410 Eosinophil.

cells in other birds, he grouped all cells in which the specific granules stained with eosin into two types of heterophils: heterophils with ellipsoidal rods and heterophils with bacillary rods.

When the criteria set up in table 8 (p. 90) are applied, as far as they may be applicable, to Hewitt's colored figures of these two cell types, the cells with the ellipsoidal rods become heterophils and those with bacillary rods become eosinophils. The close agreement between the differential counts on ducks that he used and the counts on the common mallard (p. 216) offer further confirmatory evidence that his heterophils with bacillary rods are eosinophils in spite of the fact that they superficially resemble the heterophils of other species of birds.

The percentage values for leukocytes obtained by Magath and Higgins (1934) for adult tame mallard, *Anas platyrhynchos* L., differ somewhat from those given in table 18. Like Hewitt, he found that polymorphonuclears with granules were more abundant than those with rods, namely, 24.3 and 2.1 percent, respectively.

Figures 400–402 are from the mallard, figures 403 and 404 from the baldpate duck, and figure 405 from the ruddy duck. The three were selected because they again illustrate the wide variation in the appearance of the eosinophil. Figures 403 and 404 are cells that were adjacent on the same slide. The rods of the heterophil are cigar shaped with a vacuole in the center of each rod. The spheres of the eosinophil are very large and most of them are homogeneous, but in a few there are small granules on a reticulum; the granules are arranged in a square.

The type of eosinophil in figure 405 is a source of confusion. It appears but little different from the heterophil in figure 401. The specific bodies of the eosinophil are present in the form of short rods with granules. Sometimes these granules are located at the end and sometimes in the middle of each body. The eosinophil of the turkey (fig. 407) stains almost the same color as the heterophil rods of the baldpate duck. A clear, light-staining space is present in the center of some of the spheres.

Perhaps all these variations can be resolved into some definite overall plan. Although much study still remains, there seems to be some evidence that the specific granule of the eosinophil has two morphologic forms with transitional stages between, not only in the same species but also in the same individual. In the chicken there were small, fine granules on a reticulum (fig. 179) and larger spheres, nearly homogeneous in structure (fig. 180). The condition in figure 402 is equivalent to that in figure 179. The important fact to note is that, at least in chickens, the large type eosinophilic body is actually composed of four small granules arranged in a square (fig. 180). Therefore, it is particularly significant that in the sphere located at about 1 o'clock on figure 404 there should be 4 small, distinct granules in the form of a square with homogeneous material around them. In figure 405 they have taken another form, and here the unit granules have moved apart in pairs so that a rod is produced.

These variations and their possible relationships are presented in figure 411, in which the progression is from the homogeneous sphere, stage A, to the development of an enclosed tetrad of granules, B, which in ducks may pull apart by pairs to form pseudorod structures, B' and B''. The homogeneous sphere, A, may develop into a square of four granules surrounded by much matrix, B, or only a little, C. Step D has never been observed but its existence, as a transitional configuration between the scattered tetrads of C and the reticulum with granules at the interstices of E, is assumed. Any such scheme of progression should agree with the development of the cell through myelogenic stages, maturity, and aging. During myelopoiesis, the only expression of the specific eosinophilic granule in the chicken is in the form of homogeneous spheres (figs. 379–381). The same was true in a case of eosinophil myelogenous leukemia. Of the immature stages that were drawn from circulating blood (figs. 184 and 186), the first had homogeneous spheres and the second a tetrad type of arrangement of small granules. Since the second is a more differentiated cell than the first, it might have been concluded that the spheres were changed into granules, but when figure 186, a young cell with granules, is compared with figure 180, a mature cell with three nuclear lobes, it could be concluded equally well that the process of change was going in the opposite direction.

Well executed color drawings of the blood from an African vulture have been presented by Neave (1906). He illustrates three morphologic types of eosinophilic polymorphs, but does not attempt to name them.

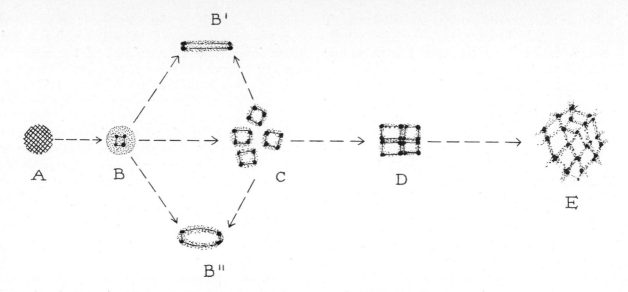

FIGURE 411.—A diagram in which relationships have been suggested for the different types of eosinophil granules that have been observed.

A   A large homogeneous sphere seen during myelopoiesis.
B   A combination of sphere and small granules arranged in a square (for example, see fig. 404).
C   The type of granule often seen in the eosinophil of the chicken—four small granules in a square, joined by lines (figs. 177, 178). The presence of a matrix around them is questionable.

B′ and B″   From the type of granule in either B or C elongation of the square into either a rod or oval shap, can be produced (fig. 405). The rod and oval forme can be confused easily with the rods of heterophils bus have no relationship.
D   A transition stage leading to E, a reticulum carrying small granules at the interstices (fig. 402).

Figures 406–410 illustrate the granulocytes found in turkeys. The rods in the heterophil (fig. 406) can be identified readily for what they are, but if they are much thinner than shown in this cell, they take on the effect of a reticulum—an effect that may cause them to resemble the fine-granule type of eosinophil. Actually, there was no confusion in the identification of heterophils and eosinophils on the slide from which figures 406 and 407 were taken because the eosinophil (407) was so strikingly different from the heterophil in both color and structure. This again emphasizes the fact that among various species the tinctorial qualities of cells of the same type are not always alike; for example, the rods of the heterophil (fig. 403) are colored about the same hue as are the granules of the eosinophil (fig. 407) and neither of these are greatly different from the dark-magenta bodies of the basophil (fig. 408).

Duplicate smears were made of blood taken from some of the species listed in table 11. One was fixed dry and the other in Petrunkevitch No. 2 and stained with May-Grünwald Giemsa. By the latter method the nuclear lobes were clearly shown and were used for Arneth counts. In the chicken heterophil (fig. 203) the rods were completely dissolved and only the protoplasmic network remained. The same picture has been seen in the turkey (fig. 409). This technic, how-ever, produced different effects on the eosinophils of these two species. In the chicken (fig. 215) the eosinophil granules are well preserved, but in the turkey (fig. 410) they are completely dissolved, with the result that heterophils and eosinophils appear quite similar in this species; a close examination of the two cell types in turkeys does reveal a difference. The protoplasmic framework around the eosinophil granules is sharp and definite and the size of the spaces is equivalent to the area of the large granules that fill them (fig. 407). The spaces within the heterophil vary in size and are irregular in shape, and the protoplasmic network is not sharply defined. Once these differences are recognized there should be no difficulty in the separation of heterophils and eosinophils when making Arneth counts in the turkey.

When smears were taken from pheasants, it was noted that the blood had a surprisingly high viscosity. When the drop collected on the pusher slide had been touched to the smear slide, it did not spread easily to the opposite corners, as does the blood of chickens and geese. Only after considerable moving around of the pusher slide did the drop spread laterally to form a uniform column of substance. This property of the pheasant blood made it difficult to obtain a thin, uniform smear.

The erythrocytes of the species of ducks, cuckoos and the hawk mentioned in table 11 were larger than those of the chicken; the erythrocytes of all the other species had approximately the same size as those of the chicken. These statements are based on visual comparisons and not on measurements. Wintrobe (1933) has given the length and width of erythrocytes for the chicken, guinea, goose, and pigeon. A further discussion of the size of erythrocytes in the chicken will be given when table 12 is considered.

Immature stages of development and erythroplastids of all sizes were found in many of the species of wild birds; they were especially numerous in some of the slides from ducks and from the indigo bunting. In mature cells, the nucleus was slender and rodlike with dense chromatin clumps like figure 5. In slides from some specimens of mallard ducks the nuclei were so contracted and slender that the dense chromatin clumps bulged outward, giving it a mulberry appearance. Scarcely any spaces could be seen between the clumps.

Smears from ducks and pigeons showed erythrocytes that were distributed in pairs and in a crossed position. With each erythrocyte in a pair crossing the other at 90 degrees, and with the centers coinciding, a pinwheel effect was produced. This peculiarity has never been observed in chicken blood.

The thrombocytes in the shoveller duck, turkey, pheasant, pigeon, dove, owl, black-capped chickadee, cuckoo, and white-breasted nuthatch were larger than those in the chicken. Except for these differences in size, the thrombocytes in all the species listed in table 11 were similar to those of the chicken. The specific granules of the turkey thrombocyte were usually in vacuoles.

There is always a possibility that thrombocytes will be confused with lymphocytes. Confusion is especially likely to occur in the case of the pigeon. In this species the cytoplasm of thrombocytes takes a more intense coloration than it does in most avian species, and the cells are nearly round. Moreover, the thrombocytes of pigeons appear to disintegrate less readily when the smear is made than they do in most species; thus the form of the cell is retained. This, of course, aids in holding the specific granule of the thrombocyte intact so that identification can be made easily when neither lymphocytes nor thrombocytes have disintegrated. If the cytosome of these two cell types has been lost they can still be separated by the fact that the nucleus of the lymphocyte is larger than that of the thrombocyte.

Lymphocytes in all species of wild and domestic birds examined appeared the same as in chickens. Magenta bodies or reactive lymphocytes, or both, were found in nine species, including a species of duck.

Monocytes in other species are the same as found in the chicken. Those of the great horned owl were large with round nuclei and large, dense chromatin clumps.

Heterophils were variable within an individual or a species, as they were in chickens. Differences in the shape of the rods in ducks have already been mentioned; in turkeys the rods dissolve readily as they do in chicken cells; in the owl the rods were of the "typical" type, pointed at both ends. In other species of birds, as well as in the chicken, central bodies exist inside the rods, but their occurrence is not constant.

The eosinophils for some ducks have been pictured. Figure 402 represents the granular type, figure 404 the large sphere type, and figure 405 the rod type; in figure 411 these have been diagramed as *E*, *B*, and *B'*, respectively. In the pintail duck the specific bodies are spheres and vary in size from medium to large; in the green-winged teal, rods and granules are mixed; and in the shoveller duck small granules are clumped to form rods. The Canada goose and the owl have small granules, and the pheasant and the dove have large ones. In many of the passerines they are like those in the chicken but in the red-eyed vireo and purple finch they have fine granules and in the robin the bodies are almost refractile.

Basophils in other avian species appear as they do in the chicken except that the cells of the turkey are larger and those of the owl are smaller. The nucleus of the pigeon basophil is often eccentrically placed so that the granules lie at one side of the cell. This cell in the mallard duck is extremely susceptible to aqueous stains; even Wright's stain dissolves most of the granules and when this happens so that the cell contains only a few granules, the nucleus becomes more intensely stained and the cell closely resembles a lymphocyte with magenta bodies. Often it is only the pinkish ground color of the basophil cytoplasm and the blue of the lymphocyte that distinguishes one cell from the other. Both May-Grünwald Giemsa and MacNeil's tetrachrome stains dissolve the cytosome and its granules to such an extent that basophils could not be found in smears following these stains.

SIZE OF CELLS

Graphs in chapter 2 (figs. 89, 152, 153, and 197) give the average sizes of thrombocytes, lymphocytes, monocytes, and the three granulocytes. With the possible exception of the curves for the granulocytes, they are unimodal. Actually the data for these graphs represented a composite from four sources:

Stock from the U. S. Regional Poultry Research Laboratory:
    Single Comb White Leghorns, line 6—relatively resistant to lymphomatosis.
    Single Comb White Leghorns, line 15—relatively susceptible to lymphomatosis.
Stock from a commercial breeder:
    New Hampshires.
    Columbian Plymouth Rocks.

Slides were taken from individuals of each group and the various cell types were measured.

The most challenging data came from differences in size of erythrocytes. The length and width of the cytosomes and nuclei of 25 cells from each bird were measured. The ranges and the averages are given in table 12. The average length of the erythrocyte for our stock was 10.6μ, and the width was about 6.6μ; the nucleus was $4.1 \times 3.0\mu$. There was little difference between lines 6 and 15. Both breeds of chickens procured from commercial sources had erythrocytes that averaged about 1.6μ longer and the nuclei were about 1.0μ longer, but the widths of each were the same as for the smaller cells from our birds. Even among the individuals of a group there may be considerable difference in a particu-

lar set of measurements; for example, the erythrocyte nucleus of the first Columbian Plymouth Rock was 18 percent longer than that of the second one. These data raise again the questions, What is the form of a typical erythrocyte? Are the rounded cells with oval leptochromatic nuclei less mature than the longer cells with rodlike pachychromatic nuclei?

Keller (1933) studied cell and nuclear size in dwarf and normal breeds of chickens. In embryos, during the incubation period of 4 to 8 days, there was no significant difference in lengths of erythrocytes. At hatching, the average dimensions of length and width for the dwarf breed was $8.05 \times 3.88\mu$ and for the breed of normal size, $7.51 \times 3.77\mu$. In the grown birds, the dwarf showed $7.84 \times 4.19\mu$ and the chicken of normal size, $8.19 \times 4.50\mu$. It was concluded that the size of the breed had no influence on the size of the erythrocytes. It should be noted that the average values given in her work are in every case less than the minimum of the range given in table 12.

Kitaeva (1939) also studied the size of erythrocytes from three European breeds of chickens—Langshans, Brown Leghorns, and Benthams. The differences were slight. Averages computed from his data on all adult birds were, length 11.0μ and width 6.6μ. These values fall within the ranges given in table 12.

An extensive study of cell size in relation to body weight was made by Mehner (1938) on 11 breeds of chickens. He used epithelial cells, striated muscle cells, and erythrocytes. The bird weights varied from 335 to 2900 grams. The area of the erythrocytes varied from 62.3 to 77.2 sq. μ and, in spite of considerable variability, he obtained a correlation of -0.54 ± 0.08 between body weight and erythrocyte area. He studied size of erythrocytes in the White Leghorn from 1 day of age to 54 months of age. When dividing the series into those younger than 9 months and those older than 9 months, he obtained an average erythrocyte area of 70.0 sq. μ for the former and 66.5 sq. μ for the latter.

Kalabukhov and Rodionov (1934), who were interested in the problem of changes in the blood with age, gave the following figures, based on the sparrows *Passer montanus* L. and *P. domesticus* L., which have altricial young: age 1–5 days, hemoglobin 4.0 percent, number of erythrocytes

Table 12.—Dimension of erythrocytes

Breed	Source [1]	Bird [2]	Cytosome				Nucleus			
			Length		Width		Length		Width	
			Range μ	Average μ	Range μ	Average μ	Range μ	Average μ	Range μ	Average μ
Single Comb White Leghorns.	RPL 6......	1	9.6–11.8	10.8	6.2–8.0	7.0	3.4–4.9	4.3	2.7–4.1	3.1
		2	10.0–11.6	10.8	5.9–7.7	6.6	3.6–4.6	4.1	2.7–3.5	3.1
		3	9.7–11.8	10.7	6.0–7.7	6.6	3.4–4.6	4.1	3.0–3.5	3.2
Average for group....			....	10.8	....	6.7	....	4.2	....	3.1
Single Comb White Leghorns.	RPL 15.....	1	9.2–11.4	10.6	6.2–7.2	6.7	3.0–5.2	3.8	1.8–3.6	3.0
		2	9.4–11.6	10.3	6.0–7.4	6.5	3.5–4.8	4.1	2.8–3.4	3.0
		3	9.3–11.6	10.4	6.0–7.5	6.7	3.6–5.3	4.3	2.6–3.7	3.1
Average for group....			....	10.4	....	6.6	....	4.1	....	3.0
New Hampshires.......	Commercial .	1	10.9–14.0	12.4	6.0–7.5	6.8	4.1–5.7	4.9	3.0–3.7	3.4
		2	10.6–13.4	12.1	6.2–8.2	7.2	4.6–6.3	5.1	2.7–4.1	3.3
		3	10.9–13.2	12.0	4.6–7.2	6.5	3.0–6.0	5.2	2.8–3.5	3.2
Average for group....			....	12.2	....	6.8	....	5.1	....	3.3
Columbian Plymouth Rocks.	Commercial .	1	11.0–13.4	12.4	5.0–7.7	6.9	4.9–7.0	5.9	2.0–3.7	2.8
		2	11.2–12.9	12.0	6.0–7.6	6.7	4.4–6.0	5.0	2.5–3.6	3.3
		3	10.9–14.2	12.6	6.0–8.3	7.0	4.7–7.3	5.5	2.8–4.4	3.3
Average for group....			....	12.3	....	6.9	....	5.5	....	3.1

[1] RPL=stock from the U. S. Regional Poultry Research Laboratory. [2] Measurements based on 25 cells per bird.

1,028,000; age 10–15 days, hemoglobin 6.8 percent, number of erythrocytes 1,645,000, area of an erythrocyte $74.5\mu^2$; age 16–20 days, hemoglobin 7.7 percent, number of erythrocytes, 2,177,000 area of an erythrocyte $72.7\mu^2$; and age 21–30 days, hemoglobin 11.4 percent, number of erythrocytes 2,425,000, and area of an erythrocyte $55.8\mu^2$. Essentially similar changes in increase of hemoglobin and cell number, and decrease in cell size with age, occurred in the gull, *Larus ridibundus* L., which have praecocial young.

Bartsch et al. (1937) gave average length and width of erythrocytes and length and width of their nuclei for 50 species of birds from eastern North America. They say (p. 516):

"The largest cell was found in the Osprey, which yielded the length 16.5 microns, while the smallest length was observed in the Carolina Chickadee, which gave a length of 6.0 microns. The greatest diameter of the cell was found in the Osprey and the Red-headed Woodpecker, both of which gave a reading of 10.0 microns, while the Eastern Tree Sparrow yielded the least diameter, namely 4.0 microns.

"In the measurements of the nucleus the largest diameter fell to the Red-headed Woodpecker, which yielded 7.87 microns, while the shortest length of the nucleus fell to the White-breasted Nuthatch and the Yellow-throated Warbler, both registering 3.10 microns. The greatest diameter of the nucleus fell to the White-breasted Nuthatch and the Eastern Hermit Thrush, both of which yielded 1.10 microns."

These authors listed five earlier papers, not quoted here, in which erythrocyte size had been determined in wild birds.

Table 13 gives measurements of length and width of thrombocytes for the same four groups of chickens. Nuclear measurements were not taken. The cells in the New Hampshire and in the Columbian Plymouth Rock were about 1 micron longer than in the Laboratory stock of Single Comb White Leghorns, and the width was greater also.

The irregular shapes of the lymphocytes and monocytes make it impossible to take simple length and width measurements. This irregularity of form is shown in figures 150 and 151. On page 65 it was explained that the areas were determined by tracing the outlines of cells and nuclei with a camera lucida and then using a planimeter. The diameters given in table 14 are calculated values derived from the areas. The areas of lymphocytes for the three groups, RPL 6, RPL 15, and the Columbian Plymouth Rocks, were close—54.7, 52.6, and $54.2\mu^2$, respectively. But the average area for the three New Hamp-

Table 13.—Dimensions of thrombocytes

Breed	Source [1]	Bird [2]	Cytosome Length Range μ	Cytosome Length Average μ	Cytosome Width Range μ	Cytosome Width Average μ
Single Comb White Leghorns	RPL 6	4	7.0– 8.5	7.8	3.1–4.6	4.1
		5	6.6–10.5	8.8	3.3–6.1	4.4
		6	7.0– 8.9	7.8	4.3–5.9	5.1
Average for group				8.1		4.5
Single Comb White Leghorns	RPL 15	4	7.7– 9.9	8.6	3.6–5.6	4.5
		5	6.7– 9.5	7.7	3.1–4.7	3.9
		6	6.1– 9.0	7.1	3.0–5.1	3.9
Average for group				7.8		4.1
New Hampshires	Commercial	1	8.9–10.8	9.8	4.8–5.9	5.4
		4	7.7–11.5	8.9	3.5–6.0	5.0
		5	7.8–10.4	9.0	5.1–6.4	5.7
Average for group				9.2		5.4
Columbian Plymouth Rocks	Commercial	1	8.3–10.1	9.2	4.3–5.9	5.1
		2	6.8–10.9	8.6	3.6–5.4	4.7
		4	7.4– 9.5	8.5	4.6–6.1	5.2
Average for group				8.8		5.0

[1] RPL=stock from the U. S. Regional Poultry Research Laboratory.　[2] Measurements based on 10 cells per bird.

Table 14.—Area and diameter of lymphocytes

Breed	Source [1]	Bird [2]	Cytosome Area μ² Range	Cytosome Area μ² Average	Cytosome Diameter μ Range	Cytosome Diameter μ Average	Nucleus Area μ² Range	Nucleus Area μ² Average	Nucleus Diameter μ Range	Nucleus Diameter μ Average
Single Comb White Leghorns.	RPL 6	1	20.5–102.7	49.7	5.1–11.4	7.8	12.8–57.8	34.5	4.0– 8.6	6.5
		2	38.5–105.3	61.1	7.0–11.6	8.7	23.1–88.6	42.1	5.4–10.6	7.3
		3	25.7–118.1	53.2	5.7–12.3	7.9	20.5–60.3	35.0	5.1– 8.8	6.6
Average for group				54.7		8.1		37.2		6.8
Single Comb White Leghorns.	RPL 15	1	38.5–106.6	65.5	7.0–11.6	9.1	28.2–61.6	40.9	6.0– 8.9	7.2
		2	30.8–118.1	48.7	6.3–12.3	7.7	25.7–69.3	35.1	5.7– 9.4	6.6
		3	25.7–100.1	43.5	5.7–11.3	7.3	23.1–59.1	35.8	5.4– 8.7	6.7
Average for group				52.6		8.0		37.3		6.8
New Hampshires	Commercial	1	25.7– 79.6	39.4	5.7–10.1	7.0	18.0–43.7	29.0	4.8– 7.4	6.0
		2	15.4– 53.9	37.1	4.4– 8.3	6.8	12.8–38.5	27.4	4.0– 7.0	5.8
		3	12.8– 64.2	30.4	4.0– 9.0	6.1	10.3–41.1	22.1	3.6– 7.2	5.2
Average for group				35.6		6.6		26.2		5.7
Columbian Plymouth Rocks.	Commercial	1	20.5– 92.4	42.8	5.1–10.8	7.3	15.4–48.8	28.8	4.4– 7.9	6.0
		2	25.7– 92.4	50.7	5.7–10.8	7.9	20.5–46.2	32.8	5.1– 7.7	6.4
		3	28.2–110.4	69.1	6.0–11.8	9.2	20.5–53.9	39.1	5.1– 8.3	7.0
Average for group				54.2		8.1		33.6		6.5

[1] RPL=stock from the U. S. Regional Poultry Research Laboratory.　[2] Measurements based on 25 cells per bird.

shires was definitely smaller—35.6μ^2. The same difference in size for this breed is reflected, as would be expected, in the nuclear area and in the diameters of the cells and nuclei. If the lymphocytes and their nuclei when flattened had been circular and the nucleus had been in the center, the cytoplasm would have formed a rim around it hardly more than a half micron in width.

The striking difference in size and nucleocell ratios of lymphocytes and of monocytes is well brought out by comparing the data of table 14 with those of table 15. The monocyte area for both lines of Laboratory stock was large, and for both the commercial lines it was small. In other words, in 3 of the 4 groups lymphocyte and monocyte areas appeared to be positively correlated, but in the Columbian Plymouth Rocks the association was negative. The area of the monocyte nucleus is approximately half the area of the total cell or, comparing nucleus with cytosome, the ratio is approximately 1:1.1 in contrast to the lymphocyte, where the ratio is approximately 1:0.5.

Heterophils show a greater variability among birds within a group than among groups (table 16) and from this there is probably relatively little significance to the difference in size from 7.9μ diameter for RPL line 6 birds and 9.9μ for the New Hampshires. The data for the eosinophils emphasize a point that was brought out when the eosinophil of circulating blood was discussed—so often an individual chicken showed almost exclusively a large or a small type of cell. This is evident in table 16, where maximum size was 6.0μ for bird 6 of RPL line 15, but the minimum for bird 4 was greater—6.4μ. Almost the same situation existed in birds 4 and 6 of RPL line 6, and in 1 and 4 of the Columbian Plymouth Rock.

The average for the basophil diameter of 7.8μ for Laboratory birds is less than 8.1 and 9.1μ for chickens from commercial sources, but the samples are probably too small to have much significance in view of ranges in diameter as great as 4.9 to 10.9μ within a bird and rather wide variability in the averages among groups of birds.

CELL COUNTS, HEMOGLOBIN LEVELS, AND HEMATOCRITS

An important function of an atlas on blood is to aid in cell identification so that accurate differential counts can be made. A review of earlier cell counts in some cases, as well as tabulation of new data of their own has been given by

Table 15.—**Area and diameter of monocytes**

Breed	Source [1]	Bird [2]	Cytosome				Nucleus			
			Area μ^2		Diameter μ		Area μ^2		Diameter μ	
			Range	Average	Range	Average	Range	Average	Range	Average
Single Comb White Leghorns.	RPL 6	1	107.9–151.5	129.0	11.7–15.9	12.9	46.2–66.8	57.9	7.7– 9.2	8.6
		2	102.7–151.5	125.4	11.4–15.9	12.7	43.7–64.2	54.2	7.4– 9.0	8.3
		3	97.6–146.4	124.2	11.1–13.6	12.5	43.7–66.8	56.7	7.4– 9.2	8.5
Average for group				126.2		12.7		56.3		8.5
Single Comb White Leghorns.	RPL 15	1	84.7–146.4	120.7	10.4–13.6	12.4	43.7–64.2	54.3	7.4– 9.0	8.3
		2	105.3–226.0	151.9	11.6–17.0	13.9	46.2–84.7	67.4	7.7–10.4	9.2
		3	87.3–138.7	113.2	10.5–13.3	12.0	48.8–71.9	57.0	7.9– 9.6	8.5
Average for group				128.6		12.8		59.6		8.7
New Hampshires	Commercial.	1	66.8–179.8	100.3	9.2–15.1	11.2	38.5–97.6	50.5	7.0–11.1	8.0
		2	77.0–169.5	107.7	9.9–14.7	11.6	41.1–79.6	51.8	7.2–10.1	8.1
		3	53.1–136.1	101.1	8.7–13.2	11.3	36.0–66.8	51.4	6.8– 9.2	8.0
Average for group				103.0		11.4		51.2		8.0
Columbian Plymouth Rocks.	Commercial.	1	61.6–148.9	93.4	8.9–13.8	10.8	36.0–69.4	49.2	6.8– 9.4	7.9
		2	51.4–133.5	95.7	8.1–13.0	11.0	23.1–64.2	47.4	5.4– 9.0	7.7
		3	71.9–143.8	114.7	9.6–13.5	12.0	38.5–69.3	52.9	7.0– 9.4	8.2
Average for group				101.3		11.3		49.8		7.9

[1] RPL=stock from the U. S. Regional Poultry Research Laboratory. [2] Measurements based on 25 cells per bird.

Table 16.—**Diameter of granulocytes**

Breed	Source [1]	Bird [2]	Heterophil		Eosinophil		Basophil	
			Range μ	Average μ	Range μ	Average μ	Range μ	Average μ
Single Comb White Leghorns........	RPL 6.......	4	6. 2– 7. 8	6. 8	5. 3– 6. 8	6. 1	6. 1– 8. 3	7. 4
		5	6. 0–10. 0	7. 6	5. 5– 8. 8	6. 7	6. 3–10. 0	7. 3
		6	8. 8–10. 1	9. 4	6. 7–10. 9	8. 3	7. 9– 9. 2	8. 8
Average for group..................				7. 9		7. 0		7. 8
Single Comb White Leghorns........	RPL 15......	4	8. 6–10. 6	9. 4	6. 4–10. 1	8. 0	4. 9–10. 9	9. 3
		5	5. 1– 9. 2	7. 6	5. 7– 7. 6	6. 6	6. 1– 7. 8	7. 1
		6	6. 6– 7. 9	7. 2	4. 8– 6. 0	5. 4	6. 0– 7. 6	6. 9
Average for group..................				8. 1		6. 7		7. 8
New Hampshires....................	Commercial...	1	9. 8–11. 4	10. 6	6. 3– 8. 5	7. 8	5. 3– 9. 2	7. 3
		4	8. 2–10. 5	9. 4	6. 1– 8. 3	7. 1	8. 2–10. 6	9. 3
		5	8. 4–10. 5	9. 7	7. 5– 9. 4	8. 4	5. 7– 9. 6	7. 8
Average for group..................				9. 9		7. 8		8. 1
Columbian Plymouth Rocks..........	Commercial...	1	6. 5–10. 3	8. 9	6. 3– 8. 8	7. 8	6. 9– 9. 1	8. 1
		2	7. 4– 8. 4	7. 9	6. 2– 7. 3	6. 7	7. 9– 9. 8	9. 2
		4	9. 1–10. 6	9. 6	8. 5–10. 1	9. 3	9. 0–10. 5	9. 9
Average for group..................				8. 8		7. 9		9. 1

[1] RPL=stock from the U. S. Regional Poultry Research Laboratory. [2] Measurements based on 10 cells per bird.

Burnett (1908), Goodall (1909), Burckhardt (1912), Forkner (1929), Hayden (1929), Blakemore (1934), Cook and Dearstyne (1934), Magath and Higgins (1934), Biely and Palmer (1935), Kelly and Dearstyne (1935), Palmer and Biely (1935a and b), Cook (1937), Olson (1937), Twisselmann (1939), Blount (1939a), Hamre and McHenry (1942b), and Rhian, Wilson, and Moxon (1944). Twisselman clearly demonstrated that there has not always been agreement in regard to cell identification or cell terminology. Breusch (1928) mentions the high variability of cell counts for chickens and considers it to be normal. Palmer and Biely (1935a), in an exhaustive study, concluded that ". . . the erythrocyte and leucocyte counts of a bird fluctuate around a certain level characteristic of the individual." Similar observations were made on cattle by Ferguson, Irwin and Beach (1945). Excellent reviews on variability in blood counts have been given by Garrey and Bryan (1935) and by Sturgis and Bethell (1943). Although these reviews deal primarily with a discussion of cell counts of blood samples taken from mammals, the problems and principles involved are equally applicable to the avian species.

Diesem (1956) and Lucas and Denington (unpublished data) have sought to establish the 95-percent fiducial interval for the normal blood values of chickens. The latter authors also noted that the variability of blood-cell counts in birds was no greater than that reported in mammals.

A superficial comparison of tables 18, 19, 20, and 21 (for ducks, geese, pheasants, and pigeons) with table 17 (for chickens) might give the impression that the first four species were highly variable in comparison with the last. However, this is not the case, and individual records for chickens are just about as variable as for wild birds. The values in table 17, which seem relatively uniform, are based on large groups of chickens—33 to more than 100 in each group. The data from the Laboratory stock were part of a project carried out under a grant from the United States Atomic Energy Commission. Two inbred lines were used, 6 and 15, and data from the two lines have been combined in table 17. Line 6 was developed toward resistance to avain lymphomatosis and line 15 toward susceptibility to this pathologic condition (Waters, 1945). There was a statistically significant difference between the means for each line on almost every type of blood determination; thus the values for erythrocyte count, hemoglobin, hematocrit, and buffy coat were higher for line 6 than for line 15. The only values not significantly different were the eosinophil averages.

In view of the high variability in counts on individual birds, two questions are raised:

Table 17.—Normal blood values for chickens

| Blood component | RPL [1] stock—Single Comb White Leghorns | | | | Farm stock | |
| | Female | | | Male adult | Single Comb White Leghorns—female adult | Rhode Island Reds—female adult |
	6 weeks	12 weeks	Adult			
Erythrocytes..........millions/mm.³..	3.02	3.02	3.00	3.78	2.96	2.88
Hemoglobin..........gms./100 cc...	10.10	9.80	9.70	13.50	10.70	11.00
Hematocrit..............percent..	30.90	30.40	30.80	40.00	31.90	30.80
Buffy coat................percent..	1.00	1.00	1.00	.80	....	....
Thrombocytes.............mm.³..	30,457	26,254	30,856	27,586	37,211	60,311
Total white cells...........mm.³..	28,612	31,256	29,397	16,615	28,863	35,787

	Number per cu. mm.	Percent	Number per cu. mm.	Percent	Number per cu. mm.	Percent	Number per cu. mm.	Percent	Number per cu. mm.	Percent	Number per cu. mm.	Percent
Lymphocytes.....................	23,328	81.5	24,310	77.8	22,371	76.1	10,626	64.0	20,704	71.7	20,794	58.1
Monocytes......................	1,286	4.5	1,542	4.9	1,663	5.7	1,065	6.4	326	1.1	880	2.5
Heterophils.....................	2,898	10.1	3,654	11.7	3,917	13.3	4,288	25.8	6,831	23.7	12,551	35.1
Eosinophils.....................	438	1.5	1,210	3.9	728	2.5	241	1.4	410	1.4	440	1.2
Basophils......................	662	2.3	540	1.7	718	2.4	395	2.4	592	2.1	1,121	3.1

[1] RPL=stock from the U. S. Regional Poultry Research Laboratory.

1. How much value is there in blood determinations based on a single bird?

2. How many birds must be included in one population to give mean values that are significantly different?

At present the opinion is held that some types of blood values, for a single bird, offer relatively little information about the health of that particular bird. This is particularly true for total white cell and differential counts.

This is evident not only in chickens but also in other species of birds. Cook and Dearstyne (1934) arrived at an estimate of the importance of the value given by a single count by grouping all counts into classes in a frequency distribution table. This method is more informative than either an average or a range.

Some types of blood data on chickens gave a narrow range in values for the normal population. Under such conditions, a wide departure

Table 18.—Blood values for common mallard duck (adult males)

[Differential counts in percent]

Bird [1]	Lymphocytes	Monocytes	Heterophils	Eosinophils	Basophils
1..........	47	7	32	11	3
2..........	31	3	55	6	5
3..........	28	8	44	9	11
4..........	30	8	53	5	4
5..........	49	7	31	8	5
6..........	31	15	42	10	2
7..........	24	15	53	6	2
8..........	31	6	55	5	3
9..........	24	7	57	3	9
10........	29	4	53	10	4
Average....	32	8	48	7	5

[1] 100 cells counted from each bird.

Table 19.—Blood values for Canada goose (adult males)

[Differential counts in percent]

Bird [1]	Lymphocytes	Monocytes	Heterophils	Eosinophils	Basophils
1..........	66	4	24	3	3
2..........	33	2	54	10	1
3..........	37	2	50	8	3
4..........	49	5	37	6	3
5..........	30	5	57	8	0
6..........	52	10	32	3	3
7..........	59	11	19	10	1
8..........	32	10	38	15	5
9..........	53	6	39	2	0
Average....	46	6	39	7	2

[1] 100 cells counted from each bird.

from the average, even by a single bird, may indicate ill health. A shift of probably as little as a half million erythrocytes per cubic millimeter could be significant. Likewise, hemoglobin values show a relatively narrow range of variability, and a difference of as little as 1 gram per 100 cc. might be viewed with suspicion. Hematocrit values do not as a rule vary more than about 5 percent either way. The average hematocrit values in table 17 are only 1 to 2 percent higher than those given by Hamre and McHenry (1942a) except for the males. Buffy coats were read in the Van Allen hematocrit tubes with a low-magnification hand lens and as long as there was no hemolysis the normal values usually did not vary more than ±0.2 percent.

On the other hand, thrombocytes, total white cells, and individual cell types often varied from half to twice the average, and thus individual readings do not mean much. This was found to be the case whether the comparison was among different individuals or among repeated bleedings from the same bird. Palmer and Biely (1935a) studied the variability of cell counts in great statistical detail and concluded that when careful attention has been given to technics the fluctuations in normal erythrocytes can be reduced to 15 percent. In their data, the coefficient of variability was generally quite low.

This brings us to the second question. An answer based on some figure derived from a statistical analysis takes into account the variability within and between groups and thus could be different, depending on the scope of the population under study. In the Atomic Energy studies on two inbred lines of Single Comb White Leghorn chickens, birds 6 weeks and 12 weeks of age in groups of 15 to 25 birds were used, but in laying hens the numbers were reduced for various reasons to 7 to 12 birds in a group. Working with these data led to the conclusion that 10 was the minimum desirable number in an experimental group and that 15 was preferable.

This is only a rough estimate derived from studies by Lucas and Denington on whole body X-ray irradiation. In this same study they found (unpublished data) that if the coefficient of variability for the 95-percent fiducial interval were to be held to some fixed value, for example, ±10 percent of the group mean, then the following number of birds would be needed for a study on each of the components of the blood:

Blood component:	Number of chickens in a group
Red blood cells/mm.³	10
Hemoglobin, gms./100 ml.	12
Hematocrit in percent	8
Buffy coat in percent	33
Thrombocytes/mm.³	140
White blood cells/mm.³	106
Lymphocytes/mm.³	130
Monocytes/mm.³	352
Heterophils/mm.³	240
Eosinophils/mm.³	3615
Basophils/mm.³	551

Table 20.—Blood values for ring-necked pheasant (adult males)

[Differential counts in percent]

Bird [1]	Lympho-cytes	Mono-cytes	Hetero-phils	Eosino-phils	Baso-phils
1	28	11	42	0	19
2	49	6	40	0	5
3	43	5	41	0	11
4	17	8	60	0	15
5	43	8	34	1	14
6	63	3	23	2	9
7	29	2	65	0	4
8	24	23	47	0	6
9	29	7	53	0	11
10	20	18	52	3	7
11	44	9	38	2	7
12	42	3	41	1	13
13	26	4	65	2	3
14	10	5	75	4	6
15	41	6	39	0	14
Average	34	8	48	1	10

[1] 100 cells counted from each bird.

Table 21.—Blood values for laboratory pigeon

[Differential counts in percent]

Bird [1]	Lympho-cytes	Mono-cytes	Hetero-phils	Eosino-phils	Baso-phils
1	19	11	61	4	5
2	28	4	64	0	4
3	14	25	60	0	1
4	32	8	58	0	2
5	14	23	59	0	4
6	42	14	42	0	2
7	50	11	37	1	1
8	8	20	66	1	5
9	51	14	29	0	6
10	46	19	32	0	3
11	49	12	34	0	5
Average	32	15	49	0.5	3

[1] 100 cells counted from each bird.

These calculations were based on normal adult female Single Comb White Leghorn chickens. It is evident, therefore, that the desirable number of birds to be used in an experimental group is determined by the blood component that is of particular concern to the problem at hand. Fewer birds would be needed in each group if red-cell counts were of chief concern than if eosinophils were to be followed critically. The high variability for some of the blood components makes it necessary for practical reasons to accept high coefficients of variability in order that the number of birds involved in each experimental group can be small enough to make the experiment practical.

Another problem studied by Lucas and Denington (unpublished data) has been the number of cells that should be tabulated from a slide when making a differential count. The accuracy increases by the square root of the multiples of 100 cells counted. In other words, 400 cells give values that are twice as accurate as when 100 cells are counted, and 900 cells give values three times as accurate as when 100 cells are counted.

The question arises, When is the point of diminishing returns in accuracy reached for the time spent in making the counts? In the studies made by Lucas and Denington, it was found that 100 cells were sufficient for lymphocytes and heterophils; but for monocytes, eosinophils, and basophils, 292 cells were needed to give the maximum accuracy for the time spent in making the counts. In making the counts, 300 cells were used. Lucas and Denington found also that the number of birds used in an experiment can be reduced if the number of cells counted per bird is increased. The gain comes chiefly in those blood components having high variability— especially so when the variability within birds is as great as the variability between birds.

In the same experiment there were males from the same source and they were killed at about 550 days of age. Thirty-three individuals went into the averages presented in table 17. Laboratory males showed higher values than Laboratory females for number of erythrocytes, grams of hemoglobin, and volume of packed cells (hematocrit percentage). The total white-cell count was lower for males than for females. The sexes did not differ widely in the percentage values for monocytes, eosinophils, and basophils. Female chickens showed a higher percentage value for lymphocytes than did male chickens. The reverse was true for heterophils.

A higher erythrocyte number for adult males than for adult females agrees with the work of Juhn and Domm (1930). Before maturity there was no difference between the sexes. The average values given for males of 3,600,000 and for females of 2,700,000 given by Taber et al. (1943) agree fairly well with those given in table 17. The averages computed from Kitaeva's data (1939) for adult birds were 3.40 million erythrocytes per mm.[3] for males and 2.92 million per mm.[3] for females. Domm and Taber (1946) obtained an average erythrocyte count for males of 3,250,000 and for females of 2,610,000. They sought to determine if a diurnal rhythm for erythrocytes in the circulating blood existed in chickens, comparable to that which had been found in some mammals. They took their samples at noon, 6 p. m., midnight, and 6 a. m. They found a definite tendency in males to give highest values at midnight and lowest at noon. The same tendencies were evident in females also, but the difference in averages at these two times of the day was not as great in females as in males. Domm and Taber found a seasonal variation in erythrocyte counts; the lowest counts came at the period of highest reproductive activity and the highest counts at the time of lowest activity. See also Domm, et al. (1943).

Kakara and Kawasima (1939) found that birds sitting on eggs had a lower red-cell count, lower thrombocyte count, and lower total white cells than did laying hens.

Chickens moved to a high altitude, 6,000 feet, showed a slight increase in hemoglobin and erythrocyte count, according to Vezzani (1939).

An extensive study of erythrocyte numbers for many species of birds was made by Nice et al. (1935). Counts on wild birds ranged from 3,930,000 (tufted titmouse) to 7,645,000 (junco). The median count was 5,230,000. All of the counts are higher than the average for chickens. In the bobwhite, a gallinaceous bird, the average was 3,532,000. Erythrocyte counts and hemoglobin determinations on pigeons and on doves by Riddle and Braucher (1934) gave higher values for males than for females. They observed seasonal differences also, with the highest values occurring in the autumn and lowest values in the summer.

Venzlaff (1911) made erythrocyte counts from 45 species of birds. In collecting his material he attempted to obtain a reasonably uniform representation of most of the families of birds—from the Struthioniformes to the Passeriformes. Body weight and size of the erythrocytes were given, also, but the interrelationship of these variables is still open to question.

Percentage values are often misleading—the real differences between sexes are seen more clearly in the data giving the number of cells per cubic millimeter (table 17). The Rhode Island Reds had a high thrombocyte count, and a slightly elevated total white-cell count in comparison with the others. The monocytes of both farm stocks were low both in absolute and in percentage values. This may be the reason why some investigators group monocytes with lymphocytes in their differential counts. Heterophils were even more variable than lymphocytes, ranging from 10 percent to 25 percent, and on the basis of absolute numbers per cubic millimeter, the differences are even greater—2,900 to 12,600—over a fourfold difference. The range in average number for the lymphocyte groups was slightly over twofold.

The low heterophil count for our birds may be due to the fact that these chickens are held indoors throughout their lives and are relatively free from parasites and common poultry infections except lymphomatosis. The count was the highest for Rhode Island Reds, yet in all groups of chickens it was definitely less than in wild birds (tables 18, 19, 20, and 21). In fact there are several points of difference between the percentage values of leukocyte types in chickens and wild birds, the most striking being the low value for lymphocytes, the high value for heterophils, and a consistently high level for monocytes. Eosinophils in the Canada goose and the mallard duck ran 7 percent and in pigeon and pheasant the averages were low. Basophils ranged from 2 to 10 percent. Any comparison of these tables with the data on the chicken indicates that absolute values have greater usefulness than percentage values, and any extensive studies on comparative avian hematology should include data on the actual number of cells per cubic millimeter.

The values on counts made by Wickware (1947) should be compared with those given in table 17 for the leukocyte types. About the only generalization that can be made is that these data further emphasize that there is high variability among different groups of chickens.

Cell counts on pigeons, more extensive than given here (table 21), were made by DeEds (1927). He found a very high variability for the counts of each cell type; for example, small lymphocytes varied from 5 to 53 percent, large lymphocytes from 9 to 67 percent, heterophils from 0 to 25 percent and the remaining cell types showed a similar variability. Thrombocytes varied from 8,000 to 89,000 per mm.[3]

Less variability was experienced in a later study on pigeon blood cells by Schoger (1939). In his data, lymphocytes varied from 40.5 to 62.0 percent, monocytes from 4.0 to 6.5 percent, heterophils from 29.0 to 48.5 percent, eosinophils from 2 to 4 percent, and basophils from 0.5 to 2.0 percent. He used 16 mature, healthy birds. The variability in his data was less than shown in table 21. Red cell counts, hemoglobin, and differential counts for leukocytes were made by Gauger et al. (1940) on normal pigeons and on pigeons infected with paratyphoid. Their counts on both normal and infected birds were also highly variable. They concluded that, due to this variability, chronic carriers of this pathogen could not be distinguished from noninfected pigeons by blood-cell counts.

The values given by Hewitt (1942) of differential counts on laboratory ducks (breed not given) agree closely with our averages in table 18, based on common mallards. Hewitt's averages were: Lymphocytes, 40.4 percent; monocytes, 5.3 percent; heterophils, 44.4 percent; eosinophils, 7.1 percent; and basophils, 2.4 percent. Normal differential blood counts for turkeys, as given by Johnson and Lange (1939), are: Lymphocytes, 50.6 percent; monocytes, 1.9 percent; heterophils, 43.4 percent; eosinophils, 0.9 percent; and basophils, 3.2 percent. McGuire and Cavett (1952) gave the counts for normal values of turkey blood in cells per mm.[3] as follows: Total leukocytes, 38,700; lymphocytes, 17,200; monocytes, 1,900; heterophils, 16,600; eosinophils, 40; and basophils, 1,700. These data give essentially the same percentage values as obtained by Johnson and Lange. A review of earlier literature on blood values for ducks is given by Magath and Higgins (1934). They also determined for other anseriform species, the size of erythrocytes and the number per cubic millimeter.

Perhaps some of the variability in heterophil count on pigeons experienced by different investigators was due to diurnal rhythm, the existence of which was worked out by Shaw (1933). He found that heterophil counts on the average were 76 percent higher in the afternoon than in the morning. The afternoon rise for 7 birds was: 1, no change; 2, rise of 106 percent; 3, rise of 38 percent; 4, rise of 55 percent; 5, rise of 143 percent; 6, rise of 54 percent; and 7, rise of 138 percent.

ARNETH COUNTS

Arneth counts were given for a group of chickens discussed in chapter 2, page 85; and in

heterophils and eosinophils no more than 5 lobes were found. Likewise, no more than 5 were found for turkeys (table 22), pheasants (table 23) and geese (table 24). The index values for male turkeys ranged from 1.75 to 2.16, with an average of 1.95; for females, it was from 1.65 to 2.45, with an average of 2.09. For pheasants it was from 1.84 to 2.58, with an average of 2.27. Only two slides were obtained from the geese; they read 2.06 and 2.38. Counts were not made on eosinophils for any species except the Canada goose—after considerable searching 16 cells were found on each slide. The indices were 3.75 and 4.25; thus there is a preponderance of cells with 3, 4, and 5 lobes—a situation that thus far has not been observed either in eosinophils or in heterophils for this or any other species studied.

Sugiyama (1938) gave Arneth counts for 8 species of birds. His data for the domestic

Table 22.—**Domestic turkey (White Holland): Arneth counts on heterophils**

Bird	Class (nuclear lobes)					Index
	I	II	III	IV	V	
MALES						
1............	28	69	3	0	0	1.75
2............	9	72	19	0	0	2.10
3............	13	80	7	0	0	1.87
4............	19	72	9	0	0	1.90
5............	11	64	23	2	0	2.08
6............	13	84	3	0	0	1.90
7............	26	70	4	0	0	1.78
8............	25	64	9	2	0	1.88
9............	7	73	17	3	0	2.16
10............	9	73	17	1	0	2.10
Average......	......	......	......	......	......	1.95
FEMALES						
1............	39	57	4	0	0	1.65
2............	7	59	30	3	1	2.32
3............	6	62	29	3	0	2.29
4............	8	82	9	1	0	2.03
5............	8	78	13	1	0	2.07
6............	9	61	25	5	0	2.26
7............	6	90	4	0	0	1.98
8............	8	73	18	1	0	2.12
9............	8	84	8	0	0	2.00
10............	10	77	11	2	0	2.05
11............	8	45	41	6	0	2.45
12............	16	66	16	2	0	2.04
13............	15	66	16	3	0	2.07
14............	12	68	17	3	0	2.11
15............	13	75	10	2	0	2.01
16............	10	83	7	0	0	1.97
17............	12	68	18	2	0	2.10
18............	16	60	24	0	0	2.08
19............	10	61	28	1	0	2.20
Average......	......	......	......	......	......	2.09

Table 23.—**Ring-necked pheasant (adult males): Arneth counts on heterophils**

Bird	Class (nuclear lobes)					Index
	I	II	III	IV	V	
1............	5	32	12	1	0	2.18
2............	7	37	6	0	0	1.98
3............	3	32	15	0	0	2.24
4............	6	32	10	2	0	2.16
5............	8	33	9	0	0	2.02
6............	4	31	13	2	0	2.26
7............	5	25	17	3	0	2.36
8............	2	28	19	1	0	2.38
9............	1	34	15	0	0	2.28
10............	4	14	28	4	0	2.64
11............	2	19	24	4	1	2.66
12............	13	32	5	0	0	1.84
13............	5	36	9	0	0	2.08
14............	1	30	15	4	0	2.44
15............	3	21	20	6	0	2.58
Average......	......	......	......	......	......	2.27

Table 24.—**Canada goose (adult males): Arneth counts on eosinophils and heterophils**

Cells	Class (nuclear lobes)					Index
	I	II	III	IV	V	
Heterophils...	1	30	18	1	0	2.38
	3	41	6	0	0	2.06
Average....	......	......	......	......	......	2.22
Eosinophils...	0	1	1	7	7	4.25
	0	2	4	6	4	3.75
Average....	......	......	......	......	......	4.00

chicken have already been reported (p. 85). The values for the remaining 7 are given here, since many libraries do not have the journal. The classes are indicated by Roman numerals, followed by a figure that is the percentage having this number of nuclear lobes. At the end of the series, the mean or index is given by an italicized number:

Cockatoo: I, 36.0; II, 60.0; III, 4.0; *1.68*
Quail: I, 27.0; II, 59.0; III, 13.5; IV, 0.5; *1.88*
Sparrow: I, 26.0; II, 60.0; III, 12.5; IV, 1.5; *1.90*
Swallow: I, 12.5; II, 65.5; III, 22.0; *2.10*
Pigeon: I, 20.5; II, 63.0; III, 15.5; IV, 1.0; *1.97*
Owl: I, 20.0; II, 48.0; III, 29.0; IV, 3.0; *2.15*
Bunting: I, 14.0; II, 57.0; III, 23.0; IV, 6.0; *2.21*

Perhaps the first investigator to compile Arneth counts on birds was Shaw (1933) in his study on pigeons. He took blood samples from April through September. The index varied from 1.76 to 2.11 but there was no seasonal trend. The average index for the 6-month period was 1.95, which is almost the same as Sugiyama found in the pigeons he studied. However, the breakdown into classes was somewhat different. Shaw found: Class I, 33 percent; II, 42 percent; III, 23 percent; and IV, 2 percent. Shaw also studied an owl, and the percentages in the various classes were as follows: I, 34; II, 48; III, 18; IV, 0. The index was 1.84. This was somewhat lower than found in the owl studied by Sugiyama.

Shaw compared the Arneth counts of the bone marrow with the counts of the blood of pigeons. The averages based on three specimens were as follows:

Blood: I, 36, II, 41; III, 22; IV, 1; *1.87*
Bone marrow: I, 75; II, 30; III, 5; IV, 0; *1.30*

It seems odd that during the twenty years, and more, since the publications of Sugiyama and of Shaw on Arneth counts for normal birds, this technic, so common in the mammalian field, has not been applied to the study of blood diseases in birds.

CHAPTER 7

Technics for Avian Blood

Lack of satisfactory technics is one of the reasons why studies of avian blood have not been carried forward as energetically and successfully as have studies of mammalian blood. Students of avian hematology have found that they frequently get unsatisfactory results when they attempt to apply technics that are known to be suitable for studying the blood of mammalian species.

Over a period of years this Laboratory has modified a number of commonly used technics to suit the needs of avian hematology.

THE MICROSCOPE AND LIGHT

Perhaps the greatest deterrents to accurate and critical study are (1) lack of a good microscope, (2) lack of a good light source, and (3) deficiencies in setting up and using microscope and light.

Here is what one often finds in a laboratory: The "good" microscope is tucked away in a box. When a special occasion arises, it is brought forth and placed on a table close to a 75- or 100-watt bulb or a lamp with a frosted glass in front. Then the condenser is dropped below the level of the stage until the amount of light is right, or the diaphragm is closed so that the object shows up well.

For a quick look with low magnification, such procedure may be satisfactory, but efforts are often made to do critical studies under an oil immersion lens with this type of set-up. The efforts are disappointing because the microscope is prevented from giving top-quality performance.

Many good books have been written on the use of the microscope. Nevertheless it is not uncommon to see research workers, technicians, veterinarians, and physicians using the instrument as if there were no directions. Correct use is emphasized here not only because the authors hope that their comments may be helpful to other workers, but also because it is desired to assure the reader that the structures depicted in the illustrations have actually been seen in specimens. The reader who fails to locate, in specimens of his own, the small structural and tinctorial differences depicted here should not conclude that they do not exist; he should consider the possibility that he is not working under optimum conditions.

The information that follows was obtained from the late Dr. Max Poser of the home office of Bausch & Lomb Optical Co. and from Mr. H. L. Shippy of the Detroit office of that company. Similar information has been presented by Dr. Oscar W. Richards in *Color and Illumination*, published by the Spencer Lens Co. Two other useful reference items by Dr. Richards will be found in Literature Cited (Richards, 1938 and 1949). Another reference (Spitta, 1920) has provided particularly helpful explanations of the differences between achromatic and apochromatic lenses, and of why Huyghenian eyepieces should be used with the former and compensating oculars with the latter.

An ideal light source is a small, brilliant point of light that is passed through a lens designed to produce parallel or nearly parallel rays. All the drawings in this Atlas were made with a tungsten arc light.

The lamp should be placed about 2 feet in front of the microscope and the image of the light source brought to a focus on a white card placed in front of the microscope mirror. Adjustments in focus can be made by moving the lamp condenser in and out. Just in front of the condenser lens of the lamp is a leaf diaphragm, which should be wide open at this stage of setting up the lamp and microscope. The next step is to place a *clear* blue daylight filter in one of the three slots in front of the lamp diaphragm. The slots are constructed to hold 2″ x 2″ filters. One may purchase a good lamp capable of giving critical or Köhler illumination,[1] then nullify its value by placing a ground glass in the path of the light.

[1] The essential differences between critical and Köhler illumination are given by Richards (1954) in a booklet accompanying each research microscope when purchased. This booklet also contains a helpful bibliography.

In order to do critical microscopic work, one should have a box of neutral intensity filters, graded 0.3, 0.6, 0.9, and 1.2. These numbers represent the logarithms of the opacity; each filter has double the opacity of the one preceding it. By placing filters, one can reduce the light until there is no danger of eye injury. Place a prepared slide on the stage of the microscope. Adjust the flat mirror so that, when the low-power objective focuses on the specimen, the light falls directly in the center of the microscope field. To ascertain that it is centered, close the lamp diaphragm as far as it will go and then elevate the microscope condenser until the opening of the lamp diaphragm appears as a sharp ring. With the flat glass mirror usually present on research microscopes, there will be three circles instead of one. Critical work can be carried out with the glass mirror but for these studies on avian blood, this mirror was replaced with a flat, front-surfaced mirror, which eliminated all images except one.

After manipulating the mirror to bring the light to the center of the field—or to what appears to be the center—and after focusing the condenser to the level of the specimen, check to see that the circle of light really is in the center of the field. This is the time to ask the question, Is the condenser perfectly in line with the optical axis of the objective, tube, and eyepiece? To find the answer, proceed as follows:

Open the diaphragm on the lamp as far as it will go, then close the microscope diaphragm—all the way. Lift out the eyepiece and look through the tube. There will be a circle of light that does not fill the front lens of the objective. Is this circle of light in the center? It is difficult to tell, because moving the head makes the light appear to move. Freedom from the uncertainty can be gained by using a pinhole eyepiece, which has a small hole in the exact center (but no lens). With this in place the position of the circle of light can be determined easily and accurately. If it is not in the center there are two or three screws with which adjustment can be made. The screws are on most microscopes. They are not on some of the less expensive student instruments.

If an adjustment is necessary to bring the image of light to the center of the front lens, make it, then return the regular eyepiece to the tube. Now open the microscope diaphragm and close the lamp diaphragm. Is the image still in the

center of the field. If it is not, readjust the mirror, look through the open tube of the microscope, and check again with the pinhole eyepiece.

When, finally, the condenser seems to be in perfect alignment, it can be checked by moving the tube up and down. The circle of light will enlarge above and below the focal point. If these two light cones remain on the same axis within the tube the task has been completed. But if the light beam shifts to one side of the tube axis as the tube is moved up and down, the adjustment procedure should be repeated. Books by Belling (1930) and by Beck (1938) should be consulted for further refinements on testing the alignment of the condenser.

After the tests on alignment have been completed, put in the eyepiece and open the lamp diaphragm all the way. It probably has already been noted that the field of light from the lamp illuminates only a small circle in the center of the low-power field and that the marginal half or two-thirds of the field is dark. The tendency of many is to drop the condenser until the field is fully lighted. Doing this is unobjectionable if you wish only to examine large masses in the slide, but it is objectionable if you are interested in details. The correct procedure for filling the low-power field with light will be given after adjustments relating to the use of the oil immersion lens have been described.

Starting with the microscope condenser elevated so that the edge of the lamp diaphragm is in sharp focus and wide open, shift to the objective of next highest magnification and note whether the field of light is still in the center. Do the same for the other objectives. If all the lenses do not show the circle of light in the center of the field, at least one is not par centered. This adjustment should be made at the factory or with the help of a competent representative of the company. If most of the microscope work can be done with only one lens, all adjustments can be made to fit the particular lens. (Most of the work reported in this Atlas was done with the oil immersion lens.) All the lenses screwed into one nosepiece should be par focal: as each is moved into position, only a slight movement of the fine-adjustment screen should be necessary to bring it into focus. Shifting lenses in this way is recommended for the "dry" lenses but certainly it cannot be recommended as standard procedure for the oil immersion lenses. How to bring the oil immersion lens into focus is described in most of the instruction booklets provided by manufacturers of microscopes.

After the oil immersion lens has been focused on the cells or tissues on the slide, the lamp diaphragm is again closed and the mirror adjusted slightly so that the circle of light is centered in the field. Then the lamp diaphragm is opened slowly until its margin barely passes out of the microscope field. If one goes much further a flare is produced across the objects on the slides, which is disturbing.

Next the eyepiece lens is removed and the microscope condenser diaphragm is opened slowly; this action enlarges the circle of light seen through the back lens of the objective. The movement should be stopped as soon as a point is reached where further opening of the diaphragm no longer enlarges the circle. An unlighted rim remains on the margin of the back surface of the lens. This is due to the fact that air separates the top of the condenser from the bottom of the slide, setting a theoretical limit of a numerical aperture (N. A.) of 1.0 for the entire lens system. If oil is placed on the condenser and the condenser is again brought to a focus at the level of the objects on the slide, it will be found, after the microscope diaphragm has been opened still further, that the back lens of the objective is fully illuminated. This will occur if the numerical aperture of the condenser is as high as, or higher than, the numerical aperture of the oil immersion objective. If less—for example, an N. A. 1.25 condenser and an N. A. 1.3 objective—there will still remain a narrow dark ring.

Oil on the condenser and on the bottom of the slide often makes a mess if the slide is moved around much. The use of oil between condenser and slide is necessary if a single cell or part of a cell is to be photographed or if objects within the cell are much less than a micron in diameter. The procedure outlined gives maximum resolving power. The resolving power can be estimated by means of a monogram (Richards, 1938). The objects usually studied in blood cells are large enough to preclude the need for oil between the condenser and slide.

It has been said that use of an air-space instead of oil gave a theoretical limit of N. A. 1.0 but Spitta (1920) suggests that in actual practice it is an average of the theoretical limit of 1.0

and the N. A. of the objective; thus for an N. A. 1.3 the effective N. A. would be 1.15.

In selecting the most desirable filter, each worker should consider the sensitivity of his eyes to light; he should try a number of filters and select the one that enables him to study cellular details without suffering eye fatigue.

Do not close the microscope diaphragm or drop the condenser out of focus to reduce the intensity of light. Closing the diaphragm reduces the effective N. A. and hence the resolving power, but it increases the apparent refractivity of cells and their parts. Sometimes individuals mistake this effect for what is described as "seeing the objects better." A worker must have considerable experience in the correct use of the microscope before he realizes that he can see more with the condenser focused and the diaphragm open. If preparations of unstained cells, either living or dead, are to be studied satisfactorily, the diaphragm must be closed nearly all the way. The cells are distinguished by differences in refractibility, and closing the diaphragm emphasizes these differences.

On page 223 it was said that the problem of filling the field at low magnification with a lamp giving collimated light would be discussed later. The procedure for the high dry (4 mm. focal length objective) lenses is the same as for the oil immersion lenses. In general, there are lenses manufactured at three numerical apertures—0.66, 0.85, and 0.95. Each has its advantages and disadvantages; only the N. A. 0.66 has sufficient working distance to be used with the usual thick cover glass of the blood-counting chamber.

When the 8 or 16 mm. objectives are used the light does not fill the field. If the work is not critical, a quick examination of a section is sufficient to see whether it is flat and whether the stain and counterstains are balanced. For counting objects in the sections, a frosted blue light bulb in a gooseneck lamp (or similar adjustable lamp) brought close to the flat mirror of the microscope is adequate. If the lamp is close enough it will fill the field with light. When the condenser is focused, an image of the light bulb appears in the field. To avoid the printing, take the light from the side of the bulb rather than from the end. The mirror should not be moved when the frosted bulb is brought into position. If movement is limited to the lamp bulb the light from the microscope lamp behind it is still in alignment when the bulb is taken away.

If critical studies are to be made under low magnification, or if photomicrographs are to be taken, an ordinary light bulb is not adequate, and one returns to the arc or ribbon filament lamp or other light source which will provide critical or Köhler illumination. The upper and lower lenses of condensers on most research microscopes can be separated—usually by sliding or screwing them apart. The upper element is laid aside and the lower element is moved up or down until the light source itself or the edge of the diaphragm in front of it is sharply in focus at the level of the objects on the slide. After the condenser has been lowered as far as possible (up to the point just short of touching the edge of the mirror) it may still be necessary to elevate the slide above the level of the stage by as much as 1.5 cms., in order to bring the image of the light source or its diaphragm into focus. With another make, the condenser is moved down close to the mirror but the slide does not have to be elevated above the stage in order to bring the light to a focus on the slide.

Technicians accurately identified cell types and their developmental stages when microscopes provided with N. A. 1.3 apochromatic objectives and N. A. 1.4 condensers were furnished and when the light sources were carefully aligned with the microscope.

The illustrations shown in this Atlas were used during the training of the technicians.

PROCURING BLOOD

Preparation of cannulas for taking blood from early embryos

The problem of drawing out glass tubing to a small diameter seemed on the face of it to be a rather simple one, but it was soon discovered that a broken, jagged tip would not smoothly enter the dorsal aorta of embryos, 2 to 3 days old, or the tip of the heart of older embryos. The task called for a delicate, almost microscopic tip with a smooth-beveled point like that of a hypodermic needle.

Pyrex tubing, 2 mm. inside diameter and 4.5 mm. outside diameter, was used. An area in the center was heated with an oxygen-gas flame. The ends were pulled apart quickly in order to give a rapid taper and to keep the walls thin. As the tubing was pulled, a 60° angle was made between the thin center portion and the unheated ends. After a dozen or so of these had been made, the thin portion was broken off several centimeters from the point where the taper began.

The next step was the preparation of a microburner. Any burner will do if the flame can be reduced to a height of about 2 mm. A glass sleeve, tapered to a small opening, was placed over the metal tube of a microburner, and this gave a small flame. Even though the flame was small, it was approached cautiously. While the thin part of the tube was heating a slight tension was exerted so that as soon as the thin glass had softened it could be pulled quickly to a thin, short tip. If pulled too quickly the tip was long and thin and not stiff enough to push through the tissues of the embryo and, if one hesitated too long, the walls thickened and the bore became excessively small. The best tips were selected from those made and the delicate, thin tubing was broken off about a half centimeter from the portion of intermediate thickness.

The next step was to grind the end to a bevel tip. The method followed was not the best—there was a certain amount of breakage—but after studying the principles set forth one can add refinements that will make the process easier. A small highspeed motor that carried a three-jawed chuck over the end of the shaft was used. It was mounted vertically in a bracket and two rheostats were hooked in series to the current line. One rheostat of the correct type would be sufficient if it could be regulated delicately enough; the only requirement is that the motor turn at a slow, constant speed. The speed was not measured but it was estimated to be 1 to 4 revolutions per second. Into the chuck was inserted a small spindle that carried near the end a flat emery disk about an inch in diameter. When the emery disk was in place and rotating slowly, a flat dish of water was lifted up beneath it so that the disk turned just below the surface of the water. With the set-up described, the increased friction often stopped the motor; probably a worm-gear reducing unit would have given greater power and a nearer constant speed.

The fine glass tip of the cannula was lightly touched to the flat surface of the moving emery wheel. The first trial demonstrated that the particles of emery and glass would completely plug the small bore of the glass tip. A thin-walled flexible rubber tubing was attached to the large end of the tip. An effort was made to dislodge the particles by blowing through the tubing during the grinding process. But blowing by mouth did not keep the bore free. It was found necessary to make a connection to an air or oxygen pressure tank in order to keep a flow of air or oxygen that would prevent the entrance of particles into the glass tip. The progress of grinding was checked under the microscope and was considered finished when there was a beveled, smooth, sharp tip.

When the grinding was finished the tubes were cleaned with alcohol and ether, and dried with air.

Method for taking blood from the dorsal aorta of the 48- to 72-hour embryo

Eggs that are presumed to be fertile are taken from the cool room where they have been held at a temperature of about 55 degrees since they were laid. They are placed in the incubator with a record of the hour and date. In these studies the age has been taken as 3 hours less than the total time held in the incubator. When the embryo has reached 48 hours, incubation age (51 hours actual time in the incubator), it is removed, opened carefully, and slid into a bowl of warm saline or Ringer's solution. Sugiyama (1926) followed Sabin's suggestion and increased the salt content of Locke-Lewis solution to 1.04-percent NaCl for an embryo on the second day of incubation, to 1.0-percent for an embryo on the third day of incubation, and to 0.9-percent for an embryo on the fourth day of incubation and older. These improvements in technic are useful if the embryos are to be held for study over a period of time. Where the whole procedure can be completed within a few minutes, the use of 0.85-percent or 0.90-percent solution of sodium chloride alone produces no ill effects.

Prior to opening the embryo, rings from filter paper were cut. These had an outside diameter slightly larger than the margin of the area vasculosa, and the inner diameter was slightly less than this margin. The saline was removed from the bowl until the embryo lay above the level of the surrounding fluid. The vitelline membrane

FIGURE 412.—A tripod to hold an infrared lamp, used to warm slides and to drive off moisture before the smear is made and to dry the blood after it is spread.

was lifted off and the filter ring was placed over the embryo, which usually adhered readily to the surface. With fine curved scissors and forceps the embryo was cut free from the yolk sac, washed in saline, and lifted to a Syracuse watch glass. It was then placed under a low-power dissecting microscope.

In the meantime clean microscope slides were drying and warming under the infrared lamp (fig. 412). The slides should feel warm, not hot, to the back of the hand or the cheek. A flexible, thin rubber tubing of the type used for taking blood in erythrocyte counts was attached to the glass cannula, and under the low power of the dissecting microscope the cannula was guided into the dorsal aorta. The heart must be beating and the blood flowing in order to obtain a satisfactory preparation. A slight positive pressure is set up with air from the mouth as the tip approaches the moist surface of the embryo. If this is not done capillary attraction tends to draw saline and embryonic fluids into the tube and these fluids quickly distort the embryo blood cells.

The blood was drawn quickly by suction and then immediately expelled from the tube onto the warmed glass slide. As the blood leaves the cannula the tip is moved back and forth so as to distribute the cells and prevent them from piling up in heaps. If there is any delay in entering the aorta, in taking the blood, in making the preparation, or in drying it, the cells will be distorted. This is especially likely to happen if contaminating fluids have entered the cannula ahead of the cells or along with them. Efforts to prevent distortion of cells by other means were made. Heparin and silicone coatings over the inside of the cannulas were tried. Neither method gave improvement over careful, rapid use of a clean, dry tube. Essentially the same procedure was used for embryos a day older. The filter-paper rings used to hold the embryo were slightly larger than those for 48-hour embryos.

Method of taking blood from the heart of embryos of 96 hours and older

The same type of cannula was used as described previously except that it had a slightly larger bore. A cannula with a still larger bore was used when embryo age increased. A different technic was used to procure blood from the second week of incubation to hatching.

After 5 to 6 days of incubation the procedure of moving the tip of the cannula back and forth across the slide, as the blood was being expelled, was discontinued and a new procedure was begun—a drop of blood was placed on the end of the smear slide and distributed with a pusher slide. In still older embryos, the tip of the heart was cut open and the drop collected directly onto the end of a pusher slide, but in doing this there must be freedom from fluids around the heart, and the heart should be elevated above the surrounding tissue. At about mid-embryonic age of incubation this drop of blood will often be carried across from one end of the slide to the other and will leave only a few scattered cells over the surface of the slide. The ways in which the physical properties of the blood at this age differ from those that obtain just before hatching and after hatching is not known, but obviously the blood has a poor affinity for glass. Schechtman (1952) showed that the surface tension was less in the embryo than in the chick after hatching, and this may be one of the factors that influence the spread of the blood over the glass slide. The difficulty usually can be circumvented by placing the pusher slide at a low angle, by barely touching it against the smear slide, and by giving it one quick movement to the opposite end.

The infrared lamp and its use in drying and warming slides

A tripod carrying an infrared bulb vertically suspended (fig. 412) has been used for many years in this Laboratory in making blood smears. The legs and braces were made from $\frac{1}{8}$-inch wires welded together. On top was a flat triangle of sheet metal with a hole large enough to receive a light socket. An infrared bulb was placed in the socket. Clean paper toweling or cloth was spread on a table beneath the bulb, and on this the slides were stacked. Usually the slides were stacked around the margin of the circle of light and then about a dozen were spread under the light.

The heat from the lamp drives the moisture from the slides, and when the smear is made the film of cells dries quickly. It was necessary to have the warmed slides close to the point where they were being used; otherwise, the slide cooled before the film was spread. The pusher slides should not be heated. If the slide is too hot, artifacts will appear. They will be similar to those that appear in erythrocytes (see chapter 2). After the smear is made the slides may be returned to the lamp for complete drying of the cells or they may be put directly into a box. In either case, they are gently heated again just before staining in order to drive off any moisture that may have accumulated when the slides were cooled.

Method for collecting and carrying blood samples

Denington and Lucas (1955) have described a box in which 15 units can be carried conveniently and safely (fig. 413). The tray holding the red-cell pipettes is removable. Upon returning to the laboratory, the worker can separate the tray from the rest of the equipment and place

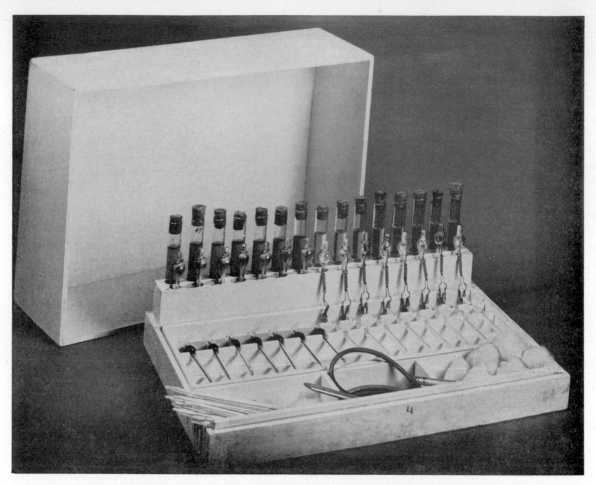

FIGURE 413.—A box and cover suitable for carrying 15 tubes for the hemoglobin test, the same number of Van Allen hematocrit tubes, and red-cell pipettes. The tray holding the last of these can be lifted out and stored in the refrigerator until they are ready for counting. Front compartments carry hemoglobin pipettes, knife, cotton bats, and rubber tubes for drawing up blood and fluids.

it in the refrigerator, where it remains until other procedures involving the hemoglobin and the Van-Allen hematocrit tubes have been completed. The box with clean slides and the infrared lamp are separate items; they are not included in the box used for collecting blood samples.

STAINING

Selection, preparation, and use of Wright's stain

Solutions containing dried Wright's powder have been made at the Laboratory and used; commercially prepared solutions have also been used. The difficulty in finding a Wright's stain suitable for avian blood has been discussed by

Denington and Lucas (1955). When dried powder was used, 3.3 grams were added to a 500-cc. bottle of pure methyl alcohol, freshly opened. This quantity of stain is approximately double the quantity used in making Wright's stain for human-blood studies. The stain is ripened for several months either at room temperature or in the incubator at 38 to 40 degrees centigrade.

A great many samples of dye, both from powders made up into solution at the Laboratory and from bottles of the dye that had been put into solution by a supply house, were tested. Some gave too red a color to the cytosomes of erythrocytes and gave pale, incompletely stained nuclei, and others stained the nuclei very intensely but gave a pale bluish color to the cytosomes of erythrocytes. The color balance of other cell types was also effected. It was sometimes possible to take a solution that produced too much red and too little blue coloration of the cells and follow this with a stain that was equally out of balance in the opposite direction and so procure a reasonably satisfactory slide. Much the same result could be obtained by using a mixture of the two solutions.

Wright's stain was obtained from various commercial sources. One product was found that, as a single staining solution, gave satisfactory results. Anyone seeking a Wright's stain for use on avian blood should test out samples from different sources in the hope that one of them will be properly balanced. Buffers of various sorts were tried with samples of Wright's stain. These manipulations still gave results that were too red or too blue.

The slides are spread on a staining rack over a sink or tray and flooded with stock Wright's stain. Use enough stain. If the stain is dry 5 minutes after it is applied, too little was used. Usually after this interval of time the surface of the solution has a metallic sheen and an equal quantity of distilled water is added. The slides are allowed to stand for another 5 minutes. There is wide variation in the periods of time that can be allowed for the concentrated stain, and the water that follows it, to stand on the slide. Different standing periods should be tried before concluding that the stain is unsatisfactory. The following are some of the periods that have been used in this study for the first and second solutions: 5 minutes and 2.5 minutes, 5 minutes and 5 minutes, and up to 9 minutes and 9 minutes. It was found that as the stock solution of stain aged, longer periods were necessary.

After the staining time has been completed, the slides are drained and blotted. Before the coverglass is put on, they are again warmed under the infrared lamp and the coverglass is heated over an alcohol lamp.

Many investigators do not cover blood smears but it has been a procedure followed in these studies on blood, and it has seemed that doing so makes the colors slightly more brilliant and the small details a little sharper.

Bulk staining with Wright's stain

When many slides are to be done at one time, the job is usually speeded up by using bulk stain-ing methods. Stainless steel racks that hold 25 to 100 slides are used, and 2 stainless steel trays with covers, or glass dishes with covers, are arranged conveniently. Wright's stain is poured into one tray or dish and distilled water into the other. The slides are left in the stain 5 to 15 minutes and then dipped slowly 2 or 3 times in the water. The rack is shaken to remove the excess water and then placed on a towel in a warm place (such as on a radiator or in an incubator) to dry. Small drops of water that adhere to the surface of the smear and afterward dry slowly often produce faded round spots. These spots usually do not interfere with the study of the smear.

The bulk staining method causes greater damage to water-soluble components of cells than does the rack method. Damage is less if the second solution is stain and water, equal parts.

May-Grünwald Giemsa

Although May-Grünwald Giemsa (M. G. G.) is a more vigorous stain than Wright's, the coloration that it gives to the cytosome and nucleus is much like that given by Wright's. Wright's stain is preferred for circulating blood of the hatched chicken. The azurophilic substances in the monocyte are differentiated better with it than with M. G. G., and the heterophil rods are preserved better. But if the blood is leukemic or for some other reason contains numerous immature cells, use M. G. G. or (if two slides are available) both stains. Because M. G. G. stains intensely, it is recommended for all impression smears from hematopoietic organs, both adult and embryonic, as well as for the circulating blood of the embryo. Both May-Grünwald and Giemsa were purchased as prepared solutions and have been entirely satisfactory. The following procedure was used:

1. Dry slides under the infrared lamp and place on a staining rack.
2. Cover with May-Grünwald solution, 5 minutes.
3. Dilute with equal quantity of distilled water and mix 1–2 minutes.
4. Pour off and without rinsing add diluted Giemsa,[2] 15–20 minutes.
5. Methyl alcohol, 1–3 dips.
6. Blot immediately.
7. Put on coverglass.

------

[2] Add 40 drops of stock Giemsa solution to 40 cc. of distilled water. If the color is weak, 80 drops to 40 cc. may be used.

Wright-Giemsa

The technic for Wright-Giemsa was suggested to us by Dr. C. J. Hamre of the University of North Dakota, who has found this stain satisfactory for the study of myelopoiesis in birds. It is a valuable method and for any critical study on myelopoiesis should be used in addition to May-Grünwald Giemsa.

1. Clean slides in concentrated HNO_3, 3 hours.
2. Wash slides in running tap water, in distilled water, and in 95-percent alcohol.
3. Make smear of blood and dry in air.
4. Use Wright's stain on rack, 4 minutes. (Proper length of time is determined by appearance of metallic sheen.)
5. Add distilled water, 4–5 minutes.
6. Wash in stream of running water and without drying add Giemsa,[3] 15–20 minutes.
7. Wash in running distilled water. If precipitate is present run Wright's stain over the slide.
8. Wash off with running water.
9. Stand slides on edge—do not blot.

Petrunkevitch No. 2 and M. G. G.

Petrunkevitch No. 2 is primarily a tissue fixative. It penetrates rapidly and since it is made up in alcohol it does not require washing. The original formula as given by Petrunkevitch (1933) has been modified slightly to adapt it for use with avian tissues.

80-percent alcohol	3 liters
Nitric acid	90 cc.
Cupric nitrate	60 gms.
Paranitrophenol	150 gms.
Mix and filter	
Ether	150 cc.

Combine the chemicals in the order given. Store in a cold place and in a well-sealed bottle.

In handling the paranitrophenol, do not inhale the dust and do not allow it to remain on the wet skin. Wear rubber gloves when weighing out the material and when handling the prepared fixative; this precaution is especially pertinent if there is danger that the prepared fixative may be splashed on the skin.

The paranitrophenol should be chemically pure. Before using it, note whether there is an indication of deterioration—brownish discoloration of the clumps of powder.

Petrunkevitch No. 2 fixative was used here

chiefly to show nuclear structure of heterophils for making Arneth counts. After the blood was spread, it was held for a second or two until a dull effect, which comes with the drying of the slide, began to replace the high gloss of the wet surface. At that instant the slide is put quickly into a Coplin jar of fixative. Since the fixative contains ether, it is better to use a Coplin jar with a screw top. Fix, 1 to 24 hours. Wash in several changes of 80-percent alcohol and run up to absolute methyl alcohol. Staining with May-Grünwald Giemsa is done in a Coplin jar rather than on a rack and the staining times for one or both dyes should be increased, sometimes as much as 50 to 100 percent over that given under the technic for staining the usual dry smear with M. G. G. On one set of slides, May-Grünwald was applied for 10 minutes and Giemsa (80 drops in 40 cc. of distilled water) for 20 minutes. When used this way on blood from the early embryo, sharply defined chromosomes are obtained in mitotically dividing cells.

Methyl alcohol and thionin

The chief use in this study for the combination of methyl alcohol fixative and thionin stain has been to hold the granules of basophils in their normal size and relationships within the cell. This requires that the film of blood or impression smear be fixed before it dries.

1. Fixation in absolute methyl alcohol, 5 minutes.
2. Stain in thionin,[4] 24–48 hours.
3. Differentiate in 95-percent alcohol.
4. Clear in 100-percent alcohol, xylene, and mount with cover glass.

Reticulocyte stain

One-percent brilliant cresyl blue was made up in 25 cc. of 0.85-percent salt solution or in avian Ringer's solution—NaCl, 8.5 gms., KCl, 0.42 gms., $CaCl_2$, 0.25 gms.; and water, 1,000 cc. The solution should be kept cold and should be filtered before using. Various methods were tried, including (1) mixing a drop of blood and a drop of stain on the slide for periods varying from 1 to 5 minutes and (2) drying a film of dye made with 0.3-percent solution of dye in 95-percent alcohol and making the blood smear over this. In the second method, the films of blood dried

---

[3] Use 15 drops of Giemsa stock to 10 cc. of distilled water.

[4] Thionin, saturated solution in 50-percent alcohol.

quickly and thus the dye on the slide was in solution for an insufficient period of time to give adequate staining. For avian blood the first method worked best, but more brilliant staining was accomplished when the mixture was held for at least 2 minutes before the smear was made. The same reticle used for making thrombocyte counts can be used for making reticulocyte counts.

Graam (1934) used a method that is essentially the same as given in the preceding paragraph, but added 0.3 percent sodium citrate. Six drops of this solution were mixed with about two drops of fresh pigeon blood. The cells were allowed to stain for 10 to 30 minutes before a drop of the mixture was removed and spread across a slide to dry. This long staining time may have been the basis for the statement (p. 202), "Practically every red cell of the pigeon's blood contained some 'basophilic' substance in the protoplasm." She goes on to say, "The younger cells contain the most of this so-called 'basophilic' substance. One must learn to be consistent and he must arbitrarily decide which of these cells to call reticulocytes. I arbitrarily called those cells reticulocytes which had a complete chain of basophilic substance around the nucleus."

Peabody and Ncalc (1933) used Löffler's methylene blue in 0.85 percent solution of sodium chloride. Air-dried smears were immersed in this stain for about 3 minutes, washed briefly in water and again air-dried. This stain was useful for temporary mounts but the preparations faded after a few hours.

The basic method for staining reticulocytes from which slight variations in procedure have arisen, was given by Osgood and Wilhelm (1931). They used, for mammalian blood, equal parts of venous blood that had been mixed with 2 mg. potassium oxalate per cc. and 1 percent brilliant cresyl blue in 0.85 percent NaCl. These substances were mixed in a test tube and after one minute a drop was removed and a smear made. This is the technic used by Magath and Higgins (1934) to stain the reticulocytes of mallard ducks.

Ralph's modification of the benzidine technic for hemoglobin in cells

The method given by Ralph (1941) is applicable to air-dried blood smears. The slide is flooded with 1-percent solution of benzidine in absolute methyl alcohol and allowed to stand 1 minute. The solution is poured off the slide and, without washing, it is replaced with a 25-percent solution of superoxol in 70-percent ethyl alcohol, which is allowed to stand 1½ minutes. This is poured off and the slide rinsed for 15 seconds in distilled water, after which it is dried by blotting and covered. Cells and other structures containing, hemoglobin stain dark or light brown. The dried slide should be counterstained with Wright's in order to reveal the cells and parts of cells that do not contain hemoglobin. In this study it was found that fine, needle-shaped crystals were sometimes deposited on the slide but usually these did not interfere with study of the cells.

MISCELLANEOUS TECHNICS

Method for hemoglobin determination

This subject has been discussed by Denington and Lucas (1955) and only a summarization is presented here.

Fill a test tube with 10 cc. of 0.4-percent solution of concentrated ammonium hydroxide in distilled water. Take up a 0.02-cc. sample of blood with a hemoglobin pipette; immediately discharge it into the ammonia solution; after rinsing the pipette several times in the solution, seal the test tube with a cork that has been washed, dried, and infiltrated with paraffin. Invert the tube 2 or 3 times; after an hour add 0.36 cc. of concentrated HCl to the tube and invert the tube 1 or 2 more times. This amount of HCl, namely, 1½ times as much as previously recommended, prevents formation of cloudiness in the tube; the precipitate that does form, aggregates into large masses, which usually fall to the bottom of the tube or float on top. Hemoglobin is not bound to this precipitate. The density of color is determined colorimetrically at a wavelength of $410m\mu$. These values are compared with those on a standard curve previously prepared; the curve is based on a series of 16 dilutions of hemin. Standard curves were made both from dried commercial hemin and from fowl hemin prepared according to the method given by Elvehjem (1931); the results were the same. When the transmission value, transposed into grams of hemin per cc. of blood, is multiplied by a factor of 2.3736, the product is the number of grams of hemoglobin per 100 cc. of blood. The derivation of the constant is given by Bankowski (1942).

Method for hematocrit determination

Van Allen hematocrit tubes were found suitable for embryos, small chicks, and the adult fowl. They are simple to use, give accurate results, and are easy to clean. From a small puncture about one drop of blood was drawn into the tube. The column of blood should be stopped exactly at the 100-percent mark; then the open tip of the tube should be quickly immersed in the diluent—1.6-percent solution of sodium oxalate in distilled water—which is sucked into the tube until the bulb is half full. Then the springclip cap is placed over the open end; fluid is not allowed to fall out of the open end as this is done. The springclip cap must be firmly and carefully seated.

The tubes are placed in the brass shields of the centrifuge and the shields are filled to near the top with water and are balanced by the amount of water added. They are spun at 2000 r. p. m. for 20 minutes. The radius to the middle of the shield was 7½ inches. The level of packed cells and the thickness of the buffy layer were read with a hand lens.

After they are used, the tubes must be carefully cleaned and dried. The use of acid was avoided because, if not thoroughly washed out of the tube, it will hemolyse the red cells the next time the tube is used.

It must be remembered that the buffy coat is composed of both leukocytes and thrombocytes, and the latter constitute half or more than half of the buffy coat.

Method for making thrombocyte counts

Although an indirect method was used to determine the number of thrombocytes per cubic millimeter, it seemed reasonably accurate. At the time blood was taken for use in erythrocyte counts, a dried smear was made. After the counts had been recorded, the stained slide was examined with an ocular reticle that had been scribed with two concentric squares. The inner

square had one-twentieth the area enclosed by the larger square. The latter was of such size that it would fit within the opening made by the diaphragm ring of the eyepiece.

The thrombocytes in the large square and the erythrocytes in the small square are counted. Cells that touch two of the sides are counted; those that are crossed by the lines on opposite sides are not counted. If the small square is exactly one-twentieth of the large square, a tabulation of 250 erythrocytes in that square is the equivalent of 5,000 erythrocytes in the large square. The figures now collected are substituted in the following formula:

$$\text{Throm./mm.}^3 = \frac{\text{Throm. counted} \times \text{ery./mm.}^3}{5,000}$$

The values for erythrocytes per cubic millimeter were determined from the counts made with the hemocytometer.

If the inner square is not exactly one-twentieth of the area of the larger one, differences can be compensated for by varying the counts of erythrocytes above and below 250 by an amount needed to give the equivalent of 5,000 in the large square.

Methods for white-cell counts

The relative merits of three methods—direct, semi-indirect, and indirect—were discussed by Denington and Lucas (1955) but no conclusion as to which is the best was given. Many authors have suggested technics that fall into these three categories. The indirect method is the simplest—after a total erythrocyte count has been made, the number of white cells relative to the number of erythrocytes is counted on the stained slide and from that ratio, the number of white cells per cubic millimeter can be estimated. The same reticle and procedure that were described for thrombocytes can be used.

The Wiseman (1931a) method is classed as a semi-indirect method. It is based on the principle that the total number of white cells in a cubic millimeter can be calculated if (1) the eosin-staining cells are counted directly in the counting chamber of a hemocytometer and (2) these values are used in conjunction with the percentage of eosin-staining cells tabulated in differential counts obtained from a stained slide.

Wiseman based his method on the affinity of phloxine for cells he called eosinophils, but both heterophils and eosinophils take this dye; therefore, the extrapolation to give a total cell count from a differential count must include both cell types. If this is kept in mind, accurate results can be obtained with the Wiseman table. For convenience, the table was increased to half units so that the calculations could be made on the basis of the average of cells counted in both chambers of the hemocytometer.

The following formula, which calls for less than half as much phloxine as recommended by Wiseman, was used:

Phloxine	20 mgm.
Formalin	5 cc.
Ringer's solution	95 cc.

To each 100 cc. of dye was added 0.5 cc. of 0.1 N HCl, which gave a pH of 5.7 to the solution. The dilution in the red-cell pipette was 1 to 200. The pipette was held in the refrigerator 1 to 3 hours and then placed on a slow-moving Bryan-Garrey (1935) rotating cylinder, which does not damage the cells. The fluid in the tip of the pipette was drawn off onto a piece of gauze before the chambers of the hemocytometer were filled. Heterophils and eosinophils in all squares of both chambers were counted and divided by 2. If one chamber gave results considerably different from the other in the number of eosin-stained cells present, a new preparation was made. The volume of fluid under all the squares of one side of the counting chamber is 0.9 cubic millimeters. Therefore, if only one eosin-stained cell were seen, this would represent—

$$\frac{1 \times 200}{0.9} \text{ (dilution factor)}$$

or 222.2 cells (heterophils and eosinophils) per cubic millimeter of blood. If in the differential count these two granulocytes were the only cells present, the leukocytes would also total 222.2; but if these two types represented 50 percent of the leukocytes present, the white cells would total twice as much—444.4 cells. If the eosin-stained cells represented 1 percent, the total cell count would be 22,222.2 cells. It is possible to prepare a table by which the total number of white cells per cubic millimeter can be determined, or the table given by Wiseman can be used for this purpose. The number of eosin-stained cells counted in one side of the chamber multiplied by the factor in the table for the percentage of com-

bined heterophils and eosinophils found in the differential count gives the total number of white cells per cubic millimeter.

When the total number of heterophils and eosinophils counted in the chamber is high and the percentage level in the differential count is also high, the Wiseman method has reliable accuracy; but when both these variables are low, the probability of error is increased proportionately.

The Rees-Ecker method probably is the best of the direct methods for estimating total white-cell counts. It is an adaptation of a method designed for counting platelet number in human blood (Wintrobe, 1952) and has been used by students in the Poultry Department at Cornell University. (Ram, 1949; Goodwin, 1950; and Machado, 1951). The method was first used for making cell counts on avian blood by DeEds (1927) who based his technic on the publication of Rees and Ecker (1923). The only difference between this method and the one given here, based on Wintrobe's procedure, is in the amount of brilliant cresyl blue. Rees and Ecker (1923) used only 0.1 grams of the dye instead of 0.5 grams. The diluent is composed of:

Sodium citrate	3.8 gms.
Neutral formalin	0.2 cc.
Brilliant cresyl blue	0.5 gms.
Distilled water	100.0 cc.

Keep in a glass-stoppered bottle in the refrigerator and filter before using. If formic acid is produced from the breakdown of formaldehyde, erythrocytes will be hemolysed and the solution should be discarded.

Blood is drawn to the 0.05-cc. mark on the pipette and the diluent added to bring the fluids up to the mark above the bulb. The tube is shaken in the Bryan-Garrey pipette rotor to give an even distribution of cells; then a suitable quantity of the mixture is placed on each side of the counting chamber.

Coates (1929) adapted a different direct method, using brilliant cresyl blue, for the counting of chicken leukocytes. He used two solutions: Brilliant cresyl blue in water, and potassium cyanide in water. We have not tested the Coates method.

One of the chief difficulties in using some of the direct methods for avian blood was the confusion that came in separating thrombocytes and lymphocytes. The brilliant cresyl blue stains the specific granules of the thrombocytes. If the top lens of the microscope condenser is removed and the light brought to a focus at the level of the cells in the chamber—with the diaphragm partially closed, if preferred—there is no difficulty in separating thrombocytes from each of the leukocytes. It is recommended, however, that differential counts not be attempted in the counting chamber. It is better to make them on the slide, where each cell can be checked for its identity under the oil immersion lens.

Both with the Wiseman and the Rees-Ecker method, erythrocytes can be counted in the same preparation or, if some drying has occurred, the counting chamber can be cleaned and refilled. Erythrocytes in millions per cubic millimeter are estimated in the same way as for human blood. The correct procedure for counting erythrocytes is given in numerous books on technic of hematology for the human.

Literature Cited

ANONYMOUS. 1949. Recommended terms and definitions for cells of the leukocytic, erythrocytic and thrombocytic series. Jour. Amer. Med. Assoc. 139: 175–176.

BALFOUR, A. 1911. Fallacies and puzzles in blood examination. 4th Rpt. Wellcome Trop. Res. Labs. Khartoum. Vol. A: 109–125.

BANKOWSKI, R. A. 1942. Studies of the hemoglobin content of chicken blood and evaluation of methods for its determination. Amer. Jour. Vet. Res. 3: 373–381.

BARTSCH, P. W., BALL, W. H., ROSENZWEIG, W., and SALMAN, S. 1937. Size of red blood corpuscles and their nuclei in fifty North American birds. Auk 54: 516–519.

BECK, C. 1938. The Microscope, Theory and Practice. 264 pp. R. and J. Beck, Ltd. London.

BELLING, J. 1930. The Use of the Microscope. 315 pp. McGraw-Hill Book Co., Inc. New York.

BERMAN, L. 1947. The clinical significance of cellular gigantism in human erythropoiesis. Jour. Lab. and Clin. Med. 32: 793–806.

BIELY, J., and PALMER, E. I. 1935. Studies of total erythrocyte and leucocyte counts of fowls. III. Variation in number of blood cells in normal fowl. Canad. Jour. Res.; Sci. 13, Sec. D.: 61–71.

BIZZOZERO, G. 1889. Neue Untersuchungen über den Bau des Knochenmark bei den Vögeln. Arch. f. mikr. Anat. 35: 424–469.

———— and TORRE, A. A. 1881. Ueber die Entstehung und Entwicklung der rothen Blutkörperchen. I. Ueber Entstehung und Entwicklung der rothen Blutkörperchen bei Vögeln. Moleschotts' Untersuch. z. Naturlehre d. Menschen u. d. Thiere 12: 626–652.

BLACKFAN, K. D., DIAMOND, L. K., and LEISTER, C. M. 1944. Atlas of the Blood in Children. 320 pp. The Commonwealth Fund. New York.

BLAKEMORE, F. 1934. The leucocytes of fowl blood with special reference to fowl paralysis. Vet. Rec. 14: 417–422.

BLOOM, W. 1938. Lymphocytes and monocytes. Theories of hematopoiesis. *In* Downey's Handbook of Hematology. 374–435. P. B. Hoeber, Inc. New York.

BLOUNT, W. P. 1939a. The blood picture at birth in the chick. Vet. Jour. 95: 193–195.

———— 1939b. Thrombocyte formation in the domestic hen. Vet. Jour. 95: 195–198.

BRADLEY, B. 1937. Observations on the comparative anatomy of blood. Med. Jour. Austral. 24: 992–999.

BREUSCH, E. 1928. Beiträge zur Blutmorphologie des Huhnes. Zeit. f. Infektionshr., par. Krankh. u. Hyg. d. Haustiere. 33: 219–237.

BRYAN, W. R., and GARREY, W. E. 1935. A mechanical device that produces uniform dispersion of blood cells in the diluting pipette. Jour. Amer. Med. Assoc. 103: 1,059–1,060.

BURCKHARDT, J. L. 1912. Ueber das Blutbild bei Hühnertuberkulose und dessen Beziehungen zur sogenannten Hühnerleukämie nebst Bemerkungen über das normale Hühnerblut. Zeit. f. Immunitätsforsch. u. exp. Therapie. 14: 544–604.

BURMESTER, B. R., GENTRY, R. F., and WATERS, N. F. 1955. The presence of the virus of visceral lymphomatosis in embryonated eggs of normal appearing hens. Poultry Sci. 34: 609–617.

————, SEVERENS, J. M. and ROBERTS, E. 1941. Blood cells in the bone marrow of the chick before and after hatching. Poultry Sci. 20: 391–394.

BURNETT, S. H. 1908. The Clinical Pathology of the Blood of Domesticated Animals. 158 pp. Taylor and Carpenter. Ithaca, N. Y.

CAMERON, J. A. 1941. Primitive blood-cell generations in *Amblystoma*. Jour. Morph. 68: 231–239.

CHARIPPER, H. A., and DAWSON, A. B. 1928. Direct division of erythrocytes and the occurrence of erythroplastids in the circulating blood of *Necturus*. Anat. Rec. 39: 301–307.

COATES, I. 1929. A method of counting white cells in the blood of fowl. Rept. Ontario Vet. Col. 1928; 63. (Quoted from Biol. Abst. 1931. 5:15346.)

COMMITTEE FOR CLARIFICATION OF THE NOMENCLATURE OF CELLS AND DISEASES OF THE BLOOD AND BLOOD-FORMING ORGANS. 1948. First report. Am. Jour. Clin. Med. 18: 443–450.

COOK, F. W., and DEARSTYNE, R. S. 1934. Hematology of the fowl. A. Studies on normal avian blood. B. Studies on the hematology of avian typhoid. N. C. Agr. Expt. Sta. Tech. Bul. 44, 46 pp.

COOK, S. F. 1937. A study of the blood picture of poultry and its diagnostic significance. Poultry Sci. 16: 291–296.

COTTRAL, G. E. 1950. Avian lymphomatosis, another egg-borne disease. Proc. 53d Ann. Meet. U. S. Livest. Sanit. Assoc. 1949. 183–192.

——— 1952. Endogenous viruses in the egg. *In* The chick embryo in biological research. Ann. N. Y. Acad. of Sci. 55: 221–234.

———, BURMESTER, B. R., and WATERS, N. F. 1954. Egg transmission of avian lymphomatosis. Poultry Sci. 33: 1,174–1,184.

CULLEN, E. K. 1903. A morphological study of the blood of certain fishes and birds with special reference to the leucocytes of birds. (Including a note on the occurrence of filariae in the blood of two birds and two porcupines.) Bul. Johns Hopkins Hosp. 14: 352–356.

DANSCHAKOFF, V. 1916a. Equivalence of different hematopoietic anlages. (By method of stimulation of their stem cells.) I. Spleen. Amer. Jour. Anat. 20: 255–327.

——— 1916b. The differentiation of cells as a criterion for cell identification, considered in relation to the small cortical cells of the thymus. Jour. Expt. Med. 24: 87–105.

——— 1916c. Myeloid metaplasia of the embryonic mesenchyme in relation to cell potentialities and differential factors. Carnegie Inst. of Wash. Pub. No. 274. Contrib. to Embryol. 9: 1–32.

DANTSCHAKOFF, W. 1907. Über das erste Auftreten der Blutelemente im Hühnerembryo. Fol. Haem. 4: Supp. 2: 159–166.

——— 1908a. Ueber die Blutbildung im Dottersack des Hühnchens. Verhandl. Anat. Ges. Ber. 22: 72–81.

——— 1908b. Untersuchungen über die Entwickelung des Blutes und Bindegewebes bei den Vögeln. I. Die Entstehung der Blutzellen beim Hühnerembryo und der Dottersack als blutbildendes Organ. Anat. Hefte. 37: 471–589.

——— 1909a. Untersuchungen über die Entwickelung von Blut und Bindegewebe bei Vögeln. Das lockere Bindegewebe des Hühnchens im fetalen Leben. Arch. f. mikr. Anat. 73: 117–181.

——— 1909b. Über die Entwickelung des Knockenmarks bei den Vögeln und über dessen Veranderungen bei Blutentziehungen und Ernährungstorungen. Arch. f. mikr. Anat. 74: 855–926.

——— 1931. Keimzelle und Gonade. Die endodermale Wanderzelle als Stammzelle in der Keimbahn. Zeitschr. f. Wissenschaftliche. Biol. Abt. B. Zeitsch. f. Zellforsch. u. mikros. Anat. 14: 376–384.

DAWSON, A. B. 1931. The occurrence of atypical vacuolated erythrocytes in the circulating blood of *Necturus*. Anat. Rec. 50: 23–31.

——— 1932. Hemopoietic loci in *Necturus maculosus*. Anat. Rec. 52: 367–379.

——— 1933a. An experimental study of hemopoiesis in *Necturus*: effects of lead poisoning on normal and splenectomized animals. Jour. Morph. 55: 349–385.

——— 1933b. The leucocytic reaction in *Necturus maculosus* to intravascular injections of colloidal carbon, with special reference to the behavior of the basophils and thrombocytes. Anat. Rec. 57 (Supp.) : 351–359.

——— 1936a. Some observations on the primitive and definitive erythrocytes of the developing chick. Ztschr. f. Zellforsch. u. mikros. Anat. 24: 256–268.

——— 1936b. Prolonged observations on splenectomized *Necturus maculosus* following intravascular injection of India ink. Arch. d'Anat. Micro. 32: 235–247.

DEEDS, F. 1927. Normal blood counts in pigeons. Jour. Lab. and Clin. Med. 12: 437–438.

DENINGTON, E. M., and LUCAS, A. M. 1955. Blood technics for chickens. Poultry Sci. 34: 360–368.

DENYS, J. 1887. La structure de la moelle des os et la genese du sang chez les oiseaux. La Cellule 4: 199–240.

DIESEM, C. D. 1956. A study of avian blood cells. Thesis: Ohio State Univ. 197 pp.

DOAN, C. A. 1932. Current views on the origin and maturation of the cells of the blood. Jour. Lab. and Clin. Med. 17: 887–898.

———, CUNNINGHAM, R. S., and SABIN, F. R. 1925. Experimental studies on the origin and maturation of avian and mammalian red blood-cells. Carnegie Inst. Wash. Pub. No. 361. Contrib. Embryol. 16: 163–226.

———, TABER, E., and DAVIS, D. E. 1943. Comparison of erythrocyte numbers in normal and hormone-treated Brown Leghorn fowl. Proc. Soc. Expt. Biol. and Med. 52: 49–50.

DORST, S. E., and MILLS, C. A. 1923. Comparative studies on blood clotting in mammals, birds, and reptiles. Amer. Jour. Physiol. 64: 160–166.

DOWNEY, H., and McKINLAY, C. A. 1923. Acute lymphadenosis compared with acute lymphatic leukemia. Part I. Clinical study. Arch. Int. Med. 32: 82–112.

ELVEHJEM, C. A. 1931. The preparation of standard acid hematin solutions from hemin. Jour. Biol. Chem. 93: 203–210.

EMMEL, M. W. 1936. The etiology of fowl paralysis, leukemia and allied conditions in animals. VII. Hemocytoblastosis in chickens as induced by *Sal-*

monella aertrycke. VIII. Hemocytoblastosis in naturally occurring cases of fowl paralysis and lymphomatosis, as well as in other birds from the same flocks. Fla. Agr. Expt. Sta. Bul. 306, 42 pp.

ERDMANN, R. 1917. Cytological observations on the behavior of chicken bone marrow in plasma medium. Amer. Jour. Anat. 22: 73–125.

FENNELL, R. A. 1947. The relation between age, number, and types of cells in the peripheral circulation of chicken embryos under normal and experimental conditions. Jour. Agr. Res. 74: 217–239.

FERGUSON, L. C., IRWIN, M. R., and BEACH, B. A. 1945. On variations in the blood cells of healthy cattle. Jour. Infect. Dis. 76: 24–30.

FLEMISTER, L. J., and CUNNINGHAM, B. 1940. The effects of increased atmospheric pressure on the allantoic vascular bed and the blood picture of the developing chick. Growth. 4: 63–71.

FOOT, N. C. 1913. The growth of chicken bone marrow in vitro and its bearing on hematogenesis in adult life. Jour. Expt. Med. 17: 43–60.

FORKNER, C. E. 1929. Blood and bone marrow cells of the domestic fowl. Jour. Expt. Med. 50: 121–142.

FRANK, J. A., and DOUGHERTY, T. F. 1953. Cytoplasmic budding of human lymphocytes produced by cortisone and hydrocortisone in in vitro preparations. Proc. Soc. Expt. Biol. and Med. 82: 17–19.

FURTH, J., SEIBOLD, H. R., and RATHBONE, R. R. 1933. Experimental studies on lymphomatosis of mice. Amer. Jour. Cancer. 19: 521–604.

GAGE, S. H., and FISH, P. A. 1924. Fat digestion, absorption, and assimulation as determined in man and animals by the dark-field microscope, and as a fat soluble dye. Amer. Jour. Anat. 34: 1–77.

GARREY, W. E., and BRYAN, W. R. 1935. Variations in white blood cell counts. Physiol. Rev. 15: 597–638.

GAUGER, H. C., GREAVES, R. E., and COOK, F. W. 1940. Paratyphoid of pigeons. I. Serological, bacteriological, and hematological studies of spontaneously infected birds. N. C. Agr. Expt. Sta. Tech. Bul. 62, 71 pp.

GOODALL, A. 1909. The numbers, proportions and characters of the red and white blood corpuscles in certain animals. Jour. Path. and Bact. 14: 195–199.

GOODWIN, K. 1950. A genetic and physiological study of a sex-linked lethal in the fowl. Thesis. Grad. School, Cornell Univ.

GORDON, L. 1926. Untersuchungen über die Spindelzellen im Blute von Tieren mit kernhaltigen roten Blutzellen, ihre eigentliche Gestalt. Abstammung und funktionelle Bedeutung. Virchow's Arch. path. Anat. u. Physiol. 262: 19–38.

GRAAM, D. G. 1934. The effect of lowered temperature on reticulocyte formation in the pigeon. Proc. Ind. Acad. Sci. 43: 201–204.

——— 1935. The length of the reticulocyte cycle in pigeons. Proc. Ind. Acad. Sci. 44: 224–227.

GRAY, J. E., SNOEYENBOS, G. H., and REYNOLDS, I. M. 1954. The hemorrhagic syndrome of chickens. Jour. Amer. Vet. Med. Assoc. 125: 144–151.

HAFF, R. 1914. Bindegewebs- und Blutbildungsprozesse in der embryonalen Leber des Huhns. Arch. f. mikr. Anat. 84: 321–350.

HALLIBURTON, W. D. 1886. Note on the colouring matter of the serum of certain birds. Jour. Physiol. 7: 324–326.

HAMILTON, H. L. 1952. Lillie's Development of the Chick. Ed. 3, 624 pp. Henry Holt and Company. New York.

HAMRE, C. J. 1952. Origin and differentiation of heterophil, eosinophil and basophil leucocytes of chickens. Anat. Rec. 112: 339–340.

——— and McHENRY, J. T. 1942a. Methods of obtaining blood of fowl for complete blood examination. Poultry Sci. 31: 30–34.

——— and McHENRY, J. T. 1942b. Blood values of hens fed a yeast-fermented mash supplemented adequate diet. Poultry Sci. 31: 333–339.

HANCOX, N. M. 1946. On the occurrence in vitro of cells resembling osteoclasts. Jour. Physiol. 105: 66–71.

HARNE, O. G., LUTZ, J. F., ZIMMERMAN, G. I., and DAVIS, C. L. 1945. The life duration of the red blood cell of the Macacus rhesus monkey. Jour. Lab. and Clin. Med. 30: 247–258.

HARTMANN, E. 1925. Beiträge zur Thrombozytengenese bei niederen Vertebraten, sowie zur Frage ihrer Stellung zum Megakaryozyten der Säuger. Fol. Haem. 32: 1–14.

HAYDEN, C. E. 1929. Blood physiology of chickens. Rept. N. Y. State Vet. Col. at Cornell Univ. (1927–1928). Legislative Doc. (1929) No. 18: 213–220.

HETHERINGTON, D. C., and PIERCE, E. J. 1931. The transformation of monocytes into macrophages and epithelioid cells in tissue cultures of buffy coat (demonstrated by trypan blue). Arch. expt. Zellforsch. 12: 1–10.

HEVESY, G., and OTTESEN, J. 1945. Life-cycle of the red corpuscles of the hen. Nature. 156: 534. London.

HEWITT, R. 1940. Bird Malaria. 228 pp. The Johns Hopkins Press. Baltimore.

——— 1942. Studies on the host-parasite relationships of untreated infections with Plasmodium lophurae in ducks. Amer. Jour. Hyg. 36: 6–42.

ISAACS, R. 1925. The refractive granule red blood corpuscle. Its behavior and significance. Anat. Rec. 29: 299–313.

———— 1928. Alterations of tissue cells in the blood stream. Science. 68: 547–548.

JOHNSON, E. P., and CONNER, B. V. 1933. Blood studies of fowls with various forms of lymphomatosis (fowl paralysis). Jour. Amer. Vet. Med. Assoc. 83: 325–343.

———— and LANGE, C. J. 1939. Blood alterations in typhlohepatitis of turkeys with notes on the disease. Jour. Parasitol. 25: 157–167.

JONES, O. P. 1943. Morphologic, physiologic, chemical and biologic distinction of megaloblasts. Arch. Path. 35: 752–775.

———— 1947. Mitochondria and their relation to the so-called hyaloplasm. Jour. Lab. and Clin. Med. 32: 700–719.

———— 1948. Nuclear structure versus nuclear pattern. Blood. 3: 967–986.

———— 1949. Letters to the editor. Jour. Hemat. 4: 777–779.

JORDAN, H. E. 1936. The relation of lymphoid tissue to the process of blood production in avian bone marrow. Amer. Jour. Anat. 59: 249–297.

———— 1937. The relation of lymphoid nodules to blood production in the bone marrow of the turkey. Anat. Rec. 68: 253–259.

———— 1938. Comparative hematology. In Downey's Handbook of Hematology. 703–862. Paul B. Hoeber, Inc. New York.

———— and ROBESON, J. M. 1942. The production of lymphoid nodules in the bone marrow of the domestic pigeon, following splenectomy. Amer. Jour. Anat. 71: 181–205.

JUHN, M., and DOMM, L. V. 1930. The relation of gonadal condition to erythrocyte number in fowls. Amer. Jour. Physiol. 94: 656–661.

KAKARA, K., and KAWASIMA, M. 1939. Hematological changes in the setting hen. Seventh World's Poultry Cong. and Expo. Proc. pp. 115–116.

KALABUKHOV, N., and RODIONOV, V. 1934. Changes in the blood of animals according to age. I. Changes in the blood of rodents (Mus musculus L. and Citellus pygmaeus Pall.) and birds (Passer montanus L. and Larus ridibundus L.) during the growth period. Fol. Haem. 52: 145–158.

KASARINOFF, D. 1910. Experimentelle Blutuntersuchungen bei Vögeln. Fol. Haem. 10: 391–413.

KELLER, C. 1933. Vergleichende Zellen- und Kernmessungen bei grossen und kleinen Hühnerrassen zur Prüfung der genetisch begingten Wuchsunterschiede Zugleich ein Beitrag zur Frage des rhythmischen Wachstums der Kerne. Zeitschr. Wiss. Biol. Abt. B. Zeitschr. Zellforsch. u. mikrosk. Anat. 19: 510–536.

KELLY, J. W., and DEARSTYNE, R. S. 1935. Hematology of the fowl. A. Studies on normal chick and normal adult blood. B. Studies on the hematology of chicks suffering from pullorum infection and on adult carriers of pullorum disease. N. C. Agr. Expt. Sta. Tech. Bul. No. 50, 69 pp.

KENNEDY, W. P., and CLIMENKO, D. R. 1928. Studies on the blood of birds. I. The corpuscles of the pigeon. Quart. Jour. Expt. Physiol. 19: 43–49.

KINDRED, J. E. 1940. A quantitative study of the hemopoietic organs of young albino rats. Amer. Jour. Anat. 67: 99–149.

KIRSCHBAUM, A., and DOWNEY, H. 1937. A comparison of some of the methods used in study of hemopoietic tissues. Anat. Rec. 68: 227–235.

KITAEVA, O. N. 1939. Breed determined differences in blood indices of fowls. Comp. Rend. (Doklady) de l' Académie Sc. U. R. S. S. 25: 304–307.

KNISELY, M. H., BLOCK, E. H., ELIOT, T. S., and WARNER, L. 1947. Sludged blood. Science 106: 431–440.

KNOWLES, R., ACTON, H. W., and DAS GUPTA, B. M. 1929. Puzzles and fallacies in the examination of stained films in the tropics. Indian Med. Res. Mem. No. 13, 1–35.

KRACKE, R. R., and GARVER, H. E. 1937. Diseases of the Blood and Atlas of Hematology. 532 pp. J. B. Lippincott Co. Philadelphia.

KYES, P. 1915. The physiological destruction of erythrocytes in birds. Internat. Monatschr. f. Anat. u. Physiol. 31: 543–551.

———— 1929. Normal leucocyte content of bird's blood. Anat. Rec. 43: 197–198.

LESBOUYRIES, G. 1941. La Pathologie des Oiseaux. 868 pp. Vigot frères. Paris.

LOEWENTHAL, N. 1930. Nouvelles observations sur les globules blancs du sang chez les animaux vertébrés. Arch. d'anat. d'hist. et d'embry. 11: 245–332.

LUCAS, A. M. 1940. The cytology of fox encephalitis and the effects of centrifugation upon the intranuclear inclusions. Amer. Jour. Path. 16: 739–760.

———— 1946. Hematology of blood spots in eggs of White Leghorn chickens. Amer. Jour. Anat. 79: 431–472.

———— 1949. Lymphoid tissue and its relation to so-called normal lymphoid foci and to lymphomatosis. I. Qualitative study of lymphoid areas in the pancreas of chickens. Am. J. Path. 25: 1197–1213.

———— 1950. Lymphoid tissue and its relation to so-called normal lymphoid foci and to lymphomatosis. V. A study of lymphoid areas in the pancreas of pheasants and wild Mallard ducks. Poultry Sci. 29: 450–461.

———— 1951. Lymphoid tissue and its relation to so-called normal lymphoid foci and to lymphomatosis. VI. A study of lymphoid areas in the pancreas of doves and pigeons. Poultry Sci. 30: 116–124.

———— and BREITMAYER, J. B. 1949. Lymphoid tissue and its relation to so-called normal lymphoid foci and to lymphomatosis. III. Qualitative and quantitative comparison of lymphoid areas in the pancreas of the White Pekin duck with those in chickens. Poultry Sci. 28: 436–445.

————, CRAIG, C. C., and OAKBERG, E. F. 1949. Lymphoid tissue and its relation to so-called normal lymphoid foci and to lymphomatosis. IV. Simplification of methods for quantitative analyses and its application to the turkey. Growth 13: 339–357.

———— and DENINGTON, E. M. 1956. Morphology of the chicken liver. Poultry Sci. 35: 793–806.

————, DENINGTON, E. M., COTTRAL, G. E., and BURMESTER, B. R. 1954. Production of so-called normal lymphoid foci following inoculation with lymphoid tumor filtrate. 1. Pancreas. 2. Liver and spleen. Poultry Sci. 33: 562–584.

———— and HERRMANN, W. W. 1935. Effect of centrifugation on herpetic intranuclear inclusions with a note on cytoplasmic inclusions of unknown origin in the rabbit cornea. Amer. Jour. Path. 11: 969–975.

———— and OAKBERG, E. F. 1950. Lymphoid tissue and its relation to so-called normal lymphoid foci and to lymphomatosis. II. Quantitative analysis of lymphoid areas in the pancreas of laboratory and farm chickens. Amer. J. Path. 26: 75–111.

———— and RISER, W. H. 1945. Intranuclear inclusions in panleukopenia of cats. Amer. Jour. Path. 21: 435–465.

LUNDQUIST, C. W., and HEDLUNG, B. 1925. Über die verschiedenen Granulaformen der sog. pseudo-eosinophilen Leukozyten im Hühnerblut. Fol. Haem. 31: 253–264.

McDONALD, J. G. 1939. Avian bone marrow with particular reference to red cell development. Amer. Jour. Anat. 65: 291–307.

McGUIRE, W. C., and CAVETT, J. W. 1952. Histomonas in turkeys. Poultry Sci. 31: 610–617.

MACHADO, A. V. 1951. The effect of infectious bronchitis and Newcastle disease on the blood cells of chickens. Thesis. Grad. School, Cornell Univ.

MAGATH, T. B., and HIGGINS, G. M. 1934. The blood of the normal duck. Fol. Haem. 51: 230–241.

MAINLAND, D., COADY, B. K., and JOSEPH, S. 1935. Lymphocyte sizes in human blood films. Fol. Haem. 53: 407–425.

MARVIN, H. N. 1954. Phenylhydrazine-induced changes in metabolism of pigeon blood and bone marrow. Amer. Jour. Physiol. 179: 338–342.

MAXIMOW, A. 1909. Untersuchungen über Blut und Bindegewebe. I. Die frühesten Entwicklungsstadien der Blut- und Bindegewebeszellen beim Saügetierembryo, bis zum Anfang der Blutbildung in der Leber. Arch. f. mikr. Anat. 73: 444–561.

———— and BLOOM, W. 1931. A Textbook of Histology. 833 pp. W. B. Saunders Co. Philadelphia.

MEDAWAR, P. B. 1941. The rate of penetration of fixatives. Jour. Roy. Micr. Soc. London. Ser. 3, 61: 46–57.

MEHNER, A. 1938. Beziehungen zwischen Zellgrösse und Körpergrösse. Zeit. Züchtung. Reihe B. Tierzüchtung und Züchtungsbiologie. 40: 1–48.

MICHELS, N. A. 1938. The mast cells. In Downey's Handbook of Hematology. 235–372. Paul B. Hoeber, Inc. New York.

MJASSOJEDOFF, S. W. 1926. Die Zellformen des Bindesgewebes und des Blutes und dic Blutbildung beim erwachsenen Huhn. Fol. Haem. 32: 263–296.

MURRAY, P. D. F. 1932. The development in vitro of the blood of the early chick embryo. Proc. Roy. Soc. London. Ser. B, 111: 497–521.

NATT, M. P., and HERRICK, C. A. 1954. Variation in the shape of the rodlike granule of the chicken heterophil leucocyte and its possible significance. Poultry Sci. 33: 828–830.

NEAVE, S. 1906. Report of travelling pathologist and naturalist. 2nd Rpt. Wellcome Res. Labs. Khartoum. 183–204.

NESTEROW, W. 1935. Das Schicksal von Hühnererythrozyten im Fremden Organismus. Zeitschr. f. Wissenschaftliche Biol. Abt. B. Zeitschr. f. Zellforsch. u. mikrosk. Anat. 22: 263–274.

NICE, L. B., NICE, M. M., and KRAFT, R. M. 1935. Erythrocytes and hemoglobin in the blood of some American birds. The Wilson Bul. 47: 120–124.

NITTIS, S. 1930. A surface structure (?) in normal nucleated erythrocytes. Anat. Rec. 46: 365–376.

NONIDEZ, J. F. 1920. Studies on the gonads of the fowl. I. Hematopoietic processes in the gonads of embryos and mature birds. Amer. Jour. Anat. 28: 81–115.

OAKBERG, E. F. 1949. Effect of age, sex and individual variability on lymphoid tissue of the pancreas in White Leghorn chickens. Poultry Sci. 28: 675–685.

——— 1950. Distribution and amount of lymphoid tissue in some of the splanchnic nerves of chickens in relation to age, sex and individual constitution. Poultry Sci. 29: 420–436.

——— 1951. Influence of genetic constitution on growth of lymphoid tissue in liver and pancreas of White Leghorn chickens, and correlation of lymphoid tissues with weights of some visceral and endocrine organs. Growth 15: 79–100.

OLSON, C. 1937. Variations in the cells and hemoglobin content in the blood of the normal domestic chicken. Cornell Vet. 27: 235–263.

——— 1952. Avian hematology. *In* Biester and Schwarte's Diseases of Poultry. pp. 71–91. Iowa State Col. Press. Ames, Iowa.

ORTEN, J. M. 1934. The properties and significance of the reticulocyte. Yale Jour. Biol. and Med. 6: 519–539.

——— and SMITH, A. H. 1934. The proportions of reticulocytes in the blood of albino rats. Amer. Jour. Physiol. 108: 66–73.

OSGOOD, E. E. 1935. Fenestration of nuclei of lymphocytes. Proc. Soc. Expt. Biol. and Med. 33: 218–219.

——— 1938. The histogenesis, classification and identification of the cells of the blood and marrow based on cultures and hematologic studies of human marrow and blood. Amer. Jour. Clin. Path. 8: 59–74.

——— and ASHWORTH, C. M. 1937. Atlas of Hematology. 255 pp. J. W. Stacey, Inc. San Francisco.

———, BAKER, R. L., and WILHELM, M. M. 1934. Reticulocyte counts in healthy children. Amer. Jour. Clin. Path. 4: 292–296.

——— and WILHELM, M. M. 1931. Reticulocytes. Proc. Soc. Expt. Biol. and Med. 29: 53–54.

PALMER, E. I., and BIELY, J. 1935a. Studies of total erythrocyte and leucocyte counts of fowls. I. Repeated erythrocyte and leucocyte counts. Fol. Haem. 53: 143–154.

——— and BIELY, J. 1935b. Studies of total erythrocyte and leucocyte counts of fowls. IV. Erythrocyte and leucocyte counts of birds raised in confinement. Canad. Jour. Res. 13: Sec. D: 85–88.

PAYNE, F., and BRENEMAN, W. R. 1952. Lymphoid areas in endocrine glands of fowl. Poultry Sci. 31: 155–165.

PEABODY, W. A., and NEALE, R. C. 1933. The pigeon as a hematopoietic test animal. Jour. Amer. Pharm. Assoc. 22: 1231–1237.

PETRUNKEVITCH, A. 1933. New fixing fluids for general purposes. Science 77: 117–118.

PRICE-JONES, C. 1910. The development of red blood cells in the chick. Jour. Path. & Bact. 14: 218–223.

RALPH, P. H. 1941. The histochemical demonstration of hemoglobin in blood cells and tissue smears. Stain Tech. 16: 105–107.

RAM, T. 1949. The relation of body temperature, blood cells and genetic resistance to *Salmonella pullorum* in fowls. Thesis. Grad. School, Cornell Univ.

REES, M., and ECKER, E. E. 1923. An improved method for counting blood platelets. Jour. Amer. Med. Assoc. 80: 621–622.

RHIAN, M., WILSON, W. O., and MOXON, A. L. 1944. Composition of blood of normal turkeys. Poultry Sci. 23: 224–229.

RICHARDS, O. W. 1938. A monogram for the resolving power of microscope objectives. Trans. Amer. Micr. Soc. 57: 316–318.

——— 1949. The history of the microscope. Trans. Amer. Micr. Soc. 68: 55–57, 206–207, 275–276.

——— 1954. The Effective Use and Proper Care of the Microscope. Amer. Optical Co. 63 pp. Spencer Lens Co., Buffalo.

RICHARDSON, A. P. 1937. Comparative effects of Congo red and liver extract on reticulocytes in pigeons. Proc. Soc. Expt. Biol. and Med. 37: 397–400.

RICHTER, M. N. 1938. Leucocytosis. *In* Downey's Handbook of Hematology. 2846–2886. Paul B. Hoeber, Inc. New York.

RIDDLE, O., and BRAUCHER, P. F. 1934. Hemoglobin and erythrocyte differences according to sex and season in doves and pigeons. Amer. Jour. Physiol. 108: 554–566.

ROBERTS, E., SEVERENS, J. M., and CARD, L. E. 1939. Nature of the hereditary factors for resistance and susceptibility to pullorum disease in the domestic fowl. Seventh World's Poultry Cong. 1939: 52–54.

ROBERTSON, E. I., FIALA, G. F., SCOTT, M. L., NORRIS, L. C. and HEUSER, G. F. 1947. Response of chicks to pteroylglutamic acid. Proc. Soc. Expt. Biol. and Med. 64: 441–443.

RYERSON, D. L. 1943. Separation of the two acidophilic granulocytes of turtle blood, with suggested phylogenetic relationships. Anat. Rec. 85: 25–49.

SABIN, F. R. 1920. Studies on the origin of blood-vessels and of red blood-corpuscles as seen in the living blastoderm of chicks during the second day of incubation. Carnegie Inst. of Wash. Pub. No. 272. Contrib. to Embryol. 9: 213–262.

SCHECHTMAN, A. M. 1952. Physical and chemical changes in the circulating blood. *In* The chick embryo in biological research. Ann. N. Y. Acad. of Sci. 55: 85–98.

SCHILLING, V. 1929. The Blood Picture and Its Clinical Significance. Translated and edited by P. B. H. Gradwold. 408 pp. C. V. Mosby Co. St. Louis.

SCHOGER, A. 1939. Beitrag zum Blutbild der Laboratoriumstiere unter besonderer Berücksichtigung des Bluttplättchenbildes. Das Blutbild der Taube. Pflüger's Arch. ges. Physiol. 242: 494–503.

SCHWARZ, E. 1946. Cellular gigantism and pluripolar mitosis in human hematopoiesis. Amer. Jour. Anat. 79: 75–115.

SEYFARTH, C. 1927. Experimentelle und klinische Untersuchungen über die vitalfärbbaren Erythrozyten. Fol. Haem. 34: 7–38.

SHATTUCK, G. E. 1928. Hemolysis of chicken blood. Jour. Gen. Physiol. 12: 17–28.

SHAW, A. F. B. 1933. The leucocytes of the pigeon with special reference to a diurnal rhythm. Jour. Path. and Bact. 37: 411–430.

SHIPLEY, P. G. 1916. The development of erythrocytes from hemoglobin-free cells and the differentiation of heart muscle fibers in tissue cultivated in plasma. Anat. Rec. 10: 347–353.

SPEIDEL, C. C. 1932. Studies of living nerves. I. The movements of individual sheath cells and nerve sprouts correlated with the process of myelin-sheath formation in amphibian larvae. Jour. Expt. Zool. 61: 279–331.

SPITTA, E. J. 1920. Microscopy. Ed. 3, 534 pp. John Murray. London.

STURGIS, C. C., and BETHELL, F. H. 1943. Quantitative variation in normal leukocytes. Physiol. Rev. 23: 279–303.

SUGIYAMA, S. 1926. Origin of thrombocytes and of different types of blood-cells as seen in the living chick blastoderm. Carnegie Inst. of Wash. Pub. No. 363. Contrib. to Embryol. 18: 123–147.

——— 1938. The nuclear shift of leucocytes and its clinical significance. Trans. Soc. Path. Jap. 28: 649–672.

SUNDBERG, R. D. 1947. Lymphocytogenesis in human lymph nodes. Jour. Lab. and Clin. Med. 32: 777–792.

TABER, E., DAVIS, D. E., and DOMM, L. V. 1943. Effects of sex hormones on the erythrocyte number in the blood of the domestic fowl. Amer. Jour. Physiol. 138: 479–487.

TAKAGI, S. 1931. Studien über die Differenzierung der Blutzellen, Beobachtet aus dem Standpunkt der Chondriosomenforschung. Hämatopoese im Dottersack des Hühnerembryos. Annot. Zool. Jap. 13: 105–115.

——— 1932. Über das Verhalten der Chondriosomen bei der mitotischen Zellteilung der jüngeren Blutzellen. Annot. Zool. Jap. 13: 355–359.

TATE, P., and VINCENT, M. 1932. The occurrence of peculiar bodies in blood cells of animals after treatment with some chemical compounds. Parasitology 24: 284–288.

TORYÛ, Y. 1930. Changes in the blood picture, and in the oxygen capacity of the blood haemoglobin of the carrier-pigeon following splenectomy. Sci. Rpt. Tohoku Imp. Univ. 4th Ser. Biol. 5: 391–402.

——— 1931. Haemopoiesis in the liver and bone marrow of the carrier pigeon after splenectomy (Japanese with the English summary.) Ni Zyu. Gak. Ztschr. 10: 381–390. 1933. Abs. Jap. Jour. Zool. 4: (39).

TWISSELMANN, N. M. 1939. A study of the cell content of the blood of normal chickens, with special reference to comparative differential leucocyte counts made with supravital and Wright's staining technics. Poultry Sci. 18: 151–159.

UNDERHILL, B. M. L. 1932. The rate of penetration of fixatives. Jour. Roy. Micr. Soc. London. Ser. 3, 52: 113–120.

VENZLAFF, W. 1911. Über Genesis und Morphologie der roten Blütkörperchen der Vögel. Arch. f. mikr. Anat. Abt. I. 77: 377–432.

VEZZANI, V. 1939. Influence of a sojourn in the mountains on the blood composition, body development, and egg production of White Leghorn pullets. Proc. World's Poultry Cong. and Expo. 7: 117–119.

WASSJUTOTSCHKIN, A. 1913. Untersuchungen über die Histogenese der Thymus. I. Über den Ursprung des myoiden Elemente der Thymus des Hühnerembryos. Anat. Anz. 43: 349–366.

——— 1914. Untersuchungen über die Histogenese der Thymus. II. Über den myoiden Elemente der Thymus in zusammenhange mit degeneratinen Veränderungen der Muskelfaser. Anat. Anz. 46: 577–600.

WATERS, N. F. 1945. Breeding for resistance and susceptibility to avian lymphomatosis. Poultry Sci. 24: 259–269.

WELDENREICH, F. 1911. Die Leukozyten und verwandte Zellformen. Wiesboden. (Quoted from Lundquist and Hedlung.)

WEISS, L. P., and FAWCETT, D. W. 1953. Cytochemical observations on chicken monocytes, macrophages and giant cells in tissue culture. Jour. Histochem. and Cytochem. 1: 47–65.

WICKWARE, A. B. 1947. The differential blood picture in chickens before and after administration of embryonated eggs of *Heterakis gallinae* with notes on pathogenicity. Canad. Jour. Comp. Med. 11: 78–83.

WILLS, L. 1932. Spontaneous fluctuations in the reticulocyte count in pigeon's blood. Brit. Jour. Expt. Path. 13: 172–175.

241

WILSON, E. B. 1925. The Cell in Development and Heredity. 1232 pp. The Macmillan Co. New York.

WINTROBE, M. M. 1933. Variations in the size and hemoglobin content of erythrocytes in the blood of various vertebrates. Fol. Haem. 51: 32–49.

―――― 1952. Clinical Hematology. Ed. 3, 1,048 pp. Lea and Febiger. Philadelphia.

WIRTH, D. 1950. Grundlagen einer Klinischen Hamatologie der Haustiere. 375 pp. Urban and Schwarzenberg. Vienna.

WISEMAN, B. K. 1931a. An improved method for obtaining white cell counts in avian blood. Proc. Soc. Expt. Biol. and Med. 28: 1,030–1,033.

―――― 1931b. Criteria of the age of lymphocytes in the peripheral blood. Jour. Expt. Med. 54: 271–294.

―――― 1932. The identity of the lymphocyte. Fol. Haem. 46: 346–358.

WISLOCKI, G. B. 1943. Hemopoiesis in the chorionic villi of Platyrrhine monkeys. Anat. Rec. 85: 349–363.

WRIGHT, G. P. 1930a. Factors influencing the respiration of erythrocytes. I. Primitive avian erythrocytes. Jour. Gen. Physiol. 14: 179–199.

―――― 1930b. Factors influencing the respiration of erythrocytes. II. Mammalian reticulocytes. Jour. Gen. Physiol. 14: 201–213.

―――― and VAN ALSTYNE, M. 1931. The development of primitive avian red corpuscles on incubation in vitro. Fol. Haem. 46: 26–36.

ZUCKERMAN, A. 1946. Infections with *Plasmodium gallinaceum* in chick embryos induced by exoerythrocytic and blood stages. J. Infect. Dis. 79: 1–11.

ADDENDUM

ACKERMAN, G. A., and KNOUFF, R. A. 1959. Lymphocytopoiesis in the bursa of Fabricius. Amer. Jour. Anat. 104: 163–177.

BESSIS, M. 1956. Cytology of the Blood and Blood-Forming Organs. 629 pp. Grune and Stratton. New York.

BIGGS, P. M. 1957. The association of lymphoid tissue with the lymph vessels in the domestic chicken (*Gallus domesticus*). Acta Anat. 29: 36–47.

BIGLAND, C. H., and TRIANTAPHYLLOPOULOS, D. C. 1960. A re-evaluation of the clotting time of chicken blood. Nature 186: 644.

CLELAND, J. B., and JOHNSON, T. H. 1911. Relative dimensions of the red blood cells of vertebrates, especially of birds. Emu 11: 188–197.

COOK, F. W. 1959. Staining fixed preparations of chicken blood cells with combination May-Greenwald-Wright-Phloxine B stain. Avian Dis. 3: 272–290.

CRASS, G., and RIGDON, R. H. 1954. Histologic study of the bone marrow in normal White Pekin ducks. A.M.A. Arch. Path. 58: 159–167.

DENINGTON, E. M., and LUCAS, A. M. 1960. Influence of heat treatment on the number of ectopic lymphoid foci in chickens. Amer. Jour. Vet. Res. 21: 734–739.

DIESEM, C. D., BLETNER, J. K., and VENZKE, W. G. 1957. The effect of estradiolcyclopentylproprionate (ECP) on the blood cells of chickens. Avian Dis. 2: 63–75.

――――, VENZKE, W. G., and MOORE, E. N. 1958. The hemograms of healthy chickens. Amer. Jour. Vet. Res. 19: 719–724.

FREDRICKSON, T. N., CHUTE, H. L., and O'MEARA, D. C. 1957. Preliminary investigations on the hematology of broiler flocks. Avian Dis. 1: 67–74.

GORDON, A. S. 1959. Hemopoietine. Physiol. Rev. 39: 1–40.

KANESADA, A. 1956. Lymphoid tissues occurring in the liver and bone marrow of reptiles and birds. Arch. Hist. Jap. 10: 471–481. (Jap. with Eng. summary and legends.)

―――― 1956. Postnatal development of lymphoid tissues in the liver and bone marrow in White Leghorn chickens. Arch. Hist. Jap. 10: 525–530. (Jap. with Eng. summary and legends.)

LUCAS, A. M. 1959. A discussion of synonymy in avian and mammalian hematological nomenclature. Amer. Jour. Vet. Res. 20: 887–897.

―――― and DENINGTON, E. M. 1957. Effect of total body x-ray irradiation on the blood of female Single Comb White Leghorn chickens. Poult. Sci. 36: 1290–1310.

―――― and DENINGTON, E. M. 1958. The statistical reliability of differential counts of chicken blood. Poult. Sci. 37: 544–549.

MEDWAY, W., and KARE, M. R. 1959. Blood and plasma volume, hematocrit, blood specific gravity and serum protein electrophoresis of the chicken. Poult. Sci. 38: 624–631.

OHNO, S., and KINOSITA, R. 1956. Three-dimensional observations on the intranuclear structure. Exp. Cell Res. 10: 569–574.

Acknowledgments

This study of avian hematology was initiated in 1944 and has received help and encouragement from many sources. We want to express our deepest appreciation in particular to the institutions and persons listed below for the contributions indicated:

Live birds: Dr. Donald W. Douglass, Dr. Lawrence Fay, Mr. Herbert J. Miller, Mr. Roy Hunt, and Mr. Martin Pollok, all in the Michigan Department of Conservation; Dr. M. R. Irwin, Department of Genetics, University of Wisconsin, Madison, Wis.; Dr. Charles C. Sheppard, Poultry Department, Michigan State University, East Lansing, Mich.; and Mr. A. G. Lohman, Manager Hamilton Farm Bureau Cooperative, Inc., Hamilton, Mich.

Slides: Dr. John W. Gowen and Miss Janice Stadler, Department of Genetics, Iowa State College, Ames, Iowa; Dr. Wade M. Smith, Jr., and Miss Enid B. Allbaugh, Hy-Line Poultry Farms, Des Moines, Iowa; Dr. E. N. Moore, Poultry Science Department, Ohio Agricultural Experiment Station, Wooster, Ohio; and Dr. George W. Sciple, Bear River Research Station, Brigham City, Utah.

The library work was greatly facilitated by the many courtesies extended by the staff of the Medical Library, University of Michigan, Ann Arbor, Mich.

The authors appreciate the help given to the project by all members of this Laboratory. Those most directly concerned were: Mr. Berley Winton, Director; Mrs. Hazel W. Garrison, secretary; Mr. Seymour Albert; Mrs. M. Gay Flokstra, Mrs. Isabelle M. Letts, Mrs. Georgiann S. McClure, Mrs. Ellen Reibeling, and Mrs. Carolyn Tull, technicians; Mrs. Anne C. Garrison, translator; and Mrs. Coletta S. Waggoner, librarian.

To Swift & Co., Chicago, Ill., we want to express our sincere appreciation for its generous financial support of this research through grants to Michigan State University. Dr. O. A. Newton, who represented the Company, fully appreciated the significance of the research and consistently encouraged its execution.

We also desire to express to Michigan State University our thanks for administering the research grants made by Swift & Co.

Index

Epiphysial center, 141
Erdmann (1917), 181
Erismatura jamaicensis. *See* Duck, ruddy
Erythroblast(s), 10, 192
  blast cells compared, 9, 192
  characteristics, 11, 26, 112, 192
  embryo, 31, 114, 158
    hemoglobin acquisition, 104, 112
    later generations, 98, 100, 114, 128
      in spleen, 156
    mitosis, 122
    nucleus, poorly stained, 122
    thromboblast, compared with, 128
    in bone marrow, 181, 182, 184, 191, 192, 200
    in circulating blood, 23, 24, 94
    in spleen, 157, 160
    intravascular and extravascular, 113
  primary
    basophil, 118
    cell size, difference, 116, 118
    changes during incubation, 113, 114, 118
    chromosome, 117
    disappearance from circulation, 112, 113
    division, 118
      mitosis, abnormal, 117
    first appearance, 112
      at 22 to 29 somites, 31
    giant, 117
    hemoglobin
      little, 26
      precocious, 112, 129
    like thrombocyte
      clumping, 130
      origin, 130
    smudged, 94
    term, synonymous with megaloblast, 116
  resembles large lymphocyte, 24
  terminology, 192
Erythrocyte(s), 17–41, 155
  abnormal, 20, 30–33, 34
  aged, 29, 30
  artifact, 33, 36, 39–41
  atypical, 27, 30–33, 34
  bone marrow, 181, 182, 184, 192, 193
  Cabot's ring, 39, 40
  count(s)
    birds, except chickens, 218, 219
    brooding vs. laying hen, 218
    chickens, 216
    diurnal effect, 218
    effect of—
      altitude, 218
      season, 218
    sexes, 216, 218
    variability, 217
  crossed cells, 210
  debris on, 146
  developmental stages
    circulating blood, 24–30, 164, 210
    tissue culture, 104, 116

Erythrocyte(s)—Continued
  effect of—
    antimalarial compounds, 33
    fixation, 94
      Petrunkevitch No. 2, 80
    splenectomy, 29
  embryo, 192
    artifact, 98, 100, 103, 124, 127
    bone marrow, 142, 144, 146
    cell, description, 115–130
    changes during incubation, 113, 114
    developmental stages in circulating blood, 94, 96, 98, 100, 104–130
    differential count, 113, 114
    division, 94, 96
    generations, 104, 114, 128–130
    life span, 114
    mature, 103, 113, 142, 144
    polychromatic
      early, 100, 124
        mitosis, 128
      late, 100, 103, 106, 113, 114, 124, 128, 129, 142
      mid-, 100, 106, 113, 114
    spleen, 157, 160
    mitosis, 157
  generations of, 9, 104–105, 114
  giant, 17, 117
  hemoglobin and basophilia, 29
  immature, 23
  in bone marrow, 182
  life span, 32
  line differences, 215
  mature, 10, 11, 23, 108, 111, 146, 182, 184
    cytoplasm texture, 11
    in bone marrow, 200
    normal, 17–24, 29
    typical, 17, 18, 20, 23, 211
      deviations from, 17, 18
  multipolar, 17
  nucleus, 20
    age of, 11
    aged, 23, 30
    double, 23, 27
    size, 211, 212
    squashed, 18
  origin, intravascular, 104, 113, 128, 141
  orthochromatic, 23, 26
  percent rise and fall, 113
  polychromatic, 24, 25, 26, 27, 192, 198
    artifact, 33, 144
    basophil, synonym, 24
    early, 10, 11, 23, 181, 182, 184, 192, 200
    late, 10, 11, 23, 26, 108, 182, 184, 192, 200
      atypical, 23
      mitosis, 157, 160
    mid-, 10, 11, 23, 26, 184, 192, 200
      enters circulation, 164
      mitosis, 160
  primary, 115–120, 127–128
    abnormal, 120
    amitosis, 128

Magenta granule, body, ring, sphere
  associated with—
    avian leukosis, 64
    health of bird, 65
    lymphocyte, 52, 53, 64
      pathologic significance, 64, 65
  chromidial type, 131
  granule, different from—
    azurophilic granule, 49
    magenta ring, 195
  in myelocyte, description of, 195
  new term, 54
  occasionally present in—
    embryo thrombocyte, 131
    heterophil mesomyelocyte, 12
    monocyte, 71
  present in—
    basophil promyelocyte, 13, 196–197
    heterophil
      mesomyelocyte, 154
      promyelocyte, 12, 74, 156, 188, 194
    lymphocyte
      abnormal, 49, 54
      in mitosis, 53, 54
      wild birds, 210
    mononuclear osteoclast, 148
    multinuclear osteoclast, 142, 153
    primordial osteogenic cell, 142
  relation to—
    azurophilic body, 54, 71
    orange spheres, 195
  See also Heterophil; Lymphocyte
Magnification
  high power, 4, 14
  low power, 4, 14, 15, 17, 32
  optical, 14
  projected, 14
  scale, 4
Mainland et al. (1935), 66
Makinodan (personal communication), 166
Mammal, mammalian, man
  Arneth count, 221
  basket cell, 72
  blood, 25, 73, 84
  erythrocyte
    aged cell, 30
    maturation delay, 30
    protoplasmic process, 41
    reticulocyte, 28
  giant cell, 153
  leukemia cells resemble chick immature cells, 112
  lymphocyte, 49
    azurophilic granules, 64
    stages from lymphoblastic leukemia, 53
  monocyte and lymphocyte from same organ, 167
  neutrophil, 86
    band and juvenile cells, 155
    toxic granules, 87
  platelets, 41
  serum, fewer granules than in birds, 41
  smudged cells, mouse, 39
  spleen, 156

Mareca americana. See Duck, baldplate
Marvin (1954), 199
Mast cell, 47, 91
Maturation rate, erythrocyte, 29–30
Mature—
  basophil, 10, 13, 78, 91, 111, 146, 155, 172, 182,
        191, 200
    specific granule, 197
  eosinophil, 10, 13, 76, 89, 158, 200, 208
  erythrocyte, 10, 11, 17, 18, 20, 23, 25, 26, 28, 29,
        108, 111, 146, 182, 184, 198, 200
    later embryonic, 103, 106, 113, 114, 124, 142, 144
    primary, 100, 103, 106, 113, 120, 127, 142
  heterophil, 10, 12, 18, 20, 47, 73, 74, 111, 144, 146,
        154, 155, 163, 164, 167, 172, 182, 188, 199, 200
  lymphocyte, 10, 12, 18, 48, 50, 54, 111, 163, 166,
        167, 168, 172, 174, 191, 199, 200
  macrophage, embryo, 139
  monocyte, 10, 12, 49, 58, 72, 111, 200
  osteoblast, 10, 13, 142, 152, 166
  plasmocyte, 10, 14, 198, 199, 203
  thrombocyte, 10, 12, 18, 33, 42, 45, 111, 186, 191,
        193, 200
    embryo, 136
Maximow (1909), 8, 104, 116
——and Bloom (1931), 47
May-Grünwald Giemsa. See Stain and staining
Medawar (1941), 167
Megakaryocyte, 41, 42, 153
Megaloblast, 115, 192
  produces thromboblast, 130
  synonymous with—
    erythroblast, 116
    karyoblast, 9
Mehner (1938), 211
Meleagrididae, 202
Meleagris gallopavo. See Turkey, domestic
Mesenchyme, 104
  nucleolus present, 168
  tissue, 9, 153, 168
Mesomyelocyte, 156
  basophil, 10, 13, 106, 182, 191, 197, 200
  eosinophil, 10, 13, 76, 91, 200
    combined with promyelocyte, 10, 13
  heterophil, 10, 12, 74, 86, 91, 144, 146, 154, 157,
        158, 160, 188, 200
Metachromatic granule, 91
  heterophil, 195
Metagranuloblast(s), 142, 144, 154, 156, 158, 160,
        182, 194, 197
  basophil, 10, 13
    combined with promyelocyte, 10, 13
  cytoplasm, vacuolated, 194
  early immature monocyte, different from, 167
  eosinophil, 10, 12, 156, 194, 196, 200
  granuloblast, changes from, 194
  heterophil, 10, 12, 86, 92, 156, 191, 194, 196, 200
  nucleus, eccentric, 154
Metamyelocyte, 182
  basophil, 10, 13, 200
  eosinophil, 10, 13, 76, 91, 160, 196, 200

Pathology—Continued
    crop
        atonicity, 51, 65
        impaction, 65
    dehydration, 65, 85
    emaciation, 61, 65, 85
    enlarged heart, ascitic fluid, 85
    gasping, 51, 65
    lymphomatosis
        neural, paralysis, 65, 85
        ocular, iritis, gray eye, 51, 85
        visceral, 65, 85
    prolapsed uterus, 51, 85
    urates in kidney, 51
    See also Avian leukosis complex; Lymphomatosis
Payne and Breneman (1952), 181
Peabody and Neale (1933), 27, 231
Penthestes atricapillus. *See* Chickadee, black-capped
Petrunkevitch (1933), 230
Petrunkevitch No. 2. *See* Fixation and fixatives
Phagocyte, phagocytic
    embryo, response to infection, 133
    endothelial cells, 139
    thrombocyte, 45
    See also Macrophage
Phasianidae, 202
Phasianus colchicus. *See* Pheasant, ring-necked
Pheasant
    basophil, 92
    blood viscosity, 210
    count(s)
        Arneth, 220
        differential, 217
        eosinophil, 219
        variability, 215
    eosinophil, 210
    ring-necked (*Phasianus colchicus*), 202
    thrombocyte size, 210
Phenylhydrazine hydrochloride, 29
Phloxine
    affinity for heterophils and eosinophils, 233
    in Wiseman's method, 232, 233
Photomicrography, adjustment of condenser, 225
Picidae, 202
Piciformes, 202
Pigeon
    basophil, 210
    count(s)
        Arneth, 221
        differential, 217, 219
            paratyphoid, 219
        eosinophil, 219
        erythrocyte, 218
        in bone marrow, 199
        sexes compared, 218
        thrombocyte, 219
        variability, 215
    effect of splenectomy, 29, 181
    erythrocyte, 210
        crossed cells, 210
    hemoglobin, sex difference, 218
    hemolysis, 39

Pigeon—Continued
    Laboratory, 202
    macrophage from endothelium, 139
    reticulocyte, 27, 28
        staining, 231
    serum, lipochrome pigment, 93
    thrombocyte, 42, 45
        confusion with lymphocyte, 210
    value of smear technic, 154
Pipilo erythrophthalmus. *See* Towhee
Planimeter, 212
Plasma. *See* Serum
Plasma cell(s), 197–198
    See also Plasmacyte
Plasmablast(s), 10, 13
    identity, 197
Plasmacyte(s)
    characteristics, 166
    immature
        early, 10, 13, 163, 197, 198, 203
        late, 10, 13, 163, 203
    in bone marrow, 166, 197, 200, 203
    in loose connective tissue, 197
    in spleen, 166, 197
    mature, 10, 165, 203
    resembles osteoblast, 166
    series, 10, 13, 200, 203
Plasmodium gallinaceum, increased heterophil num-
                                ber, 133
Platelets, 41
    clumping, 15
    See also Megakaryocyte; Thrombocyte
Poikilocytosis, 31, 34
Polychromatic
    color
        acidophilic and basophilic stains combined, 24,
                                25, 117
        terminology, 117
    measure of development, 25
    series, 26
    See also Erythrocyte
Precipitate on slide, resembles reticulocyte granules, 28
Premyelocyte, 92
Price-Jones (1910), 33
Primary—
    erythroblast. *See* Erythroblast
    erythroplastid. *See* Erythroplastid
Primordial—
    cell. *See* Cell
    germ cell, 139
        larger than blood cells, 140
Primordial osteogenic cell(s), 9, 10, 13
    count, 200
    distinct cell type, 152
    in mitosis, 142, 144
    magenta granules, 144, 148
    nucleolus, 152
    produces—
        osteoblast, 13, 152
        osteoclast, 13, 152
        plasmablast, 13, 197
    resembles reticular cell, 168